MATHEMATICS FOR TECHNICIAN ENGINEERS
A Third-Level Course

McGRAW-HILL
Book Company (UK) Limited

London
New York
St Louis
San Francisco
Auckland
Bogotá
Guatemala
Hamburg
Johannesburg
Lisbon
Madrid
Mexico
Montreal
New Delhi
Panama
Paris
San Juan
São Paulo
Singapore
Sydney
Tokyo
Toronto

GEORGE E. DYBALL, BA (Hons), T Eng (CEI), Cert Ed
Senior Lecturer and Deputy Head of Department of Technology,
Melton Mowbray College of Further Education

Mathematics for Technician Engineers
A Third-Level Course

Published by:

McGRAW-HILL Book Company (UK) Limited

MAIDENHEAD · BERKSHIRE · ENGLAND

British Library Cataloguing in Publication Data

Dyball, George E
    Mathematics for technician engineers.
    1. Shop mathematics
    I. Title
    510'.2'46   TJ1165   80-40672

    ISBN 0-07-084636-7

12345 AP   83210

Printed and bound in Great Britain by the Alden Press, Oxford.

CONTENTS

PREFACE

This book is a complete course in mathematics at level III for future technician engineers following a Technician Education Council (TEC) approved certificate or diploma programme. The overall aims of the book are identical to the aims of the standard unit U75/040 in that the concepts of level II mathematics are extended, the concepts of mathematical modelling are developed and applied, and, finally, the overall mathematical knowledge is broadened so as to form a basis for future study. The course is based on, and covers all the learning objectives laid down in, the standard unit U75/040. In the context of learning objectives, each chapter contains its own list that provides a guide to the reader as to the knowledge which should be gained after completion of that particular part of the book.

Students following engineering studies require a text which explains the theory of mathematics concisely and with examples related to the concepts. The examples chosen throughout the book are intended not only to demonstrate the theory but also to develop in the reader certain common mathematical techniques. At the end of each chapter, there are numerous problems, with solutions, for further practice. The problems have been graded according to difficulty by a system of asterisks.

Throughout the book, the mathematical notation used has been fully explained and is in common use outside of this course. However, to aid the reader, a list of the mathematical notation used and the first chapter in which it is introduced is given in the appendix. Also in the appendix the reader will find tables of formulae along with the generalized binomial coefficients and areas under the normal distribution.

Following the general aims of the standard unit, Chapter 1 stresses the concepts of mathematical modelling in the context of engineering studies. Throughout the remainder of the book, mathematical models concerned with electrical, mechanical and production engineering are discussed. Indeed, to bring some of the important concepts of this course together, the reader will find the theme of mathematical modelling continued in the form of revision within Chapter 16. At the end of Chapter 16, there are some short-answer questions, completion time approximately 4 minutes, and some long-answer questions which require approximately 15 to 25 minutes to complete.

Within the book there are some references to computers, and the table of areas under the normal distribution was produced by using this modern aid. I am extremely grateful to Mr Eric J. Bartlett, of Lowestoft College of Further Education, for computing this table and for advice on the statistics within the book. I am also indebted to Mr Alan Moss and Mr Anthony Pakes, both of Melton Mowbray College of Further Education, for their time in discussing, and advice on, the topics in level III mathematics. I would like to thank all my friends and colleagues within industry and education for the advice and help that has been given to me. And, finally, I would like to thank my wife, Celia, for her secretarial services, and her patience and encouragement during the preparation of this volume.

George E. Dyball
Melton Mowbray

ENGINEERING MATHEMATICS

Objectives After reading this chapter you should be able to:

1. Describe the process of mathematical modelling.
2. Round off numerical values using the 'odds/evens' process.
3. Use functional notation.
   - (*a*) State that $y = f(x)$ is the value of the function after substituting a given value of x.
   - (*b*) Sketch a flow diagram of a function.
   - (*c*) Calculate the value of a function given a value of x.
4. Calculate round-off errors.
   - (*a*) Describe the difference between blunders or mistakes and round-off errors.
   - (*b*) Calculate the value of a function minimizing the effect of round-off errors.

1-1 MATHEMATICAL MODELLING

Mathematical modelling is a process by which we obtain, predict, and evaluate information concerning the physical universe and, in particular, problems within industry. As mathematical modelling is a process, it can be illustrated by a flow chart as in Fig. 1-1. The flow chart shows how we formulate engineering problems in mathematical ways. It illustrates that we always start the process from the physical world and by collecting information, usually through experiments or surveys, we can obtain mathematical relationships between the variables involved. Having passed through this stage, we can use our mathematics to predict outcomes or to find other relationships.

We shall take an engineering example and follow the process through. The problem of being able to predict the amount of force required to extend a

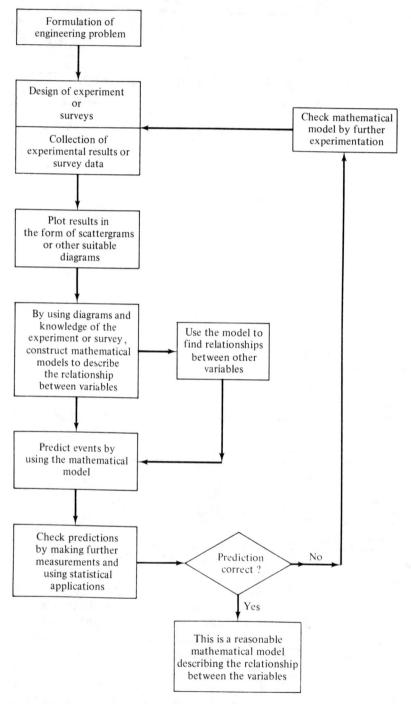

Figure 1-1 The process of mathematical modelling.

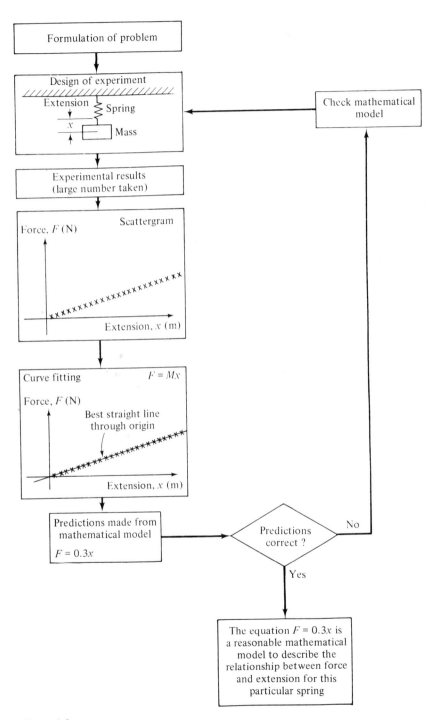

Figure 1-2

particular spring by a given distance is well known in engineering science and hence we shall use it as the vehicle to describe the process of mathematical modelling. Figure 1-2 illustrates the process starting with the formulation of the problem and the design of an experiment to obtain data relating the two variables, force and extension. We shall not go into the experiment in detail save to note that the spring is normally mounted vertically, fixed at one end and loads applied at the other. The force F and the extension x are both measured. The experimental results are collected, tabulated, and plotted on a scattergram. Here we see the general drift of points across the graph suggests that we should fit a straight line of the form $Y = MX + C$ and as we know that for *zero* load we have *zero* extension then $C = 0$. Replacing Y by F, the load, and X by x, the extension, we have the mathematical relationship

$$F = Mx$$

where M is the slope of the graph found by drawing the best straight line through the points on the scattergram and through the origin.

We now have a **mathematical model** describing the relationship between the variables **force** and **extension**. This model enables the engineer to predict the amount of force for a *given* extension when using this particular type of spring. We should note, however, that we test the model by making predictions and returning to the experiment to check these against the measurements. If these predictions are incorrect, then we have to check our mathematical model by further experimental methods. If, on the other hand, the predictions are upheld, then we have a **reasonable mathematical model** describing the relationship between force and extension for this particular spring. It must be emphasized that the *more* experimental results the *more reliable* the mathematical model describing the relationship between the variables. We shall see throughout this book how we build and use mathematical models in the electrical, mechanical, and production engineering industries.

1-2 ROUNDING OFF NUMERICAL VALUES

There are two methods in common use when rounding off numerical values. We shall demonstrate both methods by means of examples.

Example 1-2-1 Round off to 2 decimal places the numbers (*a*) 3.267, (*b*) 3.265, and (*c*) 3.275 using the '5 up' method.

SOLUTION This method involves the rounding up of numbers when the digit to be removed is greater or equal to 5, rounding down when it is less than 5. Thus

(*a*) 3.267 ⟶ 3.27,
(*b*) 3.265 ⟶ 3.27, and
(*c*) 3.275 ⟶ 3.28.

Example 1-2-2 Round off to 2 decimal places the numbers (*a*) 3.267, (*b*) 3.265, and (*c*) 3.275 by the 'odds/evens' rounding process.

SOLUTION This method involves rounding up numbers when the digit to be removed is *greater* than 5, rounding down when it is *less* than 5, and following the odds/evens rule when it is equal to 5. When the number before the 5 is *even* we round down and when it is *odd* we round the number up. Thus

(*a*) 3.267 ⟶ 3.27,
(*b*) 3.265 ⟶ 3.26, and
(*c*) 3.275 ⟶ 3.28.

We shall throughout this book use the 'odds/evens' process of rounding off numerical solutions since it reduces errors.

Example 1-2-3 Round off the numbers (*a*) 5.453 758 5, and (*b*) 4.657 895 25 to 4 decimal places by using the 'odds/evens' process.

SOLUTION
(*a*) 5.453 758 5 ⟶ 5.453 758   (6 decimal places)
     5.453 758 5 ⟶ 5.453 76   (5 decimal places)
     5.453 758 5 ⟶ 5.4538   (4 decimal places)

(*b*) 4.657 895 25 ⟶ 4.657 895 2   (7 decimal places)
     4.657 895 25 ⟶ 4.657 895   (6 decimal places)
     4.657 895 25 ⟶ 4.657 90   (5 decimal places)
     4.657 895 25 ⟶ 4.6579   (4 decimal places)

1-3 FUNCTIONS

The mathematical notation we shall adopt for functions will be $f(x)$, that is, f is a function of x. If we write

$$y = f(x)$$

then we have denoted the numerical value of $f(x)$ by the symbol y. Figure 1-3 illustrates the function $f(x) = x^3$ by showing a flow diagram and a graph based on cartesian coordinates. The y axis is a scale of **values** for the function.

Example 1-3-1 Evaluate the value of the function represented by

$$f(x) = x^3$$

when
(*a*) $x = 1$,
(*b*) $x = 2$,
(*c*) $x = -2$, and
(*d*) $x = 0$.

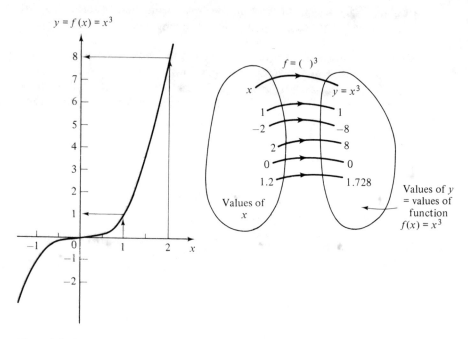

Figure 1-3 The function $f(x) = x^3$.

SOLUTION

(a) $f(x) = x^3 \Rightarrow f(1) = 1^3$
$$= 1$$

[The symbol $\Rightarrow$ denotes **implies**.]

(b) $f(x) = x^3 \Rightarrow f(2) = 2^3$
$$= 8$$

(c) $f(x) = x^3 \Rightarrow f(-2) = (-2)^3$
$$= -8$$

(d) $f(x) = x^3 \Rightarrow f(0) = 0^3$
$$= 0$$

Example 1-3-2 Evaluate the value of the function represented by

$$f(x) = \sin(x)$$

when

(a) $x = 0$,
(b) $x = 1$, and
(c) $x = -1$.

SOLUTION The reader should note that x is the **radians** (rad) and the calculator should be set in radian mode.

(a) $f(x) = \sin(x) \Rightarrow f(0) = \sin(0)$
$$= 0$$

(b) $f(x) = \sin(x) \Rightarrow f(1) = \sin(1)$
$$= 0.8415$$

(c) $f(x) = \sin(x) \Rightarrow f(-1) = \sin(-1)$
$$= -0.8415$$

Example 1-3-3 Evaluate the function
$$f(x) = x + \cos(x)$$
when
(a) $x = 0$,
(b) $x = 1$, and
(c) $x = 100$.

SOLUTION
(a) $f(x) = x + \cos(x) \Rightarrow f(0) = 0 + \cos(0)$
$$= 1$$

(b) $f(x) = x + \cos(x) \Rightarrow f(1) = 1 + \cos(1)$
$$= 1.5403$$

(c) $f(x) = x + \cos(x) \Rightarrow f(100) = 100 + \cos(100)$
$$= 100.8623$$

1-4 CALCULATIONS AND ERRORS

When we think of calculation errors we normally refer to mistakes or blunders made by the person performing the operation. There are, however, other types of error which occur through the nature of the arithmetical processes involved. Consider calculating the function
$$f(x) = x^2$$
when $x = 4.5632$. Here we have
$$f(4.5632) = (4.5632)^2$$
$$= 20.822\,794\,24$$

It is normal, however, not to write down all the decimal places. If we round the solution off to 4 decimal places, we have the result
$$f(4.5632) = 20.8228 \qquad \text{(4 decimal places)}$$

By rounding off the solution, we have introduced an error called a **rounding-off error**.

It is a general rule that when we calculate the value of more complicated functions, we round off at the end of the calculation. For example, consider calculating the value of

$$f(x) = 1000(x^2)$$

when $x = 0.0413$, to 4 decimal places.

$$f(x) = 1000(x^2) \Rightarrow f(0.0413) = 1000(0.0413)^2$$

$$= 1000(0.001\ 705\ 69)$$

$$= 1.705\ 69$$

$$= 1.7057 \qquad \text{(to 4 decimal places)}$$

However, if we round off during the squaring part of the function we have

$$f(0.0413) = 1000(0.0413)^2$$

$$= 1000(0.0017)$$

$$= 1.7$$

and we have an error caused by rounding off too early in the calculation.

Example 1-4-1 Find the arithmetic mean and standard deviation of the measurements shown in Table 1-1, to 2 decimal places.

Table 1-1

x	1.1	1.3	1.5	1.7	1.8	1.9	2.0	2.1

SOLUTION The arithmetic mean $\bar{x}$ is given by

$$\bar{x} = \frac{\sum_{i=1}^{n} x_i}{n}$$

and the standard deviation s by

$$s = \sqrt{\text{variance}}$$

$$= \sqrt{\overline{x^2} - (\bar{x})^2}$$

where $\overline{x^2}$ is the average of the measurements squared.

x	x^2
1.1	1.21
1.3	1.69
1.5	2.25
1.7	2.89
1.8	3.24
1.9	3.61
2.0	4.00
2.1	4.41
13.4	23.30

Hence

$$\bar{x} = \frac{13.4}{8}$$

$$= 1.675$$

$$= 1.68 \qquad \text{to 2 decimal places}$$

$$\overline{x^2} = \frac{23.3}{8}$$

$$= 2.9125 \qquad \text{(DO NOT ROUND OFF AT THIS STAGE)}$$

Hence

$$s = \sqrt{2.9125 - (1.675)^2}$$

$$= \sqrt{0.106\,875}$$

$$= 0.3269 \qquad \text{to 4 decimal places}$$

or

$$s = 0.33 \qquad \text{to 2 decimal places}$$

The reader should notice that we placed the value $\bar{x} = 1.675$ into the formula for the standard deviation not the rounded-off value of 1.68. If we had used $\bar{x} = 1.68$, we would obtain a standard deviation $s = 0.30$ to two decimal places, reinforcing the idea of cumulative errors in the calculation by rounding off before the end.

Finally, we would like to remind readers that an approximate calculation check, without using a calculator, will enable use to assess the order of magnitude of the solution.

Example 1-4-2 By using a calculator find the value, to 3 decimal places, of

$$\frac{(436.4)(0.000\,92)}{(3.2)(0.003)}$$

Check the result by using standard-form methods in terms of the order of magnitude.

SOLUTION By calculator we have

$$\frac{(436.4)(0.000\,92)}{(3.2)(0.003)} = 41.822$$

Using standard form we have

$$\frac{(436.4)(0.000\,92)}{(3.2)(0.003)} = \frac{(4.364)(10^2)(9.2)(10^{-4})}{(3.2)(3)(10^{-3})}$$

$$\simeq \frac{(4)(10^2)(9)(10^{-4})}{(3)(3)(10^{-3})} = 4(10^1)$$

by rounding to 1 significant figure. Hence

$$\frac{(436.4)(0.000\,92)}{(3.2)(0.003)} \simeq 40$$

which is of the same order of magnitude as the correct solution. It must be stressed that a calculator should be avoided in the approximate calculation checks.

PROBLEMS

1-1 Describe the stages of the mathematical modelling process.

1-2 Round off the numbers (a) 2.3456, (b) 3.456 525, (c) 2.765, and (d) 1.453 525 75 to 2 decimal places using the 'odds/evens' process.

1-3 Sketch a flow diagram for the function $f(x) = x^5$.

1-4 Sketch a flow diagram for the function $f(x) = \cos(x)$.

1-5 Sketch a flow diagram for the function $f(x) = \sin(x)$.

For problems **1-6** to **1-12** find the value of the function $f(x)$ at $x = 2$ to 4 decimal places.

1-6 $f(x) = x^5 + 2x$.

1-7 $f(x) = \sin(2x)$.

*1-8 $f(x) = \cos(3x) + x$.

*1-9 $f(x) = \cos(4x + 1)$.

1-10 $f(x) = x^2 - 2x + 1$.

1-11 $f(x) = x - \tan(x)$.

*1-12 $f(x) = \cos(2x) - 4\sin(2x)$.

For problems **1-13** to **1-15** find the value of the function $f(x)$ at $x = 4.3251$ to 4 decimal places.

1-13 $f(x) = x^3$.

1-14 $f(x) = \cos(2x) + x$.

1-15 $f(x) = x - \sin(x)$.

**1-16 The mathematical model $s = \frac{1}{2}gt^2$ describes the relationship between distance of a falling body starting from rest and time. Describe how you would set about checking this mathematical model.

Solutions

1-2 (a) 2.35, (b) 3.46, (c) 2.76, (d) 1.45.

1-6 36.

1-7 −0.7568.

1-8 2.9602.

1-9 −0.9111.

1-10 1.0000.

1-11 4.1850.

1-12 2.3736.

1-13 80.9074.

1-14 3.6104.

1-15 5.2510.

TWO

TRIGONOMETRY

Objectives After reading this chapter you should be able to:

1. Solve three-dimensional problems.
   (*a*) Use basic trigonometric definitions.
   (*b*) Use sine and cosine rules to solve scalene triangles.
   (*c*) Use trigonometric identities such as $\sin^2\theta + \cos^2\theta = 1$.
   (*d*) Define the angle between a line and a plane.
   (*e*) Define the angle between two intersecting planes.
   (*f*) Solve problems from engineering science using three-dimensional trigonometric theory.
   (*g*) Solve problems using three-dimensional theory capable of being specified in a rectangular block.
2. Use the compound angle formulae $\sin(A \pm B)$ and $\cos(A \pm B)$.
   (*a*) Prove the compound angle formulae.
   (*b*) Use the compound angle formulae to develop other trigonometric formulae.
   (*c*) Express $a\sin(\omega t) + b\cos(\omega t)$ in the form $R\sin(\omega t + \alpha)$.
   (*d*) Deduce the relationships between a, b, R, and α in 2(*c*).
   (*e*) Solve trigonometric equations using $R\sin(\omega t + \alpha)$.
3. Plot and sketch trigonometric graphs.
   (*a*) Define angular velocity.
   (*b*) Define frequency of a function.
   (*c*) Define periodic time.
   (*d*) Plot and sketch sinusoidal graphs of the form $R\sin(\omega t + \alpha)$.
   (*e*) Plot on the same graph $\sin(\omega t)$ and $\cos(\omega t)$.
   (*f*) Plot and sketch $\sin^2(\omega t)$ and $\cos^2(\omega t)$.

2-1 INTRODUCTION

The basic trigonometric definitions of sine, cosine, and tangent of an angle θ in a right-angle triangle are well known. That is

$$\sin \theta = \frac{\text{opposite}}{\text{hypotenuse}}$$

$$\cos \theta = \frac{\text{adjacent}}{\text{hypotenuse}}$$

$$\tan \theta = \frac{\text{opposite}}{\text{adjacent}}$$

We shall assume that the reader is familiar with the reciprocal trigonometric relationships

$$\operatorname{cosec} \theta = \frac{1}{\sin \theta}$$

$$\sec \theta = \frac{1}{\cos \theta}$$

$$\operatorname{cotan} \theta = \frac{1}{\tan \theta}$$

It will also be assumed that the following trigonometric relationships have been developed in previous work.

(a) $$\sin^2 \theta + \cos^2 \theta = 1$$

(b) $$1 + \tan^2 \theta = \sec^2 \theta$$

(c) $$a^2 = b^2 + c^2 - 2bc \cos A$$

(d) $$\frac{a}{\sin A} = \frac{b}{\sin B} = \frac{c}{\sin C}$$

(e) $$\tan \theta = \frac{\sin \theta}{\cos \theta}$$

A **scalene** triangle is one with *unequal* sides. During the formulation stage of modelling, these types of triangles often appear and it is a useful technique to be able to find any unknown sides or angles.

Example 2-1-1 Find all the unknown sides and angles associated with the triangles in Fig. 2-1.

SOLUTION (a) Using the standard notation associated with the sine rule, we have

$$A = 40° \qquad \text{and} \qquad a = ?$$
$$B = 120° \qquad \text{and} \qquad b = 2\,\text{m}$$
$$C = ? \qquad \text{and} \qquad c = ?$$

We can use the sine rule

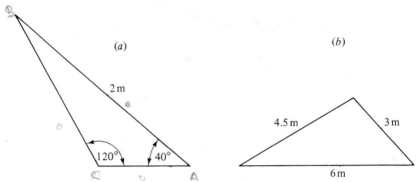

Figure 2-1

$$\frac{a}{\sin A} = \frac{b}{\sin B} = \frac{c}{\sin C}$$

Hence, on substituting the values, we have

$$\frac{a}{\sin 40°} = \frac{2}{\sin 120°}$$

or
$$a = \frac{2 \sin 40°}{\sin 120°}$$

$$= 1.4844 \, \text{m}$$

Since the three angles in a triangle add up to 180°, we have

$$C = 180 - (40 + 120)$$

$$= 20°$$

Hence, using the sine rule again, we have

$$\frac{2}{\sin 120°} = \frac{c}{\sin 20°}$$

which implies that
$$c = \frac{2 \sin 20°}{\sin 120°}$$

$$= 0.7899 \, \text{m}$$

(b) Again, using the standard notation, we have

$$A = ? \quad \text{and} \quad a = 6 \, \text{m}$$

$$B = ? \quad \text{and} \quad b = 4.5 \, \text{m}$$

$$C = ? \quad \text{and} \quad c = 3 \, \text{m}$$

Using the cosine rule

we have
$$a^2 = b^2 + c^2 - 2bc(\cos A)$$
$$36 = 20.25 + 9 - 2(4.5)(3)(\cos A)$$

which implies that
$$6.75 = -27(\cos A)$$

or
$$-0.25 = \cos A$$

Hence we have
$$A = 104.5°$$

Similarly
$$b^2 = a^2 + c^2 - 2ac(\cos B)$$
$$20.25 = 36 + 9 - 36(\cos B)$$
$$-24.75 = -36(\cos B)$$
$$0.6875 = \cos B$$

This implies that
$$B = 46.6°$$

Hence
$$C = 180 - (46.6 + 104.5)$$
$$= 28.9°$$

2-2 THE ANGLE BETWEEN A LINE AND A PLANE

The concept of a plan view in engineering drawing is founded on the ideas of projection. Here the object edges are reduced to lines and these lines are projected onto the horizontal plane. Consider one such line as shown in Fig. 2-2 by the vector arrow r. The *projected* line CD in the horizontal plane is formed by dropping a perpendicular from each endpoint of the line to the plane. The perpendiculars are known as the direction of the projection. The projected line CD is known as the **projection** of the line r onto the horizontal plane. By the definition of cosine we have

$$\cos \theta = \frac{\text{adjacent}}{\text{hypotenuse}}$$
$$= \frac{CD}{r}$$

On multiplying both sides by r we have

$$r \cos \theta = CD$$

Hence the length of the projection is $CD = r \cos \theta$. The angle θ is defined as the **angle between the line and the plane** containing the required projected length.

Example 2-2-1 A line of length 4 m lies at an angle of 30° to the horizontal plane. Find the length of the projection in the horizontal plane.

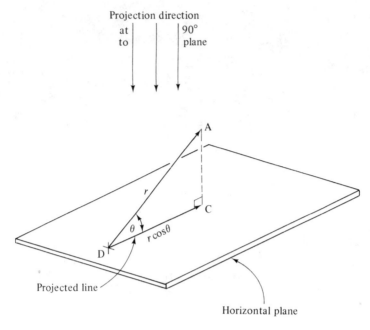

Figure 2-2

SOLUTION Since length of projection is $r \cos \theta$ where θ is the angle between the line and the plane, we have

$$r \cos \theta = 4 \cos 30°$$

$$= 3.4641 \text{ m}$$

Hence length of projection in the horizontal plane is 3.4641 m.

Example 2-2-2 A force vector of magnitude 2 newtons (N) lies at 60° to the horizontal line. Find the horizontal and vertical components.

SOLUTION The angle between the vector line and the horizontal is 60°. This implies that the projected length of the vector line in the horizontal plane is

$$r \cos \theta = 2 \cos 60°$$

$$= 1 \text{ N}$$

Hence horizontal component is 1 N.

The angle between the vertical plane and the vector line is 30°. This implies that the projected length in the vertical plane is

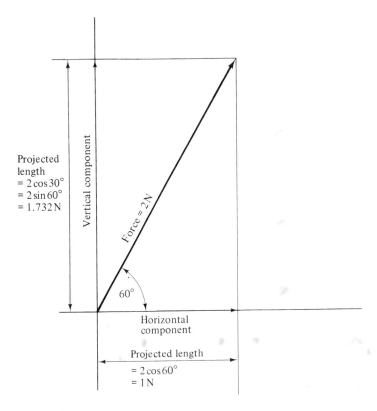

Figure 2-3

$$r \cos \theta = 2 \cos 30°$$
$$= 1.732\,N$$

Hence vertical component is 1.732 N.

The vertical and horizontal components are illustrated in Fig. 2-3.

2-3 THE ANGLE BETWEEN TWO PLANES

Figure 2-4 illustrates two planes A and B, which intersect along the line CD. This intersection is called the **trace** of the plane A onto the plane B.

We shall now define the angle between these two intersecting planes by construction. Take any point E on the intersection and draw a line in the plane A, from E perpendicular to the line of intersection CD. Draw, in plane B, another line from E also perpendicular to CD. The angle between these two lines is the **angle of intersection** or the **angle between the two planes**.

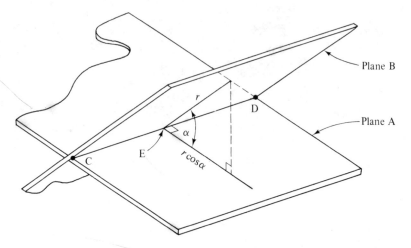

Figure 2-4 The angle of intersection α between two planes.

2-4 THREE-DIMENSIONAL TRIGONOMETRY

The standard three-dimensional coordinate system is shown in Fig. 2-5. A vector r at an angle θ from the xy plane is shown as the diagonal of a rectangular prism. The plane containing the vector r and its projection onto the horizontal plane is at an angle α from the xz plane. The projection of r onto the xy plane has a length $r \cos \theta$ by Sec. 2-2. By Pythagoras theorem, we have

$$b^2 + (r \cos \theta)^2 = r^2$$

and also

$$a^2 + c^2 = (r \cos \theta)^2$$

Hence on substituting, we get

$$b^2 + (r \cos \theta)^2 = b^2 + a^2 + c^2 = r^2$$

Therefore, the length of the line r is given by

$$r^2 = a^2 + b^2 + c^2$$

where a, b, and c are the lengths of the sides of the rectangular prism. The angle θ, the angle between the vector r and the xy plane, is given by

$$(r \cos \theta)^2 = a^2 + c^2$$

or

$$\cos^2 \theta = \frac{a^2 + c^2}{r^2}$$

or

$$\cos \theta = \sqrt{\left(\frac{a^2 + c^2}{r^2} \right)}$$

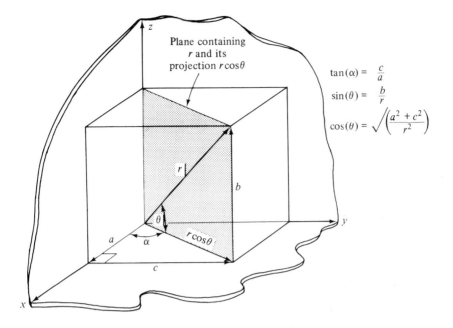

Figure 2-5

The angle α, the angle between the plane containing r and the xz plane with its trace along the z axis, is given by

$$\tan \alpha = \frac{c}{a}$$

Example 2-4-1 An oilrig 200 m high is due east of an observer. If the observer moves 300 m due south and measures the angle of elevation of the rig to be $20°$ find the distance from the base of the rig to his original position.

SOLUTION

$$\tan 25° = \frac{200}{AB}$$

where **AB** is the distance from the observer's new position to the rig base as shown in Fig. 2-6. Hence

$$AB = \frac{200}{\tan 25°}$$

$$= 428.9 \, m$$

By Pythagoras' theorem

$$(AB)^2 = (AC)^2 + (BC)^2$$

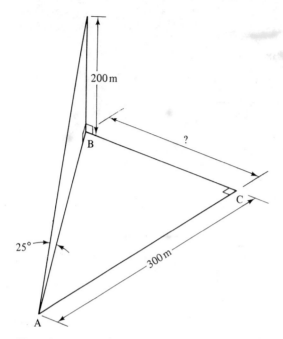

Figure 2-6

Hence

$$(BC)^2 = (AB)^2 - (AC)^2$$

$$= 428.9^2 - 300^2$$

$$\Rightarrow BC = 306.5 \text{ m}$$

Hence distance from base of rig to original position of observer is 306.5 m.

Example 2-4-2 A dynamometer measures three forces acting on a lathe tool during a turning operation. Figure 2-7 illustrates the radial, axial, and tangential forces. Find the resultant force, specifying its magnitude and the angle at which it acts to the plane containing the radial and axial force vectors.

SOLUTION Using

$$r^2 = a^2 + b^2 + c^2$$

where $a = 50\,\text{N}$ is the radial force,
$\quad b = 120\text{N}$ is the tangential force, and
$\quad c = 150\,\text{N}$ is the axial force,

the magnitude of the resultant force is

$$r = \sqrt{(50^2 + 120^2 + 150^2)}$$

$$= 198.494$$

$$= 198.5\,\text{N}$$

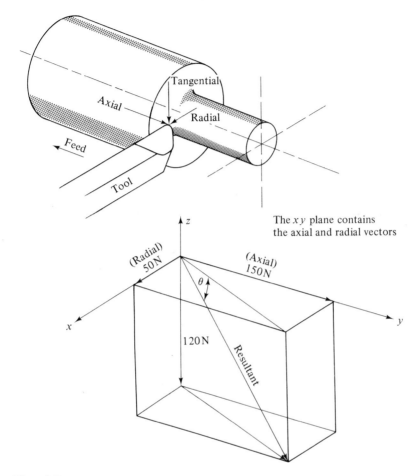

Figure 2-7

The angle between the vector line r and the plane containing the radial and axial force vectors is given by

$$\cos \theta = \sqrt{\left(\frac{a^2 + c^2}{r^2}\right)}$$

$$= 0.7965$$

which implies that

$$\theta = 37.2°$$

A second method to find θ, the angle between the resultant force and the plane containing the radial and axial force vectors, is given by

$$\sin \theta = \frac{b}{r}$$

$$= \frac{120}{198.5}$$

$$= 0.6045$$

$$\Rightarrow \qquad \theta = 37.2° \qquad \text{or} \qquad 37° \, 11'43''$$

2-5 COMPOUND ANGLE FORMULAE

The concepts of the angle between a line and a plane and its related projection can be used to develop trigonometric formulae. We shall prove the compound angle formulae

$$\sin(A \pm B) = \sin A \cdot \cos B \pm \sin B \cdot \cos A$$

and

$$\cos(A \pm B) = \cos A \cdot \cos B \mp \sin A \cdot \sin B$$

Consider the line of length r at an angle $(A + B)$ from the horizontal line OX as shown in Fig. 2-8. The line r projected onto the line OX forms a length $r \cos(A + B)$. This same line r is also projected onto the line OP forming $r \cos B$. Again the line r is projected onto WW′ forming a length $r \sin B$. Finally the line r is projected onto the line OY forming $r \sin(A + B)$.

We turn our attention to the line WW′ and project $r \sin B$ onto the line OX and onto OY giving $(r \sin B)\sin A$ and $(r \sin B)\cos A$ respectively.

Turning our attention to the line OP we project $r \cos B$ onto OX and OY giving $(r \cos B)\cos A$ and $(r \cos B)\sin A$ respectively.

Consider the lengths of the projected lines on OX. We have

$$r \cos(A + B) + (r \sin B)\sin A = (r \cos B)\cos A$$

and dividing both sides by r we have

$$\cos(A + B) + (\sin B)\sin A = (\cos B)\cos A$$

or

$$\cos(A + B) = \cos A \cdot \cos B - \sin A \cdot \sin B$$

Replace B by $-B$ and we have

$$\cos(A - B) = \cos A \cdot \cos(-B) - \sin A \cdot \sin(-B)$$

Since

$$\cos(-B) = \cos(B)$$

and

$$\sin(-B) = -\sin(B)$$

we have

$$\cos(A - B) = \cos A \cdot \cos B + \sin A \cdot \sin B$$

Consider the lengths of the projected lines on OY. We have

$$r \sin(A + B) = (r \cos B)\sin A + (r \sin B) \cos A$$

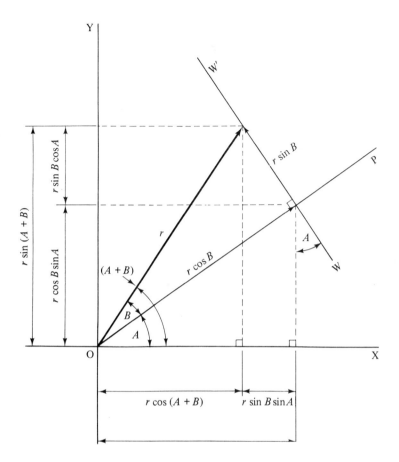

Figure 2-8

On dividing through by r this becomes

$$\sin(A + B) = \sin A \cdot \cos B + \sin B \cdot \cos A$$

As before, replace B by $-B$ and we have

$$\sin(A - B) = \sin A \cdot \cos B - \sin B \cdot \cos A$$

Example 2-5-1 Given that $\sin(30°) = 1/2$ and $\sin(45°) = 1/\sqrt{2}$, find *without* using calculators or tables the value of (*a*) $\sin(75°)$ and (*b*) $\sin(15°)$.

SOLUTION (*a*) Since

$$\sin(A + B) = \sin A \cdot \cos B + \sin B \cdot \cos A$$

we let $A = 45°$ and $B = 30°$ to give

$$\sin(45° + 30°) = \sin 45° \cdot \cos 30° + \sin 30° \cdot \cos 45°$$

$$= \frac{1}{\sqrt{2}} \cdot \frac{\sqrt{3}}{2} + \frac{1}{2} \cdot \frac{1}{\sqrt{2}}$$

Hence on factorizing

$$\sin(75°) = \frac{1}{2 \cdot \sqrt{2}}(\sqrt{3} + 1)$$

(*b*) Since

$$\sin(A - B) = \sin A \cdot \cos B - \sin B \cdot \cos A$$

we let, as before, $A = 45°$ and $B = 30°$ to give

$$\sin(15°) = \sin(45° - 30°)$$

$$= \sin 45° \cdot \cos 30° - \sin 30° \cdot \cos 45°$$

$$= \frac{1}{2 \cdot \sqrt{2}}(\sqrt{3} - 1)$$

Example 2-5-2 Given $\operatorname{cosec}(60°) = 2/\sqrt{3}$ and $\operatorname{cosec}(45°) = \sqrt{2}$ find without using tables or calculators the value of (*a*) $\operatorname{cosec}(15°)$ and (*b*) $\sec(75°)$.

SOLUTION (*a*) Since

$$\operatorname{cosec}(\theta) = \frac{1}{\sin(\theta)}$$

we have

$$\operatorname{cosec}(15°) = \frac{1}{\sin(15°)}$$

However since $60° - 45° = 15°$ we have

$$\operatorname{cosec}(15°) = \operatorname{cosec}(60° - 45°)$$

$$= \frac{1}{\sin(60° - 45°)}$$

From

$$\sin(A - B) = \sin A \cdot \cos B - \sin B \cdot \cos A$$

we have

$$\sin(60° - 45°) = \sin 60° \cdot \cos 45° - \sin 45° \cdot \cos 60°$$

Since $\operatorname{cosec}(60°) = 2/\sqrt{3}$ we have $\sin 60° = \sqrt{3}/2$ and $\cos 60° = 1/2$. Similarly $\operatorname{cosec}(45°) = \sqrt{2}$ implies that $\sin(45°) = 1/\sqrt{2} = \cos(45°)$. Hence

$$\sin(60° - 45°) = \frac{\sqrt{3}}{2} \cdot \frac{1}{\sqrt{2}} - \frac{1}{\sqrt{2}} \cdot \frac{1}{2}$$

Hence

$$\sin(15°) = \frac{1}{2 \cdot \sqrt{2}}(\sqrt{3} - 1)$$

and

$$\operatorname{cosec}(15°) = \frac{2 \cdot \sqrt{2}}{(\sqrt{3} - 1)}$$

(*b*) We have

$$\sec(75°) = \frac{1}{\cos(75°)}$$

and

$$\cos(75°) = \sin(90° - 75°) = \sin(15°)$$

By part (*a*)

$$\sin(15°) = \frac{1}{2 \cdot \sqrt{2}}(\sqrt{3} - 1)$$

and therefore we have

$$\sec(75°) = \frac{2 \cdot \sqrt{2}}{(\sqrt{3} - 1)}$$

Example 2-5-3 By using the compound formulae of $\sin(A + B)$ and $\cos(A + B)$ develop formulae for $\sin(2A)$ and $\cos(2A)$ in terms of the angle A.

SOLUTION Since

$$\sin(A + B) = \sin A \cdot \cos B + \sin B \cdot \cos A$$

we replace B by A to give

$$\sin(A + A) = \sin A \cdot \cos A + \sin A \cdot \cos A$$

or

$$\sin(2A) = 2 \sin A \cdot \cos A$$

Since

$$\cos(A + B) = \cos A \cdot \cos B - \sin A \cdot \sin B$$

we have on replacing B by A

$$\cos(2A) = \cos^2 A - \sin^2 A$$

Example 2-5-4 Show that $\sin(\theta + 90°) = \cos(\theta)$.

SOLUTION Using

$$\sin(A + B) = \sin A \cdot \cos B + \sin B \cdot \cos A$$

we have on replacing A by θ and B by $90°$,

$$\sin(\theta + 90°) = \sin \theta \cdot \cos(90°) + \sin(90°) \cos \theta$$

$$= 0 + \cos \theta$$

$$= \cos \theta$$

Example 2-5-5 Show that

$$\sin(A + B) - \sin(A - B) = 2 \sin B \cdot \cos A$$

Hence develop the formula

$$\sin(C) - \sin(D) = 2 \sin\left(\frac{C - D}{2}\right) \cos\left(\frac{C + D}{2}\right)$$

SOLUTION
$$\sin(A + B) = \sin A \cdot \cos B + \sin B \cdot \cos A$$
$$\sin(A - B) = \sin A \cdot \cos B - \sin B \cdot \cos A$$

This implies that

$$\sin(A + B) - \sin(A - B) = 2 \sin B \cdot \cos A$$

Let $(A + B) = C$ and $(A - B) = D$. Then we have

$$(C + D) = 2A$$

or

$$\left(\frac{C + D}{2}\right) = A$$

Similarly

$$(C - D) = 2B$$

$\Rightarrow$

$$\left(\frac{C - D}{2}\right) = B$$

Substitute the developed formulae for A and B into the equation

$$\sin(A + B) - \sin(A - B) = 2 \sin B \cdot \cos A$$

and we have

$$\sin(C) - \sin(D) = 2 \sin\left(\frac{C - D}{2}\right) \cos\left(\frac{C + D}{2}\right)$$

Example 2-5-6 By using the compound formulae for $\sin(A + B)$ and $\cos(A + B)$ prove that

$$\tan(A + B) = \frac{\tan A + \tan B}{1 - \tan A \cdot \tan B}$$

SOLUTION Since

$$\tan \theta = \frac{\sin \theta}{\cos \theta}$$

we have

$$\tan(A + B) = \frac{\sin(A + B)}{\cos(A + B)}$$

$$= \frac{\sin A \cdot \cos B + \sin B \cdot \cos A}{\cos A \cdot \cos B - \sin A \cdot \sin B}$$

Dividing numerator and denominator by $\cos A$ we have

$$\tan(A + B) = \frac{\tan A \cdot \cos B + \sin B}{\cos B - \tan A \cdot \sin B}$$

Dividing numerator and denominator by $\cos B$ we have

$$\tan(A + B) = \frac{\tan A + \tan B}{1 - \tan A \cdot \tan B}$$

as required.

2-6 GRAPHS OF TRIGONOMETRIC FUNCTIONS

It is very important that technician engineers can both recognize and plot graphs of common functions, particularly trigonometric curves. The curve $y = R \sin(\theta)$ in Fig. 2-9 was constructed by using the rotating-vector method. This particular rotating vector has a constant magnitude of R and rotates in an anticlockwise direction.

The graph of $y = R \sin(\theta)$ has certain features which will be useful in sketching or plotting other sinusoidal curves. These features have been collected together in Table 2-1 and consist of the zero points, maximum and minimum points, and the period. The zero points of the first **cycle** of the sine wave, $y = R \sin(\theta)$, occur at $\theta = 0$, π and 2π radians. The first cycle has a maximum point at

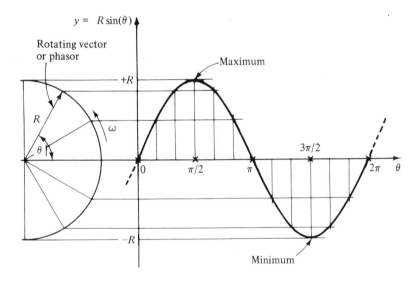

Figure 2-9 First cycle of $y = R \sin(\theta) (0 \leqslant \theta \leqslant 2\pi)$.

Table 2-1

$y = R \sin(\theta)$	Features of first cycle		
The zero points $y = 0$ occur at . . .	Maximum point	Minimum point	Period
$\theta = 0$ $\theta = \pi$ $\theta = 2\pi$	$\theta = \pi/2$ $y = R$	$\theta = 3\pi/2$ $y = -R$	$\theta_p = 2\pi$

$(\theta, y) = (\pi/2, R)$ and a minimum point at $(\theta, y) = (3\pi/2, -R)$. As the first cycle is completed in 2π radians, we say that it has a **period** of 2π and the curve $y = R\sin(\theta)$ represents a periodic function *repeating* itself every 2π radians.

2-7 CONSTANT ANGULAR VELOCITY

Consider an arm of length R attached to a rotating shaft whose angular velocity is ω rad/s. Figure 2-10 illustrates the arm at a particular time t. It is required to predict the height of the top of the arm from the horizontal axis at any time t (seconds).

Let θ be the angle turned through in t seconds. Then it follows that if the angular velocity of the shaft is constant

$$\omega = \frac{\theta}{t} \qquad \text{or} \qquad \omega t = \theta$$

From Fig. 2-10, we have

$$\sin(\theta) = \frac{y}{R}$$

or

$$R\sin(\theta) = y$$

the height of the top of the arm above the horizontal axis. We have a mathematical equation which will enable us to predict the height y for some angle θ. Since

$$\omega t = \theta$$

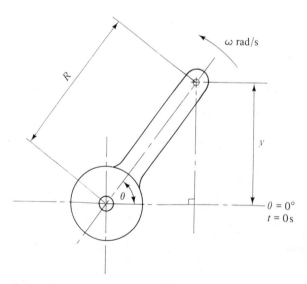

Figure 2-10

we have on substitution into $y = R \sin(\theta)$, that

$$y = R \sin(\omega t)$$

Therefore, in order to predict the height of the arm, y, from the horizontal position, we use

$$y = R \sin(\omega t)$$

The reader should note that we started the arm in the *horizontal* position and this model, $y = R \sin(\omega t)$ confirms that at $t = 0\,\text{s}, y = 0\,\text{m}$.

Example 2-7-1 An arm of length 1 m is rotated at an angular velocity of 2 rad/s. The prediction equation for the height of the top of the arm is given by

$$y = \sin(2t)$$

(*a*) Draw up a table of features for the *first cycle* of this wave.
(*b*) Using this table, plot the graph of the function $y = \sin(2t)$.

SOLUTION (*a*) Since $2t = \theta$ we have $t = \theta/2$. By using Table 2-1 we replace θ by the equivalent value for t. Hence we can form Table 2-2.

Table 2-2

$y = \sin(2t)$	Features of first cycle		
The zero points $y = 0$ occur at . . .	Maximum point	Minimum point	Period
$\theta = 0 \Rightarrow t = 0$ $\theta = \pi \Rightarrow t = \pi/2$ $\theta = 2\pi \Rightarrow t = \pi$	$\theta = \pi/2$ implies $t = \pi/4$	$\theta = 3\pi/2$ implies $t = 3\pi/4$	$\theta_p = 2\pi$ implies $T = \pi$

(*b*) To plot the graph of this function we use the rotating-vector method with Table 2-2.

We draw the axes in the usual way with the angle θ replaced by the time variable t. Using Table 2-2, we mark on the graph the zero points at $t = 0$, $\pi/2$, and π seconds, along with the maximum and minimum points of the first cycle. Intermediate values of $y = \sin(2t)$ can be found by setting the rotating vector at an angle θ and constructing the point by intersection with the respective time value. Figure 2-11 illustrates the graph showing an intermediate point at $\theta = \pi/3$ which implies that $t = \pi/6$ after using $t = \theta/2$.

Having constructed one cycle, further cycles can be sketched by noting the periodic time $T = \pi$ seconds.

Example 2-7-1 illustrated a rotating vector moving with angular velocity ω.

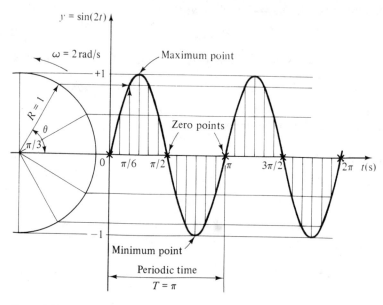

Figure 2-11

This type of rotating vector is called a **phasor**. A **phasor** then is a vector whose direction is specified in terms of an angle which is usually related to the time variable.

The **amplitude** of the function $y = R \sin(\omega t)$ is the value R. For example, if $y = 3 \sin(2t)$ then the amplitude is 3.

2-8 PHASE SHIFT

In Sec. 2-7 we started the arm on the rotating shaft at $t = 0$ in the horizontal position. Suppose we now start the arm rotating with constant angular velocity ω, from some angle α as shown in Fig. 2-12. After a time interval t, the arm will move to a position defined by the angle θ.

It has moved through an angle $A = \theta - \alpha$ which implies $\theta = A + \alpha$.

Again suppose we wish to predict the height of the top of the arm from the horizontal, then since

$$\text{Angular velocity} = \frac{\text{angle turned through}}{\text{time}}$$

$$\omega = \frac{A}{t} \qquad \text{or} \qquad \omega t = A$$

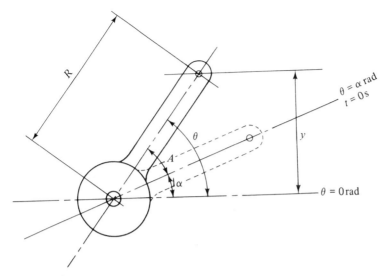

Figure 2-12

and $\theta = A + \alpha$ becomes

$$\theta = \omega t + \alpha$$

The equation for the height is

$$y = R \sin(\theta)$$
$$= R \sin(\omega t + \alpha)$$

From Sec. 2-6 we can build a table of features for the first cycle of $y = R \sin(\omega t + \alpha)$. Since

$$\theta = (\omega t + \alpha)$$

we have

$$t = \left(\frac{\theta - \alpha}{\omega} \right)$$

and using this transformation we can build the Table 2-3.

Table 2-3

$y = R \sin(\omega t + \alpha)$	Features of first cycle		
The zero points $y = 0$ occur at . . .	Maximum point	Minimum point	Period
$\theta = 0 \Rightarrow t = \dfrac{0 - \alpha}{\omega}$	$\theta = \pi/2$	$\theta = 3\pi/2$	$\theta_{\mathrm{p}} = 2\pi$
$\theta = \pi \Rightarrow t = \dfrac{\pi - \alpha}{\omega}$	implies	implies	implies
$\theta = 2\pi \Rightarrow t = \dfrac{2\pi - \alpha}{\omega}$	$t = \dfrac{(\frac{1}{2}\pi - \alpha)}{\omega}$	$t = \dfrac{(\frac{3}{2}\pi - \alpha)}{\omega}$	$T = \dfrac{2\pi}{\omega}$

Example 2-8-1 In an electrical circuit, the current (in amperes) is given by

$$i = 4 \sin\left(t + \frac{\pi}{2}\right)$$

(a) Plot the graph of this function and state the phase shift.
(b) Calculate the periodic time.
(c) State the amplitude and describe the physical significance of this value.

SOLUTION (a) Compare $i = 4 \sin(t + \pi/2)$ with $y = R \sin(\omega t + \alpha)$ and we have $R = 4, \omega = 1$ rad/s, $\alpha = \pi/2$ rad, $y = i$. Using Table 2-3 we can construct a table, Table 2-4, of features for this particular sine wave.

Table 2-4

$i = 4 \sin(t + \pi/2)$		Features of first cycle	
The zero points $i = 0$ occur at ...	Maximum point	Minimum point	Period
$t = -\pi/2$	$t = 0$	$t = \pi$	$T = 2\pi/1$
$t = \pi/2$	$i = 4$	$i = -4$	$= 2\pi$
$t = 3\pi/2$			

To plot the graph of $i = 4 \sin(t + \pi/2)$ we use the rotating-vector, or phasor, method. Construct a circle with a radius of 4 units. Mark the time axis with the three zero points from Table 2-4. Place the maximum and minimum points of the first cycle in position. As before, if intermediate points are required we have to construct these from the rotating vector line. For example, when the rotating vector is at $3\pi/4$ rad then we have a time value of

$$t = \frac{\theta - \alpha}{\omega}$$

$$= \frac{3\pi/4 - \pi/2}{1}$$

$$= \pi/4 \text{ s}$$

The final graph is shown in Fig. 2-13. It should be noted that we have plotted a cosine wave and that in general

$$y = R \sin(\omega t + \pi/2)$$

$$= R \cos(\omega t)$$

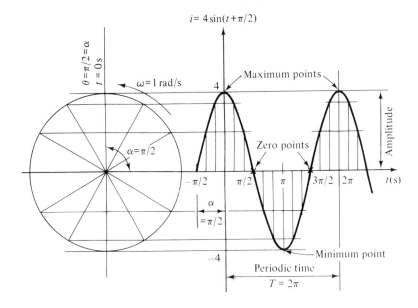

$i = 4\sin(t + \pi/2)$

Figure 2-13

(b)
$$\text{Periodic time} = T = \frac{2\pi}{\omega}$$

$$= 2\pi \, s$$

The phase shift is the amount that the sine wave $y = 4\sin(t)$ has been moved along the axis. That is the amount $\alpha = \pi/2$ rad. This has been labelled on the graph in Fig. 2-13.

(c) The amplitude of this function is 4 and its physical significance is that it represents the *maximum* possible current value flowing in the circuit. That is

$$\text{Maximum current possible} = 4 \, A$$

2-9 FREQUENCY

Frequency is a measure of how often an event repeats itself. For example, the graph of the function $y = \sin(4\pi t)$ repeats itself twice every second. In general, mathematical curves in the form of $R \cdot \sin(\omega t + \alpha)$ repeat themselves $\omega/2\pi$ every second. We have the frequency equation given by

$$\text{frequency} = \frac{\text{angular velocity}}{2\pi} \quad \text{cycles/second or hertz (Hz)}$$

From our graph plotting we have seen that the

$$\text{Periodic time} = \frac{2\pi}{\omega}$$

and hence we have the relationship

$$\text{Frequency} = \frac{1}{\text{periodic time}}$$

It should be remembered that we should translate these relationships back to the physical system we are modelling.

Example 2-9-1 Consider the rotating arm in Fig. 2-10. We can predict the height of the arm at any time t, by using the relationship

$$y = R \cdot \sin(\omega t)$$

Assuming that the arm has a radius $R = 3$ m and is rotating with constant angular velocity $\omega = 4\pi$ rad/s, find the frequency, amplitude, and periodic time of this function. Explain in all three cases the physical significance of the results.

SOLUTION Amplitude is 3 m and this is the maximum height reached by the arm. It occurs at $\frac{1}{8}$ s in the first instance.

$$\text{Frequency} = \frac{\text{angular velocity}}{2\pi}$$

$$= \frac{4\pi}{2\pi} = 2 \text{ Hz}$$

Physically the frequency of 2 Hz implies that the arm completes 2 revolutions every second.

$$\text{Periodic time} = \frac{1}{f}$$

$$\Rightarrow \qquad T = 0.5 \text{ s}$$

Physically the arm takes 0.5 s to rotate through 2π radians or one complete circle.

Example 2-9-2 Find the frequency, periodic time, and amplitude of the following sinusoidal curves:
(a) $y = 3.5 \sin(2t - 1)$,
(b) $y = -4 \sin(-2t + 1)$, and
(c) $y = -2.5 \sin(t - 1)$.

SOLUTION
(a)
$$\text{Frequency} = \frac{\text{angular velocity}}{2\pi}$$

$$= \frac{2}{2\pi}$$

$$= 0.3183 \text{ Hz}$$

$$\text{Periodic time} = 1/f$$

$$= 3.142 \text{ s}$$

$$\text{Amplitude} = 3.5 \text{ units}$$

(b) Since $\sin(-\theta) = -\sin(\theta)$ we have

$$y = -4 \sin(-2t + 1)$$

$$= 4 \sin(2t - 1)$$

and hence the angular velocity is 2 rad/s. This implies that we have a frequency of 0.3183 Hz as in part (a). The periodic time also is the same as that in part (a) namely,

$$T = 3.142 \text{ s}$$

$$\text{Amplitude} = 4 \text{ units}$$

(c) The curve $y = -2.5 \sin(t - 1)$ has an angular velocity associated with it of 1 rad/s and hence

$$\text{Frequency} = 1/2\pi$$

$$= 0.1592 \text{ Hz}$$

$$\text{Periodic time} = 1/f$$

$$= 6.2832 \text{ s}$$

$$\text{Amplitude} = 2.5 \text{ units}$$

2-10 GRAPHS OF $\sin^2(\omega t)$ AND $\cos^2(\omega t)$

To plot graphs of the curves

$$y = \sin^2(\omega t) \qquad \text{and} \qquad y = \cos^2(\omega t)$$

we cannot use the rotating-vector method directly. We will illustrate the method of plotting these graphs by considering an example.

Example 2-10-1 Plot the graph $y = 3 \sin^2(t)$.

SOLUTION We draw up a table, Table 2-5, and plot the graph as in Fig. 2-14.
It can be seen that the effect of squaring the values of the sine function is to remove the negative values and the graph of $3 \sin^2(t)$ repeats itself every π radians. The $\cos^2(\omega t)$ graphs can be plotted in a similar way.

Table 2-5

t	0	$\pi/6$	$2\pi/6$	$3\pi/6$	$4\pi/6$	$5\pi/6$	$6\pi/6$	$7\pi/6$	$8\pi/6$	$9\pi/6$
$\sin t$	0	0.5	0.866	1	0.866	0.5	0	-0.5	-0.866	-1
$\sin^2 t$	0	0.25	0.75	1	0.75	0.25	0	0.25	0.75	1
$3\sin^2 t$	0	0.75	2.25	3	2.25	0.75	0	0.75	2.25	3

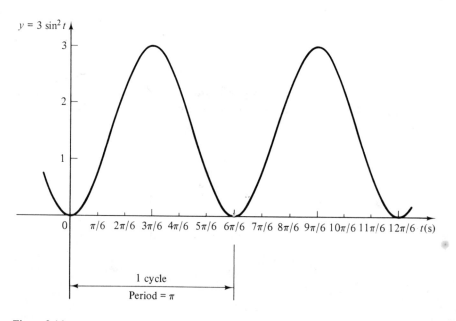

Figure 2-14

2-11 ADDITION OF SINE AND COSINE FUNCTIONS

In this section we shall consider the addition of sine and cosine functions in the form

$$a \cdot \sin(\omega t) + b \cdot \cos(\omega t)$$

where t is regarded as time in seconds and ω the angular velocity. By using the compound angle formula for $\sin(A + B)$ we can show that $a \cdot \sin(\omega t) + b \cdot \cos(\omega t)$ can be transformed into the form

$$R \cdot \sin(\omega t + \alpha)$$

Since

$$\sin(A + B) = \sin A \cdot \cos B + \sin B \cdot \cos A$$

we have on replacing A by ωt and B by α that

$$\sin(\omega t + \alpha) = \sin(\omega t) \cdot \cos\alpha + \sin\alpha \cdot \cos(\omega t)$$

$\Rightarrow \qquad R\sin(\omega t + \alpha) = R\sin(\omega t) \cdot \cos\alpha + R\sin\alpha \cdot \cos(\omega t)$

Let

$$a \cdot \sin(\omega t) + b \cdot \cos(\omega t) = R\sin(\omega t) \cdot \cos\alpha + R\sin\alpha \cdot \cos(\omega t)$$
$$= R\sin(\omega t + \alpha)$$

and comparing coefficients for $\sin(\omega t)$ we have

$$R \cdot \cos\alpha = a$$

Similarly for the $\cos(\omega t)$ terms

$$R \cdot \sin\alpha = b$$

On squaring both of these equations, we have

$$R^2\cos^2\alpha = a^2$$

and

$$R^2\sin^2\alpha = b^2$$

Adding the two equations together gives

$$R^2\cos^2\alpha + R^2\sin^2\alpha = a^2 + b^2$$

or

$$R^2(\cos^2\alpha + \sin^2\alpha) = a^2 + b^2$$

on factorizing out R^2. However $\cos^2\alpha + \sin^2\alpha = 1$ which implies that

$$R^2 = a^2 + b^2$$

Since

$$R \cdot \sin\alpha = b \qquad \text{and} \qquad R \cdot \cos\alpha = a$$

we have on dividing these equations

$$\tan\alpha = \frac{b}{a}$$

Therefore from $\tan\alpha = b/a$ and $R^2 = a^2 + b^2$ we can find the values of the phase angle α and the amplitude R.

[*A word of warning*! Be extremely careful to check within which quadrant the angle α lies by using the four-quadrant theory.]

Example 2-11-1 Place the following in the form $R\sin(2t + \alpha)$:
(a) $3\sin(2t) + 4\cos(2t)$,
(b) $-3\sin(2t) + 4\cos(2t)$, and
(c) $3\sin(2t) - 4\cos(2t)$.

SOLUTION Let

$$R \cdot \sin(2t + \alpha) = a \cdot \sin(2t) + b \cdot \cos(2t)$$

then
$$R \cdot \cos \alpha = a \qquad \text{and} \qquad R \cdot \sin \alpha = b$$

(a) In this case, $a = 3, b = 4$, and
$$R^2 = 3^2 + 4^2$$
$$= 25$$

Hence
$$R = 5 \qquad \text{(ALWAYS TAKE } R \text{ TO BE THE POSITIVE ROOT)}$$

This implies
$$5 \cos \alpha = 3 \qquad \text{and} \qquad 5 \sin \alpha = 4$$
or
$$\cos \alpha = \tfrac{3}{5} \qquad \text{and} \qquad \sin \alpha = \tfrac{4}{5}$$

Both $\cos \alpha$ and $\sin \alpha$ are positive implying that α lies in the *first* quadrant. The reader should check this by a neat sketch.

At this stage from a point of numerical work, it is good practice to take the tan α formula
$$\tan \alpha = \frac{b}{a}$$

as this, unlike the $\cos \alpha$ and the $\sin \alpha$ formulae, does not contain a calculated value, namely R. Hence
$$\tan \alpha = \tfrac{4}{3} \Rightarrow \alpha = 0.9273 \text{ rad}$$

as we are in the *first* quadrant. The reader should note that α should *never* be given in degrees when the variable time t is involved. Therefore

(b) Let
$$3 \sin(2t) + 4 \cos(2t) = 5 \sin(2t + 0.9273)$$
$$-3 \sin(2t) + 4 \cos(2t) = R \sin(2t + \alpha)$$

Hence we have
$$R \cdot \cos \alpha = -3 \qquad \text{and} \qquad R \cdot \sin \alpha = 4$$

This implies that
$$R^2 = (-3)^2 + 4^2$$
$$= 25$$

Hence
$$R = 5$$

Also
or
$$5 \cos \alpha = -3 \qquad \text{and} \qquad 5 \sin \alpha = 4$$
$$\cos \alpha = -\tfrac{3}{5} \qquad \text{and} \qquad \sin \alpha = \tfrac{4}{5}$$

With $\cos \alpha$ being negative and at the same time $\sin \alpha$ being positive we have α belonging to the *second* quadrant. From
$$\tan \alpha = \frac{4}{-3}$$

we have

$$\alpha = \pi - 0.9273$$

$$= 2.2143 \text{ rad}$$

and hence

$$-3 \sin(2t) + 4 \cos(2t) = 5 \sin(2t + 2.2143)$$

(c) Let

$$3 \sin(2t) - 4 \cos(2t) = R \sin(2t + \alpha)$$

Hence we have

$$R \cdot \cos \alpha = 3 \qquad \text{and} \qquad R \cdot \sin \alpha = -4$$

With $\cos \alpha$ being positive and $\sin \alpha$ being negative this implies that α belongs to the *fourth* quadrant. From $\tan \alpha = b/a$ we have

$$\tan \alpha = -\tfrac{4}{3}$$

and hence α is $(2\pi - 0.9273)$ or -0.9273 rad. Hence since $R = 5$, as before we have

$$3 \sin(2t) - 4 \cos(2t) = 5 \sin(2t - 0.9273) = 5 \sin(2t + 5.3559)$$

Example 2-11-2 An electrical circuit has two currents, i_1 and i_2, flowing towards the same point. If $i_1 = 0.2 \sin(3t)$ and $i_2 = 0.3 \cos(3t)$, find the current flowing away from that point. Hence find the amplitude of the resultant sine wave and the earliest time at which this output current is 0.36A.

SOLUTION Current flowing away from the point is $0.2 \sin(3t) + 0.3 \cos(3t)$. To find the resultant sine wave we place the new current

$$i_3 = 0.2 \sin(3t) + 0.3 \cos(3t)$$

in the form

$$R \cdot \sin(3t + \alpha)$$

Hence

$$R \cdot \sin(3t + \alpha) = 0.2 \sin(3t) + 0.3 \cos(3t)$$

implies that

$$R^2 = 0.2^2 + 0.3^2$$

$$= 0.13$$

$\Rightarrow$

$$R = 0.3606$$

As in Example 2-11-1, we have

$$R \cdot \cos \alpha = 0.2 \qquad \text{and} \qquad R \cdot \sin \alpha = 0.3$$

or

$$\cos \alpha = \frac{0.2}{0.3606} \qquad \text{and} \qquad \sin \alpha = \frac{0.2}{0.3606}$$

Both $\sin \alpha$ and $\cos \alpha$ are positive which implies that α belongs to the *first* quadrant. Hence $\tan \alpha = b/a$ implies

$$\tan \alpha = \frac{0.3}{0.2} = 1.5$$

or

$$\alpha = 0.9828 \text{ rad}$$

Hence

$$0.2 \sin(3t) + 0.3 \cos(3t) = 0.3606 \sin(3t + 0.9828)$$

The amplitude of the resultant sine wave is 0.3606 A. Since

$$i_3 = 0.3606 \sin(3t + 0.9828)$$

we have for $i_3 = 0.36$ A,

$$0.3606 \sin(3t + 0.9828) = 0.36$$

$$\sin(3t + 0.9828) = 0.998\,34$$

$$3t + 0.9828 = 1.5132$$

on applying the inverse sine. Hence

$$3t = 1.5132 - 0.9828$$

$$= 0.5304$$

$\Rightarrow \qquad t = 0.1768 \text{ s} \rightarrow 0.18 \text{ s} \qquad$ (to 2 decimal places)

The earliest time that the current i_3 will reach 0.36 A is 0.18 s.

Example 2-11-3 A mass is fixed at one end of a vertical spring which is attached to a beam. The mass is pulled down and released, thus setting up vertical vibrations. By using differential equations, an engineer found that he could predict the distance of the mass, in metres, from the static equilibrium position by using

$$s = 0.5 \sin(4t) + 0.4 \cos(4t)$$

Evaluate the amplitude of the vibration and state the earliest time at which the mass is at a distance of 0.5 m away from the static equilibrium position.

SOLUTION To find the amplitude of vibration, we have to place the distance equation in the form $R \cdot \sin(4t + \alpha)$. This implies that

$$R^2 = (0.5)^2 + (0.4)^2$$

or

$$R = 0.6403$$

We also have

$$R \cdot \cos \alpha = 0.5 \qquad \text{and} \qquad R \cdot \sin \alpha = 0.4$$

This implies that α belongs to the *first* quadrant and $\alpha = 0.6747$ rad. Hence

$$s = 0.5 \sin(4t) + 0.4 \cos(4t) = 0.6403 \sin(4t + 0.6747)$$

and we have an amplitude of vibration of 0.6403 m. If $s = 0.5$ m we have

$$0.6403 \sin(4t + 0.6747) = 0.5$$

$$\Rightarrow \qquad \sin(4t + 0.6747) = 0.7809$$

$$4t + 0.6747 = 0.8961$$

by taking inverse sines. Thus we obtain

$$4t = 0.2214$$

or

$$t = 0.05535 \, \text{s} \longrightarrow 0.06 \, \text{s}$$

The earliest time that the mass will reach 0.5 m away from the equilibrium position is 0.06 s.

All the steps in the transformation of $a \cdot \sin(\omega t) + b \cdot \cos(\omega t)$ to the form $R \cdot \sin(\omega t + \alpha)$ can be performed by **vector** methods. We *define* $R \cdot \sin(\omega t + \alpha)$ in vector notation as $R \underline{/\alpha}$. Hence

$$a \cdot \sin(\omega t) = a \cdot \sin(\omega t + 0) \quad = a \underline{/0}$$

and

$$b \cdot \cos(\omega t) = b \cdot \sin(\omega t + \pi/2) = b \underline{/\pi/2}$$

We can now construct a vector diagram in the usual way. As we have the direction in terms of a time angle, these vectors are called **phasors**.

Example 2-11-4 Place $3 \sin(2t) - 4 \cos(2t)$ in the form $R \cdot \sin(2t + \alpha)$ by using the phasor method.

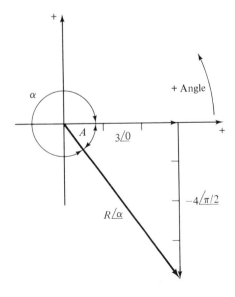

Figure 2-15 Vector addition, $3 \underline{/0} - 4 \underline{/\pi/2}$.

SOLUTION

$$3 \sin(2t) = 3 \sin(2t + 0) \qquad \longrightarrow 3 \,\underline{/0}$$

$$-4 \cos(2t) = -4 \sin(2t + \pi/2) \longrightarrow -4 \,\underline{/\pi/2}$$

Constructing the phasor diagram gives Fig. 2-15 and from this we can see by Pythagoras' theorem that

$$R^2 = 3^2 + 4^2 = 25$$

$$\Rightarrow \qquad R = 5$$

It is clear that the angle α is in the *fourth* quadrant and that $\tan A = \frac{4}{3}$ which implies that $A = 0.9273$ rad. Hence as we are in the fourth quadrant

$$\alpha = 2\pi - 0.9273$$

$$= 5.3559 \, \text{rad}$$

Therefore we have

$$3 \sin(2t) - 4 \cos(2t) = 5 \sin(2t + 5.3559)$$

PROBLEMS

For problems **2-1** to **2-4** find all the unknown sides and angles of a triangle with its sides labelled a, b, and c, and the corresponding angles A, B, and C.

2-1 $a = 13$, $b = 15$, and $B = 28°$.

2-2 $a = 11$, $b = 14$, and $B = 25°$.

2-3 $a = 12$, $c = 3.5$, and $A = 120°$.

2-4 $a = 10$, $c = 15$, and $C = 32°$.

For problems **2-5** to **2-10** find the projected length of a line lying at an angle θ to a plane and length r metres.

2-5 $r = 2$, $\theta = 30°$.

2-6 $r = 3.6$, $\theta = 28°$.

2-7 $r = 1.85$, $\theta = 45.7°$.

2-8 $r = 49.7$, $\theta = 0.5$ rad.

2-9 $r = 100.45$, $\theta = 0.5236$ rad.

2-10 $r = 3.456$, $\theta = 1.5$ rad.

For problems **2-11** to **2-15** find the length of a line which is lying at an angle of θ to a plane and whose projection in that plane has a length of x metres.

2-11 $x = 2$, $\theta = 30°$.

2-12 $x = 1.2$, $\theta = 45°$.

2-13 $x = 0.98$, $\theta = 36°$.

2-14 $x = 8.65$, $\theta = 0.5236$ rad.

2-15 $x = 6.75$, $\theta = 1.56$ rad.

For problems **2-16** to **2-20** find the angle at which a line of length r metres lies to a plane when its projected length in that plane is x metres.

2-16 $r = 2$, $x = 1.3$.

2-17 $r = 3, x = 1.45$.

2-18 $r = 4, x = 3.6$.

2-19 $r = 4.65, x = 0.987$.

2-20 $r = 456, x = 391$.

For problems **2-21** to **2-25** find the vertical and horizontal components of a force of magnitude F newtons and acting at an angle θ to the horizontal plane. In each case use the theory of projection.

2-21 $F = 2, \theta = 25°$.

2-22 $F = 2.56, \theta = 45°$.

2-23 $F = 5.78, \theta = 0.5$ rad.

2-24 $F = 6.78, \theta = 1.5$ rad.

2-25 $F = 23.5, \theta = 1.3$ rad.

*2-26 Two coplanar forces of 3 N and 6 N act at a point. Find the resultant force in magnitude and direction by the method of projection if the angle between the lines of action is $30°$.

For problems **2-27** to **2-32** find the length of the longest diagonal of a rectangular box whose sides are x, y, and z metres.

2-27 $x = 3, y = 2, z = 1$.

2-28 $x = 4, y = 3, z = 1.5$.

2-29 $x = 5, y = 2.5, z = 1.4$.

2-30 $x = 0.5, y = 0.8, z = 1.2$.

2-31 $x = 0.32, y = 0.98, z = 1$.

2-32 $x = 9.8, y = 7.5, z = 4.5$.

2-33 A rectangular box has a maximum length of its longest diagonal as 3 m. If two of its dimensions are 1 and 2 m, find the length of the third side.

**2-34 An observer sees a ship from the top of a cliff of height 100 m. The ship is seen through an instrument which measured the angle of depression to be $80°$. The observer then moved back a distance of 10 m, at which point the ship and the top of the cliff were in line. Find the distance from the base of the cliff to the ship.

**2-35 A ship is travelling at a constant speed and is observed by a person standing on top of a 150 m cliff. When the person first sees the ship, the angle of depression is $20°$. Two minutes later and having turned his instrument through a horizontal angle of $60°$, the person observes the ship at an angle of depression of $60°$. Find the speed of the ship.

*2-36 A tower 200 m high is due south of an observer. If the observer moves 250 m due east and measures the angle of elevation to be $30°$, find the distance from the base of the tower to his original position.

2-37 Three forces A, B, and C act at, and away from, the *origin* of a three-dimensional coordinate system. Force A acts along the x axis and has a magnitude of 3 N; force B acts along the y axis and has a magnitude of 5 N; force C acts along the z axis and has a magnitude of 2 N. Evaluate the magnitude of the resultant force and specify the angle to the xy plane at which it acts. The resultant force and its projection both lie in a plane at an angle α to the xz plane. Find this angle between these two planes.

2-38 Given that $\sin(30°) = 0.5$ find without tables (a) $\cos(30°)$, (b) $\cos(60°)$, (c) $\sec(30°)$, (d) $\operatorname{cosec}(30°)$, and (e) $\tan(30°)$.

2-39 Given that $\sin(30°) = 0.5$ and $\sin(45°) = 1/\sqrt{2}$ find the value of (a) $\sin(15°)$, (b) $\sin(75°)$, (c) $\cos(75°)$, and (d) $4 \sin(-15°)$ without a calculator or tables.

2-40 Given that $\sin(60°) = \sqrt{3}/2$ and that $\sin(45°) = 1/\sqrt{2}$ find the value of (a) $\sin(15°)$, (b) $\sec(15°)$, (c) $\tan(15°)$, and (d) $\operatorname{cosec}(105°)$ without using a calculator or tables.

***2-41 By using the compound formulae for $\sin(A + B)$ and $\cos(A + B)$, develop formulae for (a) $\sin(3A)$, and (b) $\cos(3A)$ in terms of $\sin(A)$ and $\cos(A)$.

For problems **2-42** to **2-54** plot the graphs $y = f(t)$ for the restricted interval stated.

2-42 $y = \sin(2.5t)$ $0 \leqslant t \leqslant 2\pi$.

2-43 $y = \sin(4t)$ $0 \leqslant t \leqslant 2\pi$.

2-44 $y = \sin(0.5t)$ $0 \leqslant t \leqslant 2\pi$.

2-45 $y = 3 \sin(t)$ $0 \leqslant t \leqslant 2\pi$.

2-46 $y = \sin(t + \pi)$ $-\pi \leqslant t \leqslant 2\pi$.

2-47 $y = \sin(2t + \pi)$ $-\pi \leqslant t \leqslant \pi/2$.

*2-48 $y = 3 \sin(t - 1)$ $-2 \leqslant t \leqslant 3$.

**2-49 $y = -2 \sin(t + 2)$ $-2 \leqslant t \leqslant 2$.

**2-50 $y = 4 \sin(3t + 1.2)$ $-2 \leqslant t \leqslant 4$.

**2-51 $y = -3 \sin(2t + 2.4)$ $-3 \leqslant t \leqslant 3$.

***2-52 $y = \sin(4.6t + 2)$ $-2 \leqslant t \leqslant 2$.

***2-53 $y = 4.5 \sin(3.2t - 3)$ $0 \leqslant t \leqslant 6$.

*2-54 $y = 2.3 \sin(2t + 2)$ $-2 \leqslant t \leqslant 2$.

For problems **2-55** to **2-64** find the frequency, amplitude, and periodic time associated with the functions $y = f(t)$.

2-55 $y = \sin(t)$.

2-56 $y = \sin(3t)$.

*2-57 $y = \sin(-2t)$.

*2-58 $y = \sin(-3t)$.

2-59 $y = 3 \sin(t)$.

*2-60 $y = -4 \sin(2t)$.

2-61 $y = 2.5 \sin(0.5t)$.

**2-62 $y = 2 \sin(2t - 1)$.

**2-63 $y = 3 \sin(3t + 4)$.

**2-64 $y = -4 \sin(2t + 100)$.

**2-65 Calculate the phase difference between $y = \sin(t)$ and $y = \sin(t - 5)$. Sketch the curves and illustrate this phase difference.

2-66 The current flowing in a circuit is given by $i = 4 \sin(2t - 0.9)$. Find the maximum value of current flowing and its frequency.

2-67 Plot the graph of $y = \sin^2(1.2t)$ for $0 \leqslant t \leqslant 2$.

*2-68 Plot the graph of $y = \cos^2(-2t)$ for $0 \leqslant t \leqslant 1$.

2-69 Plot the graph of $y = 3 \cos^2(3t)$ for $0 \leqslant t \leqslant 1$.

For problems **2-70** to **2-76** place the function given in the form $R \cdot \sin(\omega t + \alpha)$.

2-70 $4 \sin(2t) + 3 \cos(2t)$.

2-71 $-4 \sin(2t) - \cos(2t)$.

2-72 $4 \sin(2t) - 2 \cos(2t)$.

2-73 $-2 \sin(3t) - \cos(3t)$.

2-74 $5 \sin(t) + 4 \cos(t)$.

2-75 $-3 \sin(0.5t) - 4 \cos(0.5t)$.

***2-76 $2 \sin(t + 1) + \cos(t + 1)$

**2-77 An electrical circuit has two currents flowing towards the same point. If these currents are $i_1 = 3 \sin(2t)$ and $i_2 = \cos(2t)$, find the resultant current in the form $R \cdot \sin(\omega t + \alpha)$. Evaluate the frequency and periodic time of this resultant current and state its amplitude.

**2-78 A mass supported by a vertical spring is pulled downwards and released. An engineer finds that the equation $s = 0.05 \sin(0.4t) + 0.03 \cos(0.4t)$ relates the distance s from the static equilibrium position of the mass to the time t. Place s in the form $R \cdot \sin(\omega t + \alpha)$ and hence find the amplitude of vibration, its periodic time, and its frequency, and sketch the graph of the distance–time function over the first 32 seconds.

2-79 By using the phasor method place
(a) $\sin(4t) + 2 \cos(4t)$, and
(b) $-4 \sin(3t) + 3 \cos(3t)$
in the form $R \cdot \sin(\omega t + \alpha)$.

*2-80 Solve the equation $3 \sin(2t) + 4 \cos(2t) = 5$ for t between 0 and 0.5 s.

*2-81 Solve the equation $4 \sin(3t) + 3 \cos(3t) = 5$ for t between 0 and 0.5 s.

2-82 An alternating current is given by $i = 50 \sin(100t + 0.5)$. Find its frequency, periodic time, amplitude, and the value of the current at $t = 0$ s.

2-83 If $\sin(70°) + \sin(30°) = 2 \sin(A) \cos(B)$ find the values of A and B.

**2-84 Prove that $2 \cos(A) \cos(B) = \cos(A + B) + \cos(A - B)$.

***2-85 A mass of 1 kg is attached to the end of a vertically supported spring. If the mass is pulled down and released, the system vibrates. Assuming that the resistance to motion is very small so that it can be neglected, the distance s, in metres, from the equilibrium position is given by

$$s = 0.1 \sin(10t) + 0.3 \cos(10t)$$

(a) Calculate the frequency, periodic time, and amplitude of the vibration.
(b) Sketch the function s.

Solutions

2-1 $A = 24°$, $C = 128°$, $c = 25.1776$.

2-2 $A = 19.39°$ or $19° \ 24'$, $C = 135.61°$ or $135° \ 36'$, $c = 23.175$.

2-3 $C = 14.63°$ or $14° \ 38'$, $B = 45.37°$ or $45° \ 22'$, $b = 9.8609$.

2-4 $A = 20.688°$, $B = 127.312°$, $b = 22.5132$.

2-5 1.732 m.

2-6 3.1786 m.

2-7 1.292 m.

2-8 43.6158.

2-9 86.9922 m.

2-10 0.2445 m.

2-11 2.3094 m.

2-12 1.697 m.

2-13 1.2113 m.

2-14 9.9882 m.

2-15 625.2248 m.

2-16 49.46° or 49° 27'.

2-17 61.1° or 61° 06'.

2-18 25.84° or 25° 51'.

2-19 77.74° or 77° 45'.

2-20 30.97° or 30° 58'.

2-21 0.8452 N, 1.8126 N.

2-22 1.8102 N, 1.8102 N.

2-23 2.7711 N, 5.0724 N.

2-24 6.7630 N, 0.4796 N.

2-25 22.6436 N, 6.2862 N.

2-26 8.7279 N.

2-27 3.7417 m.

2-28 5.2202 m.

2-29 5.7628 m.

2-30 1.5264 m.

2-31 1.4362 m.

2-32 13.1354 m.

2-33 2 m.

2-34 576.96 m.

2-35 2.0 m/s.

2-36 239.72 m.

2-37 6.1644 N, 18.93°, 59.04°.

2-38 (a) $\sqrt{3}/2$, (b) 1/2, (c) $2/\sqrt{3}$ (d) 2, (e) $1/\sqrt{3}$.

2-39

(a) $\dfrac{1}{2\sqrt{2}}(\sqrt{3}-1),$

(b) $\dfrac{1}{2\sqrt{2}}(\sqrt{3}+1),$

(c) $\dfrac{1}{2\sqrt{2}}(\sqrt{3}-1),$

(d) $\dfrac{2}{\sqrt{2}}(1-\sqrt{3}).$

2-40

(a) $\dfrac{1}{2\sqrt{2}}(\sqrt{3}-1),$

(b) $\dfrac{2\sqrt{2}}{\sqrt{3}+1},$

(c) $\dfrac{\sqrt{3}-1}{\sqrt{3}+1},$

(d) $\dfrac{2\sqrt{2}}{\sqrt{3}+1}.$

2-41 [*Hint:* Let $B = 2A$, then expand using $\sin(A + B)$, after which substitute for $\sin(2A)$ and $\cos(2A)$.]

2-55 0.1592 Hz, 1, 6.2832 s.

2-56 0.4775 Hz, 1, 2.0944 s.

2-57 0.3183 Hz, 1, 3.1416 s.

2-58 0.4775 Hz, 1, 2.0944 s.

2-59 0.1592 Hz, 3, 6.2832 s.

2-60 0.3183 Hz, 4, 3.1416 s.

2-61 0.0796 Hz, 2.5, 12.5663 s.

2-62 0.3183 Hz, 2, 3.1416 s.

2-63 0.4775 Hz, 3, 2.0944 s.

2-64 0.3183 Hz, 4, 3.1416 s.

2-65 5 rad.

2-66 4 A, 0.3183 Hz.

2-70 $5 \sin(2t + 0.6435)$.

2-71 $4.1231 \sin(2t + 3.3866)$.

2-72 $4.4721 \sin(2t - 0.4636)$.

2-73 $2.2361 \sin(3t + 3.6052)$.

2-74 $6.4031 \sin(t + 0.6747)$.

2-75 $5 \sin(0.5t + 4.0689)$.

2-76 $2.2361 \sin(t + 1.4636)$.

2-77 $3.1623 \sin(2t + 0.3218)$, 0.3183 Hz, 3.1416 s, 3.1623 A.

2-78 $0.058\,31 \sin(0.4t + 0.5404)$, 0.058 31, 15.708 s, 0.063 66.

2-79

(*a*) $2.24 \sin(4t + 1.1071)$.

(*b*) $5 \sin(3t + 2.4981)$.

2-80 $t = 0.3218$ s.

2-81 $t = 0.3091$ s.

2-82 15.9155 Hz, 0.062 83 s, 50, 23.9713 A.

2-83 $50°, 20°$.

2-85 1.591 55 Hz, 0.6283 s, 0.316 23 m.

THREE

SERIES

Objectives After reading this chapter you should be able to:

1. Solve problems using the binomial theorem.
   (*a*) Expand expressions of the form $(a + b)^n$.
   (*b*) State the general form for the binomial coefficient for all positive integers
   n.
   (*c*) Use the binomial theorem in context of engineering applications.
2. Expand expressions of the form $(1 + X)^r$.
3. Use the exponential and logarithmic functions.
   (*a*) Define the exponential function.
   (*b*) Calculate the value of the exponential function from its power series.
   (*c*) Plot graphs of exponential and logarithmic functions.
   (*d*) Define the logarithmic function.
   (*e*) State the power series for $\ln(1 + X)$.
   (*f*) Solve problems from electrical engineering systems.
   (*g*) Solve problems in context of mechanical engineering.

3-1 BINOMIAL EXPRESSIONS

A binomial expression is one involving two terms. For example, $(a + b)$ and
$(x - 2y)$ are binomial expressions. This type of algebraic expression can be
squared, cubed, or raised to any other power.

> **Example 3-1-1** Expand and simplify the expression $(p + q)^3$ by using al-
> gebraic multiplication.
>
> SOLUTION
>
> $$\begin{aligned}
> (p + q)^3 &= (p + q)(p + q)^2 \\
> &= (p + q)(p^2 + 2pq + q^2) \\
> &= p(p^2 + 2pq + q^2) + q(p^2 + 2pq + q^2)
> \end{aligned}$$

Hence
$$(p+q)^3 = p^3 + 2p^2q + pq^2 + qp^2 + 2pq^2 + q^3$$
$$= p^3 + 3p^2q + 3pq^2 + q^3$$

It is a common technique in mathematics to perform the same operation several times and observe any resulting pattern. In Example 3-1-1 we expanded the binomial expression $(p+q)^3$ by algebraic multiplication. If we consider the expression $(a+b)^n$ and successively replace n by integers starting at 0 and then multiply out, we obtain the pattern formed from the coefficients. This pattern is known as **Pascal's triangle**.

$$(a+b)^0 = 1$$

$$(a+b)^1 = a+b$$

$$(a+b)^2 = a^2 + 2ab + b^2$$

$$(a+b)^3 = a^3 + 3a^2b + 3ab^2 + b^3$$

$$(a+b)^4 = a^4 + 4a^3b + 6a^2b^2 + 4ab^3 + b^4$$

```
              1
           1     1
        1     2     1
     1     3     3     1
  1     4     6     4     1
```

Pascal's triangle

This triangle has a distinct pattern. By adding two numbers in any row we obtain the coefficient in the row below. For example, in row four we have the coefficients 1, 3, 3, 1. By adding the first two, $1 + 3 = 4$, and we have the second coefficient in row five. Similarly, $3 + 3 = 6$, the third coefficient in row five. This process has been generalized and mathematicians have arrived at a general form for the **binomial coefficients**. Before giving the general form, we shall introduce some new notation called **factorial** notation.

3-2 FACTORIALS

The notation $n!$ where n is a positive integer or zero is known as 'n factorial' and is defined by
$$n! = n(n-1)(n-2)\ldots(3)(2)(1)$$

Example 3-2-1
(a) Calculate 3! and 6!
(b) Simplify the expression
$$\frac{n!}{(n-1)!}$$
(c) Show that $0! = 1$ by using the result of part (b).

SOLUTION

(a)
$$3! = (3)(2)(1)$$
$$= 6$$
$$6! = (6)(5)(4)(3)(2)(1)$$
$$= 720$$

(b)
$$\frac{n!}{(n-1)!} = \frac{(n)(n-1)(n-2)\ldots(3)(2)(1)}{(n-1)(n-2)\ldots(3)(2)(1)}$$
$$= n$$

(c) Using the result from part (b), that

$$\frac{n!}{(n-1)!} = n$$

we have on multiplying both sides by $(n-1)!$,

$$n! = (n)(n-1)!$$

Now replace n by the integer 1 and we have

$$1! = (1)(1-1)!$$
$$= (0)!$$

Hence we obtain

$$0! = 1$$

3-3 THE GENERALIZED BINOMIAL COEFFICIENTS

By definition the symbol

$$\binom{n}{r} = \frac{n!}{r!(n-r)!}$$

Example 3-3-1
(a) Calculate $\binom{5}{2}$.
(b) Show that the expression

$$y = \binom{n}{x}$$

can be written as

$$y = \frac{(n)(n-1)(n-2)\ldots(n-x+1)}{x!}$$

SOLUTION

(a)
$$\binom{5}{2} = \frac{5!}{2!(5-2)!}$$

$$= \frac{(5)(4)\,(3)(2)(1)}{(2)(1)\,(3)(2)(1)}$$

$$= 10$$

(b) Since we have

$$\binom{n}{x} = \frac{n!}{x!(n-x)!}$$

$$= \frac{(n)(n-1)(n-2)(n-3)\ldots(n-x+1)(n-x)\ldots(2)(1)}{x!\,(n-x)(n-x-1)\ldots(2)(1)}$$

$$= \frac{(n)(n-1)(n-2)(n-3)\ldots(n-x+1)}{x!}$$

The expression defined and calculated in this section is called the **generalized binomial coefficient**.

We have seen how $\binom{n}{r}$ can be calculated from the definition. However, to save a certain amount of time, these generalized binomial coefficients have been brought together in a table, Table A-1 in the appendix. The table allows binomial coefficients to be obtained for n ranging from 0 to 12.

3-4 THE BINOMIAL THEOREM

For any two given quantities a and b and any positive integral power n, we have

$$(a+b)^n = a^n + \binom{n}{1}a^{n-1}b + \binom{n}{2}a^{n-2}b^2 + \ldots + \binom{n}{n-1}ab^{n-1} + b^n$$

The **binomial coefficients** $\binom{n}{r}$ introduced in Sec. 3-3 can either be calculated or found in Table A-1 in the appendix. In some texts the notation $^{n}C_r$ is used instead of $\binom{n}{r}$.

Example 3-4-1 Expand using the binomial theorem (a) $(a+b)^4$ and (b) $(1+2q)^3$.

SOLUTION (a) By replacing n in the binomial theorem with the power 4, we have

$$(a+b)^4 = a^4 + \binom{4}{1}a^3b + \binom{4}{2}a^2b^2 + \binom{4}{3}ab^3 + \binom{4}{4}a^0b^4$$

From Table A-1 in the appendix

$$\binom{4}{1} = 4 \qquad \binom{4}{2} = 6$$

$$\binom{4}{3} = 4 \qquad \binom{4}{4} = 1$$

Hence we have

$$(a + b)^4 = a^4 + 4a^3b + 6a^2b^2 + 4ab^3 + b^4$$

(b) By replacing n by 3, a by 1 and b by $2q$ in the binomial theorem, we have

$$(1 + 2q)^3 = 1^3 + \binom{3}{1}(1)^2(2q) + \binom{3}{2}(1)(2q)^2 + \binom{3}{3}(1)^0(2q)^3$$

From Table A-1 in the appendix we can obtain the binomial coefficients. Hence,

$$(1 + 2q)^3 = 1 + 3(2q) + 3(2q)^2 + (2q)^3$$
$$= 1 + 6q + 12q^2 + 8q^3$$

Since by Example 3-3-1 we have

$$\binom{n}{x} = \frac{(n)(n-1)\ldots(n-x+1)}{x!}$$

we have

$$\binom{n}{1} = n \qquad \binom{n}{2} = \frac{n(n-1)}{2!}$$

$$\binom{n}{3} = \frac{n(n-1)(n-2)}{3!} \qquad \text{and so on}$$

Therefore, we can rewrite the binomial expansion in the form

$$(a + b)^n = a^n + na^{n-1}b + \frac{n(n-1)}{2!}a^{n-2}b^2 + \frac{n(n-1)(n-2)}{3!}a^{n-3}b^3 + \ldots + b^n$$

This form will be used to develop further theory in this chapter and in the chapters on differentiation and probability distributions.

Example 3-4-2 Expand by using the second form of the binomial expansion the expression $(1 + x)^5$.

SOLUTION

$$(a + b)^n = a^n + na^{n-1}b + \frac{n(n - 1)}{2!}a^{n-2}b^2 + \ldots + b^n$$

is the second form of the binomial expansion and when we replace a by 1, b by x, and n by 5, we have

$$(1 + x)^5 = 1 + 5x + \frac{5(4)x^2}{2!} + \frac{5(4)(3)x^3}{3!} + \frac{5(4)(3)(2)x^4}{4!} + x^5$$

$$= 1 + 5x + 10x^2 + 10x^3 + 5x^4 + x^5$$

3-5 EXPANSION OF $(1 + X)^r$

Expansion of $(1 + X)^r$ where r is a negative integer, fraction or a decimal, is in the form of an infinite series:

$$(1 + X)^r = 1 + rX + \frac{r(r - 1)X^2}{2!} + \frac{r(r - 1)(r - 2)X^3}{3!} + \ldots$$

This series is valid for values of X between -1 and $+1$.

Example 3-5-1 Expand $(1 + x)^{-1}$ in a power series.

SOLUTION Since

$$(1 + X)^r = 1 + rX + \frac{r(r - 1)X^2}{2!} + \ldots$$

we replace r by -1 and X by x to obtain

$$(1 + x)^{-1} = 1 - x + \frac{-1(-2)x^2}{2!} + \frac{-1(-2)(-3)x^3}{3!} + \ldots$$

Hence

$$(1 + x)^{-1} = 1 - x + x^2 - x^3 + \ldots$$

Example 3-5-2 Without using calculators or tables, find an approximate value for

$$(0.98)^{0.5} = \sqrt{(0.98)}$$

SOLUTION As the power is a decimal, we can use the expansion $(1 + X)^r$ providing we choose X to be between -1 and $+1$. Thus

$$(0.98)^{0.5} = (1 - 0.02)^{0.5}$$

We have $X = 0.02, r = 0.5$ and we substitute these values into the expansion

$$(1 + X)^r = 1 + rX + \frac{r(r-1)X^2}{2!} + \ldots$$

to give

$$(1 - 0.02)^{0.5} = 1 - 0.5\,(0.02) + \frac{0.5\,(0.5 - 1)(0.02)^2}{2!} + \ldots$$

$$= 1 - 0.01 + \frac{0.5\,(-0.5)(0.0004)}{2} + \ldots$$

$$= 1 - 0.01 - 0.00005 + \ldots$$

Hence

$$(1 - 0.02)^{0.5} \simeq 0.9900 \qquad \text{to 4 decimal places}$$

which implies that

$$0.98^{0.5} \simeq 0.9900$$

3-6 APPLICATIONS I

The binomial theorem and its related expansions have several applications, most of which are tied up with further mathematical theory as we shall see in Sec. 3-8 and in the chapters on differentiation and probability distributions. However, there is one area in which the theorem is very useful almost immediately to engineers, and that is in the field of measurement and errors. Since

A measured value = a true value + error

we can transpose to give

True value of variable = measured value of variable − error

Let X be the exact or true value of the variable and x be the measured value of the variable. Then we have

$$X = x - E$$

where E is the error in the measurement. We shall use this equation to investigate the effects of errors in measurement on any subsequent calculations.

Example 3-6-1 A cube has its side measured and the result is x metres.
(a) Assuming an error in the measurement of E, find an expression for (i) the exact volume of the cube in terms of the measured value x and the error E, and (ii) the approximate error in the calculated volume if the measured value of the side is used. It may be assumed that the error in the measurement is very, very small.
(b) If the measured value of the side is 2.01 m and the maximum possible error is 0.005 m, find the approximate error in the calculated volume.

SOLUTION
(a) (i) Exact volume = X^3

where X is the true or exact value of the side of the cube. Since

$$\text{Exact value of side} = \text{measured value} - \text{error}$$

we have

$$X = x - E$$

$\Rightarrow$
$$(X)^3 = (x - E)^3 = \text{exact volume of cube}$$

Expanding the binomial expression we have

$$X^3 = x^3 - 3x^2 E + 3xE^2 - E^3$$

and hence exact volume of cube in terms of x and E is

$$V = x^3 - 3x^2 E + 3xE^2 - E^3$$

(ii) If we used the measured side x to calculate the volume, we have

$$\text{Volume (using measured side } x) = x^3$$

However

$$\text{Exact volume} = X^3$$

$\Rightarrow$
$$\text{Error in calculated volume} = x^3 - X^3$$

Using the expression from part (i) we have

$$\text{Error in calculated volume} = x^3 - X^3 = x^3 - (x^3 - 3x^2 E + 3xE^2 - E^3)$$
$$= 3x^2 E - 3xE^2 + E^3$$

As E is very, very small, we can neglect the terms containing E^2 and E^3 to give

$$\text{Approximate error in calculated volume} = 3x^2 E$$

(b) With measured value $x = 2.01$ m and error $E = 0.005$ m, we have approximate error in the calculated volume as

$$3x^2 E = 3 (2.01)^2 (0.005)$$
$$= 0.0606 \, \text{m}^3$$

Example 3-6-2 A cube has its side measured. If the result of this measurement is 1.210 m and assuming an exact mass of 0.3 kg, find an equation for the density of the cube assuming that measurement errors are very small.

SOLUTION
$$\text{Density} = \frac{\text{mass}}{\text{volume}}$$

Assume that 0.3 kg is the *exact* mass. Let true value of side of cube be X. Hence by using

$$\text{True value of variable} = \text{measured value} - \text{error}$$

we have

$$X = 1.210 - E$$

where E is the error in the measurement. Therefore,

$$\text{Density} = \frac{\text{mass}}{\text{volume}}$$

$$= \frac{0.3}{(1.21 - E)^3}$$

$$= 0.3 \, (1.21 - E)^{-3}$$

$$= 0.3 \left[1.21 \left(1 - \frac{E}{1.21} \right) \right]^{-3}$$

$$= 0.3 \, (1.21)^{-3} \left(1 - \frac{E}{1.21} \right)^{-3}$$

$$= 0.1693 \left[1 + (-3) \left(-\frac{E}{1.21} \right) + \dots \right]$$

by using Sec. 3-5. Hence

$$\text{Density} \simeq 0.1693 \left(1 + \frac{3E}{1.21} \right)$$

3-7 LIMITS

We have seen in the last section that if we assumed that the error in a measurement was very small we could make approximations in calculations involving the measured variable. If we now allow this error to tend to zero, we can see that the approximation will tend to the true value of the variable.

Consider the expression

$$\text{True length} = \text{measured length} - \text{error}$$

Here, as the error tends to zero, the measured length tends to the true length.

From Example 3-6-2 we have

$$\text{Density} \simeq 0.1693 \left(1 + \frac{3E}{1.21} \right)$$

and as the error E tends to zero then the density tends to the value of 0.1693 kg/m^3. This can be written as

$$\underset{E \to 0}{\text{LIMIT}} \left[0.1693 \left(1 + \frac{3E}{1.21} \right) \right] = 0.1693$$

Example 3-7-1 Find the value of $3 + 2E$ as E tends to zero.

SOLUTION

$$\underset{E \to 0}{\text{LIMIT}} \, (3 + 2E) = 3$$

A demonstration of the approach to the limit 3 in the last example can be given by numerical means. We choose a starting point for E, say $E = 1$, and calculate the value of $(3 + 2E)$. Taking smaller and smaller values of E, calculating the value of $(3 + 2E)$ produces Table 3-1.

The notation 'LIMIT' can be shortened to 'LIM' or 'lim', and we use the latter.

Table 3-1

	E	$(3 + 2E)$	
E tending to zero	1	5	$(3 + 2E)$ tending to the number 3
	0.1	3.2	
	0.01	3.02	
	0.001	3.002	
	0.0001	3.0002	
	0.000 01	3.000 02	
	. . .	. . .	
	0.000 000 000 01	3.000 000 000 02	

Example 3-7-2 Evaluate the following limits:

(a)
$$\lim_{h \to 0} \, (4 + 2x + h)$$

(b)
$$\lim_{\delta x \to 0} \, [x^2 - 2(\delta x)].$$

SOLUTION

(a)
$$\lim_{h \to 0} \, (4 + 2x + h) = 4 + 2x$$

(b)
$$\lim_{\delta x \to 0} \, [x^2 - 2(\delta x)] = x^2$$

So far, we have allowed a variable to tend to zero. It has become very small. Suppose we now allow a variable to become very large and tend to infinity. For example, if we consider the expression $1/h$ and allow h to grow in size, it can be seen that $1/h$ will get smaller. This is illustrated in Table 3-2.

Example 3-7-3 Find

$$\lim_{h \to \infty} \left(x + \frac{1}{h} + \frac{2}{h} \right)$$

Table 3-2

	h	$1/h$	
h tending to a very very large number	1	1	$1/h$ tending to zero
	10	0.1	
	100	0.01	
	1000	0.001	
	...	...	
	1 000 000	0.000 001	
	...	...	
	10^{100}	10^{-100}	

SOLUTION As h tends to infinity (∞), $1/h$ and $2/h$ will tend to zero. Therefore

$$\lim_{h \to \infty} \left(x + \frac{1}{h} + \frac{2}{h} \right) = x$$

Example 3-7-4 Evaluate the following limits:
(a)

$$\lim_{n \to \infty} \left(3 + \frac{2x}{n} \right)$$

(b)

$$\lim_{h \to 0} \left(2x + x^2 h \right).$$

SOLUTION (a) As n tends to infinity, $2x/n$ tends to zero and hence

$$\lim_{n \to \infty} \left(3 + \frac{2x}{n} \right) = 3$$

(b)

$$\lim_{h \to 0} \left(2x + x^2 h \right) = 2x$$

3-8 THE EXPONENTIAL FUNCTION

The exponential function allows us to describe relationships between variables in terms of growth and decay. This function is defined by means of a **power series** which is developed from the binomial expression

$$\left(1 + \frac{x}{n} \right)$$

Consider

$$\left(1+\frac{x}{n}\right)^n = 1 + n\left(\frac{x}{n}\right) + \frac{n(n-1)}{2!}\left(\frac{x}{n}\right)^2 + \frac{n(n-1)(n-2)}{3!}\left(\frac{x}{n}\right)^3 + \dots$$

by the binomial theorem. Hence

$$\left(1+\frac{x}{n}\right)^n = 1 + x + \left(1-\frac{1}{n}\right)\frac{x^2}{2!} + \left(1-\frac{1}{n}\right)\left(1-\frac{2}{n}\right)\frac{x^3}{3!} + \dots$$

As the power n increases, the terms $1/n$, $2/n$, and so on, decrease. Therefore, allowing n to tend to infinity, we have $1/n$, $2/n$, and other similar terms tending to zero. We are left with an **infinite power series**, that is,

$$\lim_{n \to \infty} \left(1+\frac{x}{n}\right)^n = \left(1 + x + \frac{x^2}{2!} + \frac{x^3}{3!} + \dots\right)$$

This **infinite power series** is defined as the **exponential function** and is written as

$$\exp(x) = \left(1 + x + \frac{x^2}{2!} + \frac{x^3}{3!} + \dots\right)$$

There is a second notation which is extremely common. We shall define

$$e^x \equiv \exp(x)$$

and we shall use *both* notations, interchangeably, throughout the remainder of the book. To find the value of the exponential function we will have to substitute the given x into the power series.

Example 3-8-1 Find by using the power series for $\exp(x)$ the value of (*a*) e^1, (*b*) e^{-1}, and (*c*) $\exp(0.2)$, using the first nine terms and rounding to 4 decimal places.

SOLUTION

(*a*)

$$e^1 = \exp(1)$$

$$= \left(1 + 1 + \frac{1^2}{2!} + \frac{1^3}{3!} + \frac{1^4}{4!} + \frac{1^5}{5!} + \frac{1^6}{6!} + \frac{1^7}{7!} + \frac{1^8}{8!} + \dots\right)$$

$$= 2.7183$$

(*b*)

$$e^{-1} = \left(1 - 1 + \frac{(-1)^2}{2!} + \frac{(-1)^3}{3!} + \frac{(-1)^4}{4!} + \frac{(-1)^5}{5!} + \frac{(-1)^6}{6!}\right.$$

$$\left. + \frac{(-1)^7}{7!} + \frac{(-1)^8}{8!} + \dots\right)$$

$$= 0.3679$$

(c) $\exp(0.2) = e^{0.2}$

$$= \left(1 + 0.2 + \frac{(0.2)^2}{2!} + \frac{(0.2)^3}{3!} + \frac{(0.2)^4}{4!} + \frac{(0.2)^5}{5!} + \frac{(0.2)^6}{6!}\right.$$

$$\left. + \frac{(0.2)^7}{7!} + \frac{(0.2)^8}{8!} + \ldots\right)$$

$$= 1.2214$$

The values of $\exp(x) = e^x$ can be found by using electronic calculators or tables without resorting to the original definition.

Example 3-8-2 Plot the graph of

$$y = e^{-x}$$

for values of x ranging from -3 to $+3$.

SOLUTION By using a calculator, the values of the function e^{-x} can be found. These values are brought together in Table 3-3.

Table 3-3

x	-3	-2	-1	0	1	2	3
$-x$	3	2	1	0	-1	-2	-3
e^{-x}	20.09	7.39	2.72	1	0.37	0.14	0.05

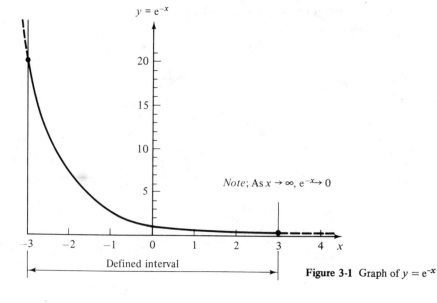

Note; As $x \to \infty$, $e^{-x} \to 0$

Defined interval

Figure 3-1 Graph of $y = e^{-x}$

The values of e^{-x} have been rounded off to 2 decimal places and these have been plotted using cartesian coordinates as shown in Fig. 3-1.

3-9 NAPIERIAN LOGARITHMS

Napierian or natural logarithms are logarithms to base 'e'. Consider

$$y = e^x$$

$$\Rightarrow \quad \log_e y = \log_e(e^x)$$

$$= x \log_e(e)$$

$$= x \quad \text{since } \log_e(e) = 1$$

Therefore $\log_e y$ is the number x which we substitute into the exponential power series to obtain the value $y = e^x = \exp(x)$. The logarithm (base e) is the **inverse** of the exponential function. This is illustrated in Fig. 3-2. It is common practice among engineers to denote the napierian or natural logarithm by the symbol 'ln'. Therefore if

$$y = e^x$$

$$\ln(y) = x$$

We can also place natural logarithmic functions in the form of a power series. For example,

$$\ln(1 + x) = \left(x - \frac{x^2}{2} + \frac{x^3}{3} - \frac{x^4}{4} + \ldots \right)$$

We shall require this series in the chapter on differentiation.

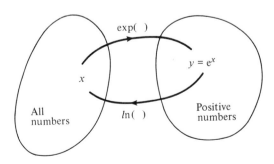

Figure 3-2

Example 3-9-1 Solve the equations (a) $10 = e^{x+1}$ and (b) $1 = e^{x+1}$.

SOLUTION

(a)
$$10 = e^{x+1}$$

$\Rightarrow$
$$\ln(10) = x + 1$$

or
$$2.302\,58 = x + 1$$

$\Rightarrow$
$$1.302\,58 = x$$

(b)
$$1 = e^{x+1}$$

$\Rightarrow$
$$\ln(1) = x + 1$$

or
$$0 = x + 1$$

$\Rightarrow$
$$x = -1$$

3-10 APPLICATIONS II

In this section, we shall consider two electrical circuits and some mathematical models which describe current flow with respect to time. All the models have been developed by using differential equations which will be described in Chapter 11.

Two electrical circuits are shown in Fig. 3-3. Consider the $L-R$ circuit which consists of an inductor and resistor in series. Suppose that when the switch is moved to position 1, the current flowing is zero. It can be shown by using differential-equation theory that

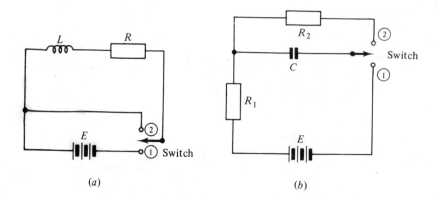

(a)   (b)

Figure 3-3 (a) $L-R$ circuit; (b) $C-R$ circuit.

$$i = \frac{E}{R}\left[1 - \exp\left(-\frac{R}{L}t\right)\right]$$

where i is the instantaneous current at time t and E is the supply voltage. This equation describes the growth of current in an inductive circuit.

If we move the switch to position 2 when the current flowing has a value of I amperes, then the decay in the current in the inductive circuit is described by

$$i = I \exp\left(-\frac{R}{L}t\right)$$

Example 3-10-1 A coil of 6 H inductance and 12 Ω resistance replaces the inductor and resistor in the L–R circuit in Fig. 3-3. The switch is moved to position 1 from position 2 when the current flowing in the circuit is zero.
(a) Write down an equation which decribes the growth of current in this circuit.
(b) Calculate the maximum possible current flowing.
(c) Calculate the current flowing at a time $t = 0.1$ s and the time at which the current reaches 0.5 A.

SOLUTION (a) The growth of current in the inductive circuit is given by

$$i = \frac{E}{R}\left[1 - \exp\left(-\frac{R}{L}t\right)\right]$$

and on substituting $R = 12\,\Omega$, $L = 6$ H, and $E = 12$ V, we have

$$i = [1 - \exp(-2t)]$$
$$= 1 - e^{-2t}$$

(b) Maximum possible current flowing is $E/R = 1$ A. The reader should note that as $t \to \infty$ the value of the current i tends to its maximum of 1 A.
(c) For $t = 0.1$ s we have

$$i = 1 - e^{-2(0.1)}$$
$$= 0.1813 \text{ A}$$

Hence, current flowing at $t = 0.1$ s is 0.1813 A.
If the current has a value of 0.5 A then

$$i = 0.5 = 1 - e^{-2t}$$

or

$$-0.5 = -e^{-2t}$$

Taking logarithms to base e we have

$$\ln(0.5) = -2t$$

$\Rightarrow$

$$-t = -0.693\,15/2$$

or

$$t = 0.3466$$

Thus at the time of 0.3466 s the current will have a value of 0.5 A.

We now consider the C–R circuit shown in Fig. 3-3 and throw the switch to position 1 when the charge on the capacitor is zero. That is, at time $t = 0$ s we have charge $q = 0$ C (coulombs). Again it can be shown that the instantaneous current is given by

$$i = \frac{E}{R_1} \exp\left(-\frac{1}{CR_1}t\right)$$

Here the current *decays* as the capacitor is charged. If we now throw the switch to position 2 when the capacitor has attained its full charge of CE, then we have the equation

$$i = -\frac{E}{R_2} \exp\left(-\frac{1}{CR_2}t\right)$$

In this equation the instantaneous current flows in the opposite direction to that of the charging current and again decays, energy being dissipated in the form of heat in the resistor R_2.

Example 3-10-2 A capacitor of $10\,\mu F$ (microfarads) is in series with a resistor $100\,\Omega$ across a 10 V supply. Calculate (*a*) the initial charging current, (*b*) the current flowing at $t = 0.03$ s, and (*c*) the time at which the current is 0.02 A.

SOLUTION (*a*) As the capacitor is charged, the current flowing is given by

$$i = \frac{E}{R_1} \exp\left(-\frac{1}{CR_1}t\right)$$

The initial charging current occurs at $t = 0$. Hence we have

$$i = \frac{10}{100} \exp(0)$$

$$= 0.1e^0$$

$$= 0.1 \text{ A}$$

(*b*) At $t = 0.03$ s we have a current flowing given by

$$i = 0.1 \exp\left(-\frac{10^6}{10^3}0.03\right)$$

$$= 0.1 \exp(-30)$$

$$= 9.4 \times 10^{-15} \text{ A}$$

(*c*) At $i = 0.02$ A we have a time t given by

$$0.02 = 0.1 \exp(-1000t)$$

or

$$0.2 = e^{-1000t}$$

Taking logarithms we have

$$\ln(0.2) = -1000t$$
$$-1.6094 = -1000t$$
$$\Rightarrow \qquad t = 0.00161 \text{ s}$$

Hence time at which the current is 0.02 A is 0.00161 s.

Example 3-10-3 A capacitor of value 20 μF is fully charged. If this capacitor is discharged through a resistor of 0.5 MΩ, find the time taken for the current flowing to reach half of its initial value.

SOLUTION Since

$$i = \frac{E}{R} \exp\left(-\frac{1}{CR}t\right)$$

represents the discharging current we have at $t = 0$,

$$i = \frac{E}{R}(e^0)$$
$$= E/R$$

Therefore the initial current is E/R amperes and half of this value is $E/2R$. Hence for the time to reach half of the initial current value, we substitute into the current discharge equation to obtain

$$\frac{E}{2R} = \frac{E}{R} \exp\left(-\frac{1}{CR}t\right)$$

or $$0.5 = \exp(-0.1t)$$

or $$0.5 = e^{-0.1t}$$

Taking logarithms we have

$$-0.693147 = -0.1t$$

or $$t = 6.9315 \qquad \text{to 4 decimal places}$$

Thus the time for the current flowing in this circuit to reach half of its initial value is 6.9315 s.

PROBLEMS

For problems **3-1** to **3-3** expand the expression by using algebraic multiplication.

3-1 $(1 + 2x)^4$.

3-2 $(x^2)(1 + x)^3$.

3-3 $(3 + 2x)^4$.

3-4 Evaluate (a) 4!, (b) 3!, and (c) 5(0!).

3-5 Evaluate $\dfrac{8!}{2!(6!)}$.

3-6 Evaluate $\dfrac{12!}{4!(8!)}$.

3-7 Show that $\dfrac{n!}{(n-2)!} = (n)(n-1)$.

For problems **3-8** to **3-12** evaluate the definition of $\binom{n}{r}$ the given expressions.

3-8 $\begin{pmatrix} 4 \\ 2 \end{pmatrix}$.

3-9 $\begin{pmatrix} 100 \\ 2 \end{pmatrix}$.

3-10 $\begin{pmatrix} 20 \\ 18 \end{pmatrix}$.

3-11 $\begin{pmatrix} 36 \\ 29 \end{pmatrix}$.

3-12 $\begin{pmatrix} 200 \\ 1 \end{pmatrix}$.

3-13 Evaluate (a) $\binom{6}{3}$ and (b) $\binom{12}{2}$ by using the table for the generalized binomial coefficients.

For problems **3-14** to **3-18** expand the given expression by using the binomial theorem.

3-14 $(3 + x)^5$.

3-15 $(x + 3y)^4$.

3-16 $(1 + 1.2x)^3$.

3-17 $(1 - x)^4$.

3-18 $(-2 + x)^4$.

For problems **3-19** and **3-20** expand the given expression in a power series giving the first four terms and stating the range of x for which the series is valid.

*3-19 $(1 + x)^{-1}$.

*3-20 $(1 + x)^{0.5}$.

*3-21 Without tables, or calculators, find an approximate value for $(0.97)^{0.5}$.

**3-22 Find an approximate value for $\sqrt[3]{0.94}$ by expanding $(1 + x)^{1/3}$ in a power series and substituting a suitable value for x.

**3-23 If $(1 + ax)^b = 1 + 6x + 12x^2 + 8x^3$, find the values of the positive integers a and b.

***3-24 A cube has its side measured and the result is 1.31 m. (a) Assuming that the error in the measurement is E metres, find an expression for (i) the *exact* volume of the cube in terms of the error E, and (ii) the approximate error in the calculated volume if the measured value of 1.31 m is used in the evaluation.

(b) If the error $E = 0.001$ m, find the approximate error in the calculated volume of the cube when using the measured side length of 1.31 m.

For problems **3-25** to **3-35** evaluate the given limits.

3-25 $\lim\limits_{h \to 0} (3x + 2h^2)$.

3-26 $\lim\limits_{\delta x \to 0} [3x + 4(\delta x)]$.

3-27 $\lim\limits_{\delta x \to 0} [4x - 2(\delta x) + 3(\delta x)^2]$.

3-28 $\lim\limits_{\delta x \to 0} \dfrac{13x(\delta x) + 3(\delta x)^2}{\delta x}$.

*3-29 $\lim\limits_{\delta x \to 0} (y)$.

*3-30 $\lim\limits_{\delta x \to 0} (3 + x)$.

3-31 $\lim\limits_{h \to \infty} \left(3 + \dfrac{1}{h}\right)$.

3-32 $\lim\limits_{h \to \infty} \left(4x + \dfrac{2}{h}\right)$.

*3-33 $\lim\limits_{h \to \infty} \left(4x + \dfrac{3x}{h}\right)$.

**3-34 $\lim\limits_{h \to \infty} \left(\dfrac{3 + h^2}{h^2}\right)$.

**3-35 $\lim\limits_{h \to \infty} \left(\dfrac{4 - 3h^3}{2h^3 - 1}\right)$.

For problems **3-36** and **3-37** find the first four terms in the power series for the given functions.

3-36 $e^{-x} = \exp(-x)$.

3-37 $e^{2x} = \exp(2x)$.

For problems **3-38** to **3-40** find the value of $y = \exp(x)$ by using nine terms of the power series definition for the given value of x.

3-38 $x = 0.5$.

3-39 $x = 2$.

3-40 $x = -0.2$.

For problems **3-41** to **3-45** plot the graph of the given function for the range $-3 \leqslant x \leqslant +3$.

3-41 $y = e^x$.

3-42 $y = e^{2x}$.

*3-43 $y = \exp(x^2)$.

**3-44 $y = e^x(\sin x)$.

***3-45 $y = e^{-x}[\sin (2x)]$.

For problems **3-46** to **3-55** find the value of x which satisfies the given equation.

3-46 $4 = e^x$.

3-47 $2 = e^{2x}$.

3-48 $5 = 10e^{0.1x}$.

*3-49 $\exp(3x^2) = 4$.

*3-50 $4 \exp(x^2) = 16$.

3-51 $\ln(x) = 3$.

3-52 $\ln(x) = -0.5$.

3-53 $\ln(x) = 0.12$,

*3-54 $\ln(2x) + \ln(x) = 1$.

**3-55 $\ln(3x^2) - \ln(x) = 0.28$.

***3-56 Solve the equation $e^{4x} + e^{2x} - 2 = 0$.

***3-57 A coil has a resistance of 12 Ω and an inductance of 3 H. Show that if the potential difference across the coil is 24 V then the current growth in the circuit can be predicted by the mathematical model

$$i = 2(1 - e^{-4t}) \qquad \text{at } t = 0, i = 0 \text{ A}$$

where t is the time in seconds.

**3-58 The current growth associated with a coil in a certain circuit is given by

$$i = 4(1 - e^{-t}).$$

(a) State the maximum possible current flowing through the coil. (b) Find the value of the current at $t = 1$ s. (c) Find the value of the time when the current is 0.5 A.

**3-59 A capacitor of 20 μF is in series with a resistor of 200 Ω across a 10 V supply. Calculate (a) the initial charging current, (b) the current flowing at $t = 0.002$ s and (c) the time at which the current is 0.01 A.

3-60 The coefficient of friction between a belt and a pulley is $\mu = 0.25$. If the angle of lap is $\theta = 1.01$ rad and the tension in the slack side is $T_0 = 25$ N, calculate the tension in the taut side using the mathematical model defined by

$$T = T_0 [\exp(\mu\theta)]$$

**3-61 The vibration of a suspension system for a particular machine is modelled by the mathematical expression

$$s = 0.2 e^{-2t} [\cos(3t)] + 0.1$$

where s is the distance from the floor in metres at a time t. Evaluate (a) the distance s when $t = 3$ s, (b) the distance s after a very long time period, and (c) the distance s when the vibration had just started.

Solutions

3-1 $1 + 8x + 24x^2 + 32x^3 + 16x^4$.

3-2 $x^2 + 3x^3 + 3x^4 + x^5$.

3-3 $81 + 216x + 216x^2 + 96x^3 + 16x^4$.

3-4 (a) 24, (b) 6, (c) 5.

3-5 28.

3-6 495.

3-8 6.

3-9 4950.

3-10 190.

3-11 8 347 680.

3-12 200.

3-13 (a) 20, (b) 66.

3-14 $243 + 405x + 270x^2 + 90x^3 + 15x^4 + x^5$.

3-15 $x^4 + 12x^3y + 54x^2y^2 + 108xy^3 + 81y^4$.

3-16 $1 + 3.6x + 4.32x^2 + 1.728x^3$.

3-17 $1 - 4x + 6x^2 - 4x^3 + x^4$.

3-18 $16 - 32x + 24x^2 - 8x + x^4$.

3-19 $1 - x + x^2 - x^3 + \dots$ $(-1 < x < 1)$.

3-20 $1 + 0.5x - 0.125x^2 + 0.0625x^3$ $(-1 < x < 1)$.

3-21 0.9849.

3-22 0.9796.

3-23 $a = 2, b = 3$.

3-24

(a) $2.248\,091 - 5.1483E + 3.93E^2 - E^3$, $5.1483E$.

(b) $0.005\,1483\,\text{m}^3$.

3-25 $3x$.

3-26 $3x$.

3-27 $4x$.

3-28 $13x$.

3-29 y.

3-30 $3 + x$.

3-31 3.

3-32 $4x$.

3-33 $4x$.

3-34 1.

3-35 -1.5.

3-36 $1 - x + \dfrac{x^2}{2!} - \dfrac{x^3}{3!} + \dots$.

3-37 $1 + 2x + 2x^2 + \frac{4}{3}x^3 + \dots$.

3-38 1.6487.

3-39 7.3891.

3-40 0.8187.

3-46 1.3863.

3-47 0.3466.

3-48 $-6.931\,47$.

3-49 $\pm\,0.679\,78$.

3-50 $\pm\,1.177\,41$.

3-51 20.0855.

3-52 0.6065.

3-53 1.1275.

3-54 $\pm\,1.165\,82$.

3-55 0.4410.

3-56 $x = 0$.

3-58 (b) 4 A, (b) 2.5285 A, (c) 0.1335 s.

3-59 (a) 0.05 A, (b) 0.0303 A, (c) 0.0064 s.

3-60 32.181 N.

3-61 (a) 0.0996 m, (b) 0.1 m, (c) 0.3 m.

CURVE FITTING

Objectives After reading this chapter you should be able to:

1. Fit curves of the form $y = ax^b$, $y = ab^x$, and $y = ae^{bx}$.
   (a) Transform $y = ax^b$, $y = ab^x$, and $y = ae^{bx}$ to the straight-line form $Y = MX + C$.
   (b) Plot the transformed variables Y against X and hence find the slope M and the intercept C.
   (c) Transform M and C back into the constants a and b.
   (d) Plot graphs of the form $y = ax^b$ on log–log paper.
   (e) Plot graphs of the form $y = ae^{bx}$ and $y = ab^x$ on log–linear paper.
   (f) Plot experimental data, having chosen the mathematical curve, on log–log, log–linear and standard graph paper.
   (g) Determine the mathematical laws from experimental data using the forms $y = ax^b$, $y = ab^x$, and $y = ae^{bx}$.

4-1 INTRODUCTION

Curve fitting is a process of building mathematical models which describe the relationships between the variables. We shall restrict ourselves to the relationship between two variables and those curves which can be transformed into the straight-line form $Y = MX + C$. The process of finding a relationship between the variables is illustrated in Fig. 4-1, and starts with the collection of experimental data. At this stage it should be emphasized, once again, that the reliability of the mathematical relationship depends to a large extent on the number of experimental results collected. As a general rule, the greater the number of experimental results, the greater the reliability of the curve describing the relationship between the variables.

Plotting a scattergram of the results from an experiment enables an engineer to observe the type of curve required. This, along with some known physical characteristics, enables a *choice* of the mathematical relationship to take place.

70

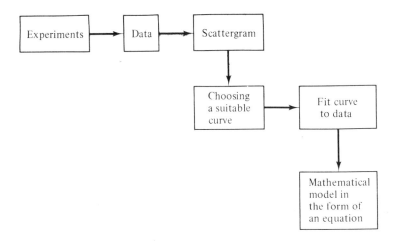

Figure 4-1 The process of curve fitting: a simplified approach.

Having chosen the form of the curve, we attempt to fit this relationship to the experimental data. It is assumed that the reader is familiar with fitting curves following the straight-line form $Y = MX + C$, and we shall use this knowledge to find other relationships between two variables.

4-2 TRANSFORMATION OF CURVES INTO STRAIGHT-LINE FORM

Consider the curve of the form

$$y = ax^b$$

where a and b are constants. If we take logarithms of base 10 the curve is transformed into

$$\log(y) = \log(a) + \log(x^b)$$

$\Rightarrow$ $$\log(y) = b \cdot \log(x) + \log(a)$$

Comparing this equation with the straight line form $Y = MX + C$, we have

$$\log(y) = b \cdot \log(x) + \log(a)$$
$$Y = M \cdot X + C$$

and we can construct Table 4-1 as shown on page 72. Hence plotting Y against X produces a straight line with a slope M and an intercept C.

Table 4-1

Straight line $Y = MX + C$		Curve $y = ax^b$
Y	$=$	$\log(y)$
X	$=$	$\log(x)$
M	$=$	b
C	$=$	$\log(a)$

Example 4-2-1 Transform to the straight-line form $Y = MX + C$, the curves $(a)\, y = a \cdot b^x$ and $(b)\, y = a \cdot \exp(bx) = a \cdot e^{bx}$.

SOLUTION (a) Since $y = a \cdot b^x$ we have, by using the theory of logarithms, that

$$\log(y) = \log(a \cdot b^x)$$

$$= \log(a) + \log(b^x)$$

$$= \log(a) + x \cdot \log(b)$$

or
$$\log(y) = \log(b) \cdot x + \log(a)$$

Comparing this equation with the straight line form $Y = MX + C$, we have

$$\log(y) = \log(b) \cdot x + \log(a)$$
$$Y \quad = \quad M \quad \cdot X + \quad C$$

and we can construct Table 4-2.

Table 4-2

Straight line $Y = MX + C$		Curve $y = a \cdot b^x$
Y	$=$	$\log(y)$
X	$=$	x
M	$=$	$\log(b)$
C	$=$	$\log(a)$

(b) Since

$$y = a \cdot \exp(bx)$$

$$= a \cdot e^{bx}$$

we use the logarithmic transformation, taking logarithms to base 'e' to obtain,

$$\ln(y) = \ln(a \cdot e^{bx})$$

$$= \ln(a) + \ln(e^{bx})$$

$$= \ln(a) + bx \cdot \ln(e)$$

$$= \ln(a) + bx \qquad \text{since } \ln(e) = 1$$

Thus $\qquad \ln(y) = bx + \ln(a)$

and comparing this equation with the straight-line form $Y = MX + C$, we have

$$\ln(y) = bx + \ln(a)$$
$$Y = MX + C$$

and we can construct Table 4-3.

Table 4-3

Straight line $Y = MX + C$		Curve $y = ae^{bx}$
Y	$=$	$\ln(y)$
X	$=$	x
M	$=$	b
C	$=$	$\ln(a)$

4-3 GRAPHICAL CURVE FITTING

We illustrated in Sec. 4-2 the transformation of the curves $y = a \cdot b^x$, $y = a \cdot x^b$, and $y = a \cdot e^{bx}$ into the straight-line form $Y = MX + C$. Fitting a curve to experimental points requires finding the constants a and b so that the chosen equation passes as close as possible to the given results. There are two methods of finding the constants and hence fitting the chosen curve. The first method is that of **graphical fitting** via the straight-line transformation, though in practice with the advent of electronic computers and calculators this method serves only as a guide. The second method is that of **numerical fitting**.

In the remainder of this chapter, the examples of curve fitting will use a small number of experimental results. It has already been pointed out that the greater the number of experimental results the more reliable is the curve that models the relationship between the two variables being measured. This should be remembered throughout the examples which fit curves to a small number of measurements.

In graphical fitting, we transform the chosen curve to the straight-line form $Y = MX + C$, and if the transformed points lie close to a straight line, it is reasonable to assume that the curve is a close fit to the experimental points. In the next two examples, we shall fit two curves of the form $y = ax^b$ and $y = a \cdot e^{bx}$ to the same set of experimental results. This will illustrate that one of these curves is a reasonable model while the other is less reliable.

Example 4-3-1 After transforming $y = a \cdot x^b$ into the straight-line form $Y = MX + C$, find by graphical methods the constants a and b such that the curve fits the experimental data shown in Table 4-4.

Table 4-4

x	1	2	3	4	5	6
y	3	12	27	48	75	108

SOLUTION Since $y = a \cdot x^b$ we have on taking logarithms to base 10, the equation

$$\log(y) = b \cdot \log(x) + \log(a)$$

As suggested in Sec. 4-2, we plot

$$Y = \log(y) \qquad \text{against} \qquad X = \log(x)$$

We construct a table, Table 4-5, to obtain the values for X and Y. These values will be rounded to 2 decimal places. The values of X and Y are plotted on graph paper as shown in Fig. 4-2 and the 'best' straight line is drawn by eye. The slope of this straight line is found by the usual method

$$M = \tan(\theta)$$

$$= 1.99$$

$$= 2.0 \qquad \text{to 1 decimal place}$$

However, $M = b$ which implies that

$$b = 2.0$$

From the graph, we can also find the intercept $C = 0.48$ and since $C = \log(a)$ we have (on taking anti-logs)

Table 4-5

x	y	$\log(x)$ or X	$\log(y)$ or Y
1	3	0.00	0.48
2	12	0.30	1.08
3	27	0.48	1.43
4	48	0.60	1.68
5	75	0.70	1.88
6	108	0.78	2.03

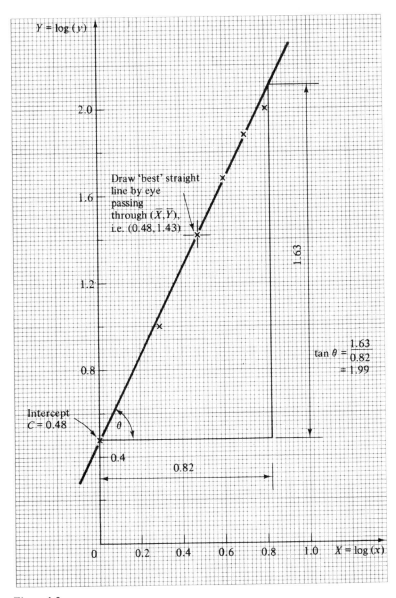

Figure 4-2

$$10^C = a$$

$$\Rightarrow \qquad 10^{0.48} = a$$

Hence the value of a is 3.02 and to 1 decimal place,

$$a = 3.0$$

Hence we have fitted the curve $y = ax^b$ having found the constants a and b. The curve fitted to the experimental results is

$$y = 3x^2$$

Example 4-3-2 Fit the curve $y = a \cdot e^{bx}$ by graphical means to the data shown in Table 4-4.

SOLUTION Since $y = a \cdot e^{bx}$ we transform to the straight-line form $Y = MX + C$ by using natural logarithms. This gives

$$\ln(y) = b \cdot x + \ln(a)$$

and from Example 4-2-1 (b) we have

$$Y = \ln(y)$$

and $$X = x$$

Hence we construct Table 4-6.

Table 4-6

x or X	y	$\ln(y)$ or Y
1	3	1.0986
2	12	2.4849
3	27	3.2958
4	48	3.8712
5	75	4.3175
6	108	4.6821

The values of X and Y are plotted on standard graph paper as shown in Fig. 4-3. The best straight line has now to be fitted by 'eye' and it can be seen that this is an almost impossible task. This suggests that the curve $y = a \cdot e^{bx}$ is *not* a suitable model for the measured data. However, going ahead with the method produces an intercept $C = 0.9$ and a slope of 0.69. Hence $M = b = 0.69$ and $C = \ln(a) = 0.9$ implies $a = 2.5$. Thus, fitting the straight line by eye produces a model

$$y = 2.5e^{0.69x}$$

The original data and the two curves from Examples 4-3-1 and 4-3-2 are shown in Fig. 4-4. It can now be clearly seen that the curve $y = 3x^2$ is closer to the data, confirming the suspicion, in the solution of Example 4-3-2, that $y = 2.5e^{0.69x}$ is *not* a suitable curve to describe the relationship between the variables.

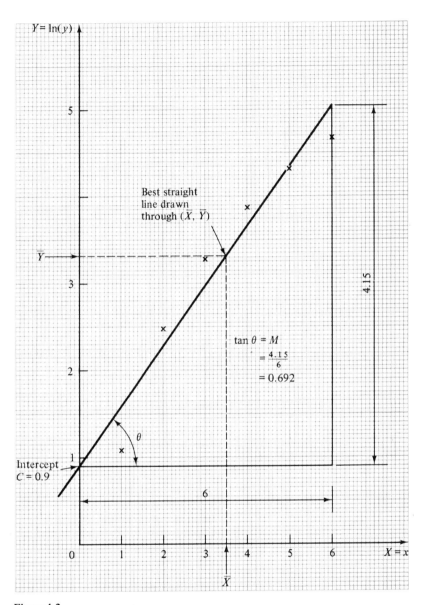

Figure 4-3

Example 4-3-3 Using the constructed equation $y = 3x^2$ for the experimental data in Table 4-4, predict the value of y for (*a*) $x = 2.5$ and (*b*) $x = 5.6$. Is it reasonable to predict, using this curve, the value of y for $x = 100$?

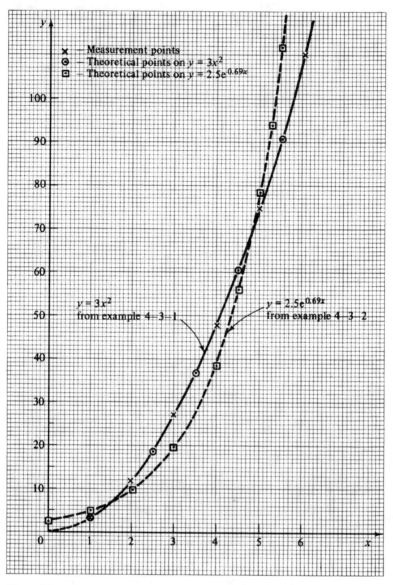

Figure 4-4

SOLUTION

(a) For $x = 2.5, y = 3(2.5)^2 = 18.75$.

(b) For $x = 5.6, y = 3(5.6)^2 = 94.08$.

It is *not* reasonable to use a value of $x = 100$ in the fitted curve equation $y = 3x^2$ as this was based on *experimental data* for x values between 1 and

6. Further measurements would now have to be made and the range extended beyond $x = 100$. The whole process of curve fitting would, of course, be repeated.

4-4 LOG–LOG PAPER

To reduce labour and errors in transforming the variables x and y to the straight-line form by using logarithmic methods, we can use a special graph paper. We shall illustrate the technique by Example 4-4-1.

Example 4-4-1 The velocity of a body at a time of t seconds is measured. The results are laid out in Table 4-7. Assuming that an engineer has chosen the curve $y = ax^b$, fit the experimental results to this form. Hence, using this fitted curve, find the expected velocity of the body at 4.5 s.

Table 4-7

t (s)	2	3	4	5	6	7	8
v (m/s)	1.1	1.9	2.6	3.4	4.3	5.2	6.0

SOLUTION Since $y = ax^b$ we choose $x = t$, the independent variable and $y = v$, the dependent variable. Therefore we have to fit the curve

$$v = a \cdot t^b$$

to the experimental results. On taking logarithms to base 10 we have

$$\log(v) = \log(a) + b \cdot \log(t)$$

On comparison with the straight-line form, $Y = MX + C$, we have Table 4-8. On standard graph paper we would plot $Y = \log(v)$ against $X = \log(t)$. However, as we require to reduce labour and errors we choose a graph paper which has been scaled in logarithmic values to base 10. In this case, *both X*

Table 4-8

Straight line $Y = MX + C$		Curve $v = at^b$
Y	$=$	$\log(v)$
X	$=$	$\log(t)$
M	$=$	b
C	$=$	$\log(a)$

and Y are logarithmic variables and hence we choose log–log paper. This type of paper has several cycles. The choice of the number of cycles depends on the experimental results. In this case, we have v values between 1 and 6 which is between 1 and 10, and the t values range from 2 to 8, again between 1 and 10. This implies that we choose log–log paper which is 1 cycle × 1 cycle. We plot the values of v and t on the log–log paper with v, the dependent variable, on the vertical axis. This is illustrated in Fig. 4-5.

We draw the 'best' straight line through the experimental points. As in Sec. 4-3, the experimental points should lie close to *any* straight line that we draw in order for the proposed curve $v = a \cdot t^b$ to be a close fit and hence a reasonable model to describe the relationship between velocity and time. In this case, the points on the log–log paper do lie close to our constructed straight line.

The **slope** of the graph is found by using a rule and measuring, in mm, the sides of the constructed triangle. In this case the slope

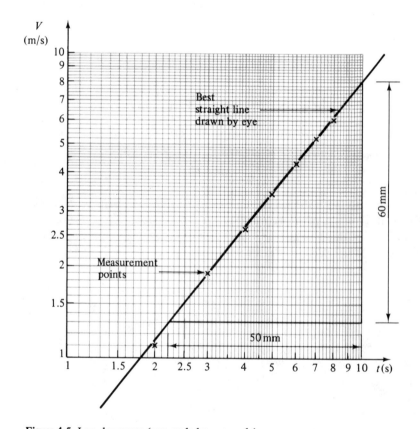

Figure 4-5 Log–log paper (one cycle by one cycle).

$$M = b = \frac{60}{50}$$

$$= 1.2$$

For the constant a, we choose a value v on the graph and read off the corresponding value of t. Hence choosing $v = 8$, we have $t = 10$. These values are substituted into the equation $v = a \cdot t^b$ along with the value of b to obtain

$$8 = a \cdot 10^{1.2}$$

or

$$a = \frac{8}{15.85}$$

$$= 0.5 \qquad \text{to 1 decimal place}$$

Hence the curve $v = 0.5t^{1.2}$ fits the experimental data.

As the curve $v = 0.5(t)^{1.2}$ lies close to the experimental points, we can use this model to predict the value of the velocity using values of time between $t = 2$ and $t = 8\,\text{s}$. As with Sec. 4-3, it must be stressed that if a velocity is required at a time value outside of the range 2 to 8 s, we should carry out more measurements and repeat the curve fitting process.

Using the curve $v = 0.5(t)^{1.2}$, at $t = 4.5\,\text{s}$, we have

$$v = 0.5\,(4.5)^{1.2}$$

$$= 3.04$$

$$= 3.0\,\text{m/s}$$

Therefore, to 1 decimal place, we have a velocity of 3.0 m/s at a time of 4.5 s.

4-5 LOG–LINEAR PAPER

Curves of the form $y = a \cdot b^x$ and $a \cdot e^{bx}$ can be fitted to experimental data by using log–linear paper.

Example 4-5-1 Fit the curve $y = a \cdot b^x$ to the experimental data shown in Table 4-9.

Table 4-9

x	2	3	4	5	6	7	8
y	0.2	0.25	0.28	0.35	0.45	0.58	0.75

SOLUTION Since $y = a \cdot b^x$ implies, after taking logarithms to base 10, that

$$\log(y) = \log(a) + x \cdot \log(b)$$

on comparison with the form $Y = MX + C$, we can construct Table 4-10.

Table 4-10

Straight line $Y = MX + C$		Curve $x = ab^x$
Y	=	$\log(y)$
X	=	x
M	=	$\log(b)$
C	=	$\log(a)$

Since $Y = \log(y)$ and $X = x$ we can use log–linear paper. The log scale should be 1 cycle in this case as the values of y are between 0.2 and 0.75. Plotting the y values using the vertical logarithmic scale, against the x values on the linear scale, and drawing the 'best' straight line through these points we have Fig. 4-6. This graph illustrates that $y = a \cdot b^x$ is a reasonable curve to fit the experimental points as these lie close to a straight line when using log–linear paper. To find the value of a, we note the intercept on the log axis. Therefore

$$a = 0.12$$

The next step is observing that

which implies

$$\log(y) = x \cdot \log(b) + \log(a)$$
$$\log(y) - \log(a) = x \cdot \log(b)$$

Taking any value of x on the graph, say $x = 8$, and noting the value of $y = 0.73$, we can obtain the slope by using the equation

Thus

$$\log(y) - \log(a) = x \cdot \log(b)$$
$$\log(0.73) - \log(0.12) = 8 \cdot \log(b)$$

or

$$0.7841 = 8 \cdot \log(b)$$

or

$$0.0980 = \log(b)$$

$\Rightarrow$

$$b = 10^{0.098}$$
$$= 1.25$$

Hence we have the curve of the form $y = a \cdot x^b$ which best fits the experimental results, that is

$$y = 0.12\,(1.25)^x$$

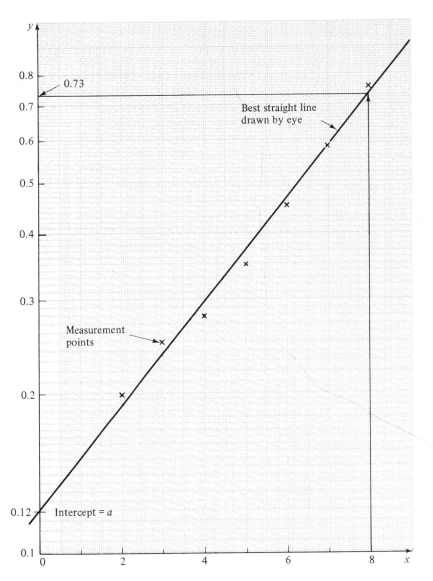

Figure 4-6 Log–linear paper.

4-6 NUMERICAL METHODS

We have seen how to fit curves via a straight-line transformation to experimental data. It has already been stressed that curve fitting can be carried out by numerical methods by computers. It is interesting to note that straight-line fitting can be completed by a preprogrammed calculator costing a few pounds.

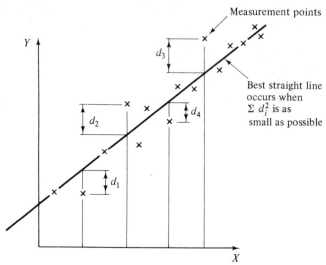

Figure 4-7

The numerical method is based on the process known as 'least squares'. Consider a set of experimental points shown in Fig. 4-7. The straight line which best fits the measurements is the one which passes through the points so that the sum of the distances squared from the points to the line is as small as possible. By the method of 'least squares' we arrive at the formulae for the slope and intercept of the best straight line. These are

slope
$$M = \frac{\Sigma XY - n\bar{X}\bar{Y}}{\Sigma X^2 - n(\bar{X})^2}$$

where n is the number of experimental results, and

intercept
$$C = \bar{Y} - M\bar{X}$$

where $\bar{X}$ is the average of the X values and $\bar{Y}$ is the average of the Y values. A reader interested in proving these formulae should consult any standard text on statistics.

In example 4-6-1 we shall demonstrate the use of these formulae in fitting a straight line of the form $Y = MX + C$.

Example 4-6-1 Fit the straight line $Y = MX + C$ to the experimental points in Table 4-11, by using numerical techniques.

Table 4-11

X	1	2	3	4	5
Y	3	5	7	9	10

SOLUTION It should be observed that with this set of data we can spot the result and hence the best straight line is $Y = 2X + 1$. The method adopted for numerical fitting begins with the formation of Table 4-12.

Table 4-12

X	Y	X^2	XY
1	3	1	3
2	5	4	10
3	7	9	21
4	9	16	36
5	11	25	55
15	35	55	125

Each column in Table 4-12 has been summed and the result given. Hence using

$$M = \frac{\Sigma XY - n\bar{X}\bar{Y}}{\Sigma X^2 - n(\bar{X})^2}$$

we see that the values of $\bar{X}$ and $\bar{Y}$ are required. Since

$$\bar{X} = \frac{\Sigma X}{n}$$

we have

$$\bar{X} = \frac{15}{5}$$

$\Rightarrow$ $\qquad\qquad \bar{X} = 3$

and by a similar process,

$$\bar{Y} = 7$$

Since $\Sigma XY = 125$ and $\Sigma X^2 = 55$ we have

$$M = \frac{125 - (5)(3)(7)}{55 - (5)(3)^2}$$

$$= \frac{125 - 105}{55 - 45}$$

$\Rightarrow$ $\qquad\qquad M = 2$

Hence, using $C = \bar{Y} - M\bar{X}$, we have

$$C = 7 - 2(3)$$

$\Rightarrow$ $$C = 1$$

Hence the best straight line as expected is

$$Y = 2X + 1$$

Example 4-6-2 Table 4-13 is a set of results from an experiment measuring the current flowing in a particular circuit. Fit the law $i = a \cdot e^{bt}$ and hence predict the value of the current flowing at 3.5 s.

Table 4-13

t (s)	1	2	3	4	5	6	7
i (A)	12.32	6.12	3.04	1.51	0.75	0.37	0.18

SOLUTION Since $i = a \cdot e^{bt}$ we have $\ln(i) = bt + \ln(a)$ by Sec. 4-2. Comparing this equation with the straight-line form $Y = MX + C$, we have Table 4-14.

Using Table 4-14 we now form a second one, Table 4-15.

Table 4-14

Straight line $Y = MX + C$		Curve $i = ae^{bt}$
Y	$=$	$\ln(i)$
X	$=$	t
M	$=$	b
C	$=$	$\ln(a)$

Table 4-15

	$t = X$	i	$\ln(i) = Y$	X^2	XY
	1	12.32	2.5112	1	2.5112
	2	6.12	1.8116	4	3.623
	3	3.04	1.1119	9	3.3357
	4	1.51	0.4121	16	1.6484
	5	0.75	−0.2877	25	−1.4385
	6	0.37	−0.9942	36	−5.9652
	7	0.18	−1.7148	49	−12.0036
Σ	28		2.8501	140	−8.2890

Hence we have

$$\Sigma XY = -8.289$$

$$\Sigma X^2 = 140$$

$$\bar{X} = \frac{28}{7} = 4$$

$$\bar{Y} = \frac{2.8501}{7} = 0.40716$$

Hence the slope

$$M = \frac{\Sigma XY - n(\bar{X}\bar{Y})}{\Sigma X^2 - n(\bar{X})^2}$$

$$= \frac{-8.289 - 7(4)(0.40716)}{140 - 7(4)^2}$$

$$= \frac{-19.68948}{28}$$

$$= -0.7032$$

Thus since $M = b$ we have

$$b = -0.7032$$

From $C = \bar{Y} - M\bar{X}$ we have

$$C = 0.40716 - (-0.7032)(4)$$

$$= 3.21996$$

But $C = \ln(a)$ and therefore $e^C = a$ which implies that

$$a = e^{3.21996}$$

$$= 25.0 \qquad \text{(to 1 decimal place)}$$

Hence the law is

$$i = 25.0(e^{-0.7t})$$

Before using the equation $i = 25.0(e^{-0.7t})$ to predict current values, we should establish whether this curve follows the general drift of the experimental points. This can be carried out by plotting the curve on the scattergram of the measurements as shown in Fig. 4-8. It can be seen that the curve found passes close to the experimental points. There is a numerical method of measuring this 'closeness' which is usually carried out by using the computer program designed to establish the law.

Returning to our prediction, we have a value of time, $t = 3.5$ s, which we substitute into the law

$$i = 25.0(e^{-0.7t})$$

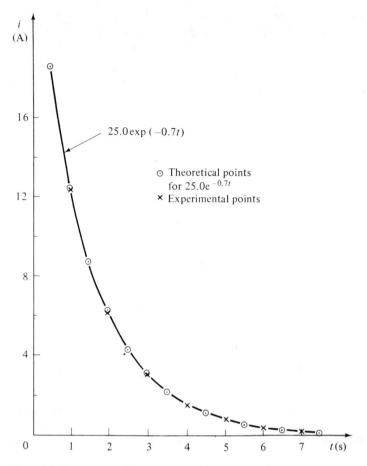

Figure 4-8 Scattergram of experimental points with graph of curve $i = 25.0e^{-0.7t}$.

This implies that

$$i = 25.0(e^{-0.7(3.5)}) \qquad \text{at } t = 3.5\,\text{s}$$

Hence we have a current of 2.16 A at a time of $t = 3.5$ s.

PROBLEMS

For problems **4-1** to **4-6** transform the given equation into the straight-line form $Y = MX + C$.

4-1 $y = 3a(x^b)$, a and b are constants.

4-2 $y = 1.2a(x^b)$, a and b are constants.

4-3 $y = a(x^{2b})$, a and b are constants.

4-4 $y = 4a(e^{2bx})$, a and b are constants.

4-5 $y = 6b(e^{3ax})$, a and b are constants.

4-6 $y = 3a(b)^{2x}$, a and b are constants.

For problems **4-7** to **4-10** the curve $y = a \cdot x^b$ has been transformed, using $\log_e$, into the straight-line form $Y = MX + C$. For the given values of M and C, find the constants a and b.

4-7 $M = 0.8, C = -1.2$.

4-8 $M = 3.4, C = 2.345$.

4-9 $M = 31.8, C = -0.68$.

4-10 $M = 321, C = 0.7532$.

For problems **4-11** to **4-15** the curve $y = a \cdot e^{bx}$ has been transformed, using $\log_e$, into the straight-line form $Y = MX + C$. For the given values of M and C, find the constants a and b.

4-11 $M = 2, C = 0.5$.

4-12 $M = 1.2, C = -2$.

4-13 $M = -1, C = 2$.

4-14 $M = 3.1, C = 0.89$.

4-15 $M = 2.6, C = 3.8$.

For problems **4-16** to **4-20** the curve $y = a \cdot b^x$ has been transformed into the straight-line form $Y = MX + C$ using $\log_e$. For the given values of M and C, find the constants a and b.

4-16 $M = -0.5, C = -0.08$.

4-17 $M = -1.3, C = -0.4$.

4-18 $M = 1.56, C = 0.35$.

4-19 $M = 0.786, C = -1.2$.

4-20 $M = 2.1, C = 2.472$.

For problems **4-21** to **4-23** fit the curve $y = a \cdot b^x$ to the given experimental data.

4-21

x	1	2	3	4	5
y	1.0	0.5	0.25	0.125	0.0625

4-22

x	1	2	3	4	5	6
y	0.6	0.36	0.216	0.1296	0.07776	0.046 656

4-23

x	1	2	3	4	5
y	3.6	10.8	32.4	97.2	291.6

For problems **4-24** to **4-26** fit the curve $y = a \cdot x^b$ to the given experimental data.

4-24

x	1	2	3	4	5	6
y	2	16	54	128	250	432

4-25

x	1	2	3	4	5	6	7
y	1	4.29	10.04	18.38	29.36	43.06	59.52

4-26

x	1	2	3	4	5	6
y	1.30	1.97	2.51	2.99	3.41	3.81

For problems **4-27** to **4-29** fit the curve $y = a \cdot e^{bx}$ to the given experimental data.

4-27

x	1	2	3	4	5
y	2.7	7.4	20.1	54.6	148.4

4-28

x	0.1	0.2	0.3	0.4	0.5	0.6
y	0.61	0.75	0.91	1.11	1.36	1.66

4-29

x	10	11	12	13	14
y	0.74	0.90	1.10	1.35	1.64

*4-30 The current in part of an electrical circuit was measured and the results laid down in Table 4-16.

Table 4-16

t (s)	1	2	3	4	5	6
i (A)	0.98	1.04	1.06	1.08	1.10	1.13

From electrical theory, a law of the form $i = a \cdot e^{bt}$ has been suggested. Fit this law to the experimental data and hence predict the current at $t = 1.6$ s.

*4-31 For the experimental results in Table 4-16, find constants such that a curve of the form $i = c \cdot d^{t}$ best fits the data.

***4-32 The velocity of a moving object travelling in a straight line is measured. The experimental results are given in Table 4-17.

Table 4-17

t (s)	1	2	3	4	5	6	7	8
V (m/s)	0.3	1.2	2.7	4.8	7.5	10.8	14.7	19.2

(a) Fit the curves $V = a \cdot t^b$ and $V = a \cdot e^{bt}$.

(b) Which of the two curves fitted in part (a) would be recommended for predicting the velocity?

(c) Is it wise to use either fitted curve to predict the velocity of the body at $t = 200$ s? Give reasons for your decision.

***4-33** Show that if the two curves $y = a \cdot e^{bx}$ and $y = c \cdot d^x$ are fitted to the same data then, provided a, c, and d are positive constants, we have $a = c$ and $b = \ln(d)$.

Solutions

The reader should note that the solutions given may not be unique and variations may occur owing to the method of finding particular curves. The logarithmic transformation may be base 10 or e.

	Y	X	M	C
4-1	$\log(y)$	$\log(x)$	b	$\log(3a)$
4-2	$\log(y)$	$\log(x)$	b	$\log(1.2a)$
4-3	$\log(y)$	$\log(x)$	$2b$	$\log(a)$
4-4	$\ln(y)$	x	$2b$	$\ln(4a)$
4-5	$\ln(y)$	x	$3a$	$\ln(6b)$
4-6	$\log(y)$	x	$2\log(b)$	$\log(3a)$

4-7 $b = 0.8, a = 0.3012$.

4-8 $b = 3.4, a = 10.4333$.

4-9 $b = 31.8, a = 0.5066$.

4-10 $b = 321, a = 2.1238$.

4-11 $b = 2, a = 1.6487$.

4-12 $b = 1.2, a = 0.1353$.

4-13 $b = -1, a = 7.389$.

4-14 $b = 3.1, a = 2.4351$.

4-15 $b = 2.6, a = 44.7012$.

4-16 $b = 0.6065, a = 0.9231$.

4-17 $b = 0.2725, a = 0.6703$.

4-18 $b = 4.7588, a = 1.4191$.

4-19 $b = 2.1946, a = 0.3012$.

4-20 $b = 8.1662, a = 11.8461$.

4-21 $y = 2(0.5)^x$.

4-22 $y = 0.6^x$.

4-23 $y = 1.2(3)^x$.

4-24 $y = 2(x^3)$.

4-25 $y = x^{2.1}$.

4-26 $y = 1.3(x^{0.6})$.

4-27 $y = 0.996(e^x)$.

4-28 $y = 0.5(e^{2x})$.

4-29 $y = 0.1(e^{0.2x})$.

4-30 $i = 0.972(e^{0.026t})$, 1.01A.

4-31 $i = 0.972(1.026)^t$.

4-32

(a) $V = 0.357(e^{0.55t})$, $V = 0.3(t^2)$.

(b) $V = 0.3t^2$.

(c) No! It is not wise, as 200 s is outside the time interval defined by the experiment.

4-33 [*Hint:* Let $a \cdot e^{bx} = c \cdot d^x$ and take logs. Compare both sides of new equation and the result follows. Note that if a, c or d are not positive, then we *cannot* transform by using logs.]

DIFFERENTIATION

Objectives After reading this chapter you should be able to:

1. Determine the derivatives of sums, products, and quotients of functions and evaluate them for a given value.
   (*a*) Determine the derivative of trigonometric, logarithmic, exponential, and polynomial functions.
   (*b*) Calculate the value of the derivative at a given point.
   (*c*) State the product rule.
   (*d*) State the quotient rule.
   (*e*) State the chain rule.
   (*f*) Apply the basic rules in 1(*c*), (*d*), and (*e*) to functions of a single variable.
2. Determine the second derivative.
   (*a*) Determine the second derivative for trigonometric, logarithmic, exponential, and polynomial functions.
   (*b*) State the relationship between the first and second derivatives of a function.
   (*c*) Calculate the value of the second derivative.
3. Apply the differential calculus to solve engineering problems.
   (*a*) State the definitions of velocity and acceleration of a body moving in a straight line.
   (*b*) Formulate velocity and acceleration equations from a given displacement equation.
   (*c*) Calculate the magnitude of the velocity and the acceleration of a body moving in a straight line for a given time value.
   (*d*) Formulate potential difference (p.d.) equations for resistors and inductors using a given current equation.
   (*e*) Calculate the p.d. across a resistor and an inductor for a given time value using the equations developed in 3(*d*).

5-1 INTRODUCTION

Differentiation can be regarded as the *process* of finding a slope equation for a given curve which represents a function $f(x)$. Consider the function represented by

93

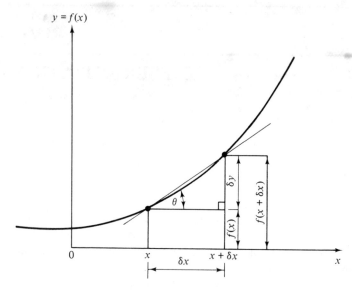

Figure 5-1 [The reader should note that δx is a single quantity and *not* the product of δ and x.]

$y = f(x)$ shown in Fig. 5-1. We choose a point x and a second point $x + \delta x$ along the x axis. Using these two points we form a right-angle triangle, the hypotenuse of which can be defined as the **approximate slope** of the curve at the point x. From Fig. 5-1 the

$$\text{Approximate slope} = \tan \theta$$

$$= \frac{\delta y}{\delta x}$$

$$= \frac{f(x + \delta x) - f(x)}{\delta x}$$

We initially chose δx, the base of the triangle, to have any value but now we let δx tend to zero and the approximate slope tends to the true slope at x. Thus,

$$\lim_{\delta x \to 0} \frac{\delta y}{\delta x} = \lim_{\delta x \to 0} \frac{f(x + \delta x) - f(x)}{\delta x}$$

We call this limit the **first derivative** and label it

$$\frac{dy}{dx} \quad \text{or} \quad f'(x)$$

Hence,

$$\frac{dy}{dx} = \lim_{\delta x \to 0} \frac{\delta y}{\delta x} = \lim_{\delta x \to 0} \frac{f(x + \delta x) - f(x)}{\delta x}$$

Example 5-1-1 Differentiate from first principles the function represented by $y = x^2$.

SOLUTION Let

$$f(x) = x^2$$

then

$$f(x + \delta x) = (x + \delta x)^2$$
$$= x^2 + 2x(\delta x) + (\delta x)^2$$

Using the definition of the first derivative we have

$$\frac{f(x + \delta x) - f(x)}{\delta x} = \frac{x^2 + 2x(\delta x) + (\delta x)^2 - x^2}{\delta x}$$
$$= \frac{2x(\delta x) + (\delta x)^2}{\delta x}$$
$$= 2x + (\delta x)$$

Therefore the approximate slope at x is

$$\frac{\delta y}{\delta x} = 2x + (\delta x)$$

and

$$\lim_{\delta x \to 0} \frac{\delta y}{\delta x} = \lim_{\delta x \to 0} 2x + (\delta x)$$
$$= 2x$$

We have the **first derivative**

$$\frac{dy}{dx} = 2x$$

This equation is also called the **slope equation** for the curve $y = f(x)$.

5-2 DIFFERENTIATION OF ax^n

Consider $y = ax^n$ and let

$$f(x) = ax^n$$

so

$$f(x + \delta x) = a(x + \delta x)^n$$
$$= a\left[x^n \left(1 + \frac{\delta x}{x} \right)^n \right]$$

Using the **binomial theorem**, we can expand the $f(x + \delta x)$ equation to give

$$f(x + \delta x) = ax^n \left(1 + \frac{n(\delta x)}{x} + \frac{(n)(n-1)(\delta x)^2}{2!} \frac{}{x^2} + \ldots \right)$$

Therefore the **approximate slope** is given by

$$\frac{\delta y}{\delta x} = \frac{f(x + \delta x) - f(x)}{\delta x}$$

$$= \frac{(ax^n + ax^{n-1}n(\delta x) + ax^{n-2}n(n-1)(\delta x)^2/2! + \dots) - ax^n}{\delta x}$$

$$= nax^{n-1} + \frac{n(n-1)ax^{n-2}(\delta x)}{2!} + \dots$$

Hence,

$$\lim_{\delta x \to 0} \frac{\delta y}{\delta x} = \frac{dy}{dx}$$

$$= nax^{n-1}$$

Example 5-2-1 By using the first derivative, find the value of the slope of the curve $y = 3x^4$ at $x = 1$.

SOLUTION If $y = ax^n$ then

$$\frac{dy}{dx} = nax^{n-1}$$

Since $y = 3x^4$ we have $\frac{dy}{dx} = 12x^3$ which is the **slope equation**.

At $x = 2, \frac{dy}{dx} = 12(2)^3 = 96$.

Therefore the value of the slope at $x = 2$ for the curve $y = 3x^4$ is 96.

5-3 GRAPHS AND SLOPE DIRECTIONS

If the slope value at x is *positive* then the value of the function, $f(x)$, is *increasing* as x increases. On the other hand, if the slope value is *negative* then the value of the function decreases as x increases. This is illustrated in Fig. 5-2.

Example 5-3-1 Find the slope value at (a) $x = 2$ and (b) $x = -2$ for the curve $y = x^4 + 2$. State whether the value of y is increasing or decreasing in the neighbourhood of these points.

SOLUTION We write

$$y = x^4 + 2$$

as $y = x^4 + 2x^0$ since $x^0 = 1$, and on using the formula for differentiating ax^n we have

$$\frac{dy}{dx} = 4x^{4-1} + (0)(2)(x^{0-1})$$

$$= 4x^3$$

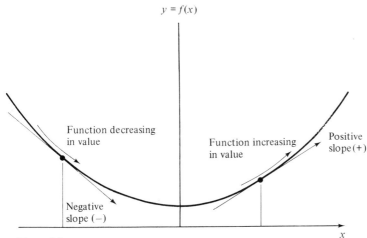

$y = f(x)$

Function decreasing in value

Function increasing in value

Positive slope (+)

Negative slope (−)

x

Figure 5-2

We note that a constant function always has a zero slope. Thus if $y = K$ where K is a constant.

$$\frac{dy}{dx} = 0$$

(a) At $x = 2$, $dy/dx = 32$ which is positive and the value of y is increasing as x increases.

(b) At $x = -2$, $dy/dx = -32$ which is negative and the value of y is decreasing as x increases.

5-4 DIFFERENTIATION OF exp(x)

By definition

$$\exp(x) = 1 + x + \frac{x^2}{2!} + \frac{x^3}{3!} + \ldots + \frac{x^n}{n!} + \ldots$$

Let

$$y = \exp(x)$$

$$= 1 + x + \frac{x^2}{2!} + \ldots + \frac{x^n}{n!} + \frac{x^{n+1}}{(n+1)!} + \ldots$$

From Sec. 5-3 we have that if $y = ax^n$, then $dy/dx = nax^{n-1}$, and so, on differentiating the exponential series term by term we have

$$\frac{dy}{dx} = 0 + 1 + \frac{2x}{2!} + \frac{3x^2}{3!} + \ldots + \frac{nx^{n-1}}{n!} + \frac{(n+1)x^n}{(n+1)!} + \ldots$$

$$= 1 + x + \frac{x^2}{2!} + \frac{x^3}{3!} + \ldots + \frac{x^{n-1}}{(n-1)!} + \frac{x^n}{n!} + \ldots$$

After the process of differentiation we have found that the same series appears as exp(x). Thus, if

$$y = \exp(x)$$

then

$$\frac{dy}{dx} = \exp(x)$$

Example 5-4-1 Differentiate (a) 4 exp(x) and (b) $14e^x + 3x$.

SOLUTION (a) Let

$$y = 4 \exp(x)$$

then

$$\frac{dy}{dx} = 4 \exp(x)$$

(b) Let

$$y = 14e^x + 3x$$

then

$$\frac{dy}{dx} = 14e^x + 3$$

5-5 FUNCTION OF A FUNCTION

If we apply more than one function to a variable in succession, we have the situation of a 'function of a function'. For example, let

$$F(x) = \exp(x^2)$$

$$= e^{x^2}.$$

$F(x)$ is a **function of a function** since we applied the function of squaring the value of x followed by the 'exp' function. This is illustrated in Fig. 5-3.

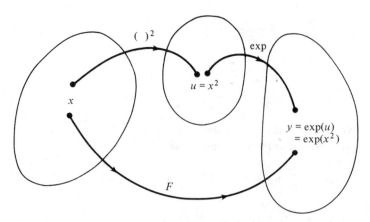

Figure 5-3 F – a function of a function, $F(x) = \exp(x^2)$.

To differentiate this type of function we use the **chain rule**. This states that

$$\frac{dy}{dx} = \frac{dy}{du} \cdot \frac{du}{dx}$$

Example 5-5-1 Differentiate $y = \exp(x^3)$.

SOLUTION Since $y = \exp(x^3)$ we let $u = x^3$ and substituting u into the equation $y = \exp(x^3)$ gives

$$y = \exp(u)$$

$\Rightarrow$
$$\frac{dy}{du} = \exp(u)$$

by Sec. 5-4. However,

$$u = x^3$$

$\Rightarrow$
$$\frac{du}{dx} = 3x^2$$

and on using the **chain rule** we have

$$\frac{dy}{dx} = \frac{dy}{du} \cdot \frac{du}{dx}$$

$$= \exp(u)\, 3x^2$$

This becomes, on substituting in the value of u,

$$\frac{dy}{dx} = 3x^2 \exp(x^3)$$

Example 5-5-2 Differentiate the function represented by $y = (x^4 + x^6 + 1)^{100}$.

SOLUTION Since

$$y = (x^4 + x^6 + 1)^{100}$$

we let

$$u = (x^4 + x^6 + 1)$$

$\Rightarrow$
$$\frac{du}{dx} = 4x^3 + 6x^5$$

However,

$$y = u^{100}$$

$\Rightarrow$
$$\frac{dy}{du} = 100u^{99}$$

Using the chain rule

$$\frac{dy}{dx} = \frac{dy}{du} \cdot \frac{du}{dx}$$

we have

$$\frac{dy}{dx} = (100u^{99})(4x^3 + 6x^5)$$

Replacing u by $(x^4 + x^6 + 1)$ we have

$$\frac{dy}{dx} = 100(x^4 + x^6 + 1)^{99}(4x^3 + 6x^5)$$

Example 5-5-3 Prove that if $y = e^{ax}$, where a is a constant, then $dy/dx = ae^{ax}$. Using this fact find the first derivative of e^{3x}.

SOLUTION Since $y = e^{ax}$ we let $u = ax$ and on substitution

$$y = e^u$$

By Sec. 5-4 we get

$$\frac{dy}{du} = e^u$$

Since

$$u = ax$$

$$\frac{du}{dx} = a$$

and using the chain rule

$$\frac{dy}{dx} = \frac{dy}{du} \cdot \frac{du}{dx}$$

$$\frac{dy}{dx} = e^u a$$

$$= ae^{ax}$$

Let $y = e^{3x}$, then $a = 3$ and using $dy/dx = ae^{ax}$ we have

$$\frac{dy}{dy} = 3e^{3x}$$

Example 5-5-4 Find the slope of the curve $y = 4e^{-2x}$ at $x = 0.5$.

SOLUTION Since $y = e^{ax}$ implies $dy/dx = ae^{ax}$ (by Example 5-5-3), we have for

$$y = 4e^{-2x}$$

$$\frac{dy}{dx} = -8e^{-2x}$$

At $x = 0.5$ we have

$$\frac{dy}{dx} = -8e^{-2(0.5)}$$

$$= -8e^{-1}$$

$$= -2.9430$$

Therefore the slope of the curve $y = 4e^{-2x}$ has a value of -2.9430 at $x = 0.5$.

5-6 DIFFERENTIATION OF LOGARITHMIC FUNCTIONS

Consider $y = \ln(x)$ and let

$$f(x) = \ln(x)$$

so

$$f(x + \delta x) = \ln(x + \delta x)$$

$$= \ln\left[x\left(1 + \frac{\delta x}{x}\right)\right]$$

$$= \ln(x) + \ln\left(1 + \frac{\delta x}{x}\right)$$

by the theory of logarithms. The approximate slope

$$\frac{\delta y}{\delta x} = \frac{f(x + \delta x) - f(x)}{\delta x}$$

$$= \frac{\ln(x) + \ln[1 + (\delta x/x)] - \ln(x)}{\delta x}$$

$$= \frac{\ln[1 + (\delta x/x)]}{\delta x}$$

By using the power series for

$$\ln(1 + X) = \left(X - \frac{X^2}{2} + \frac{X^3}{3} - \ldots\right)$$

we can expand the logarithmic part of the approximate slope. Replacing X in the power series by $\delta x/x$ we have

$$\ln\left(1 + \frac{\delta x}{x}\right) = \left(\frac{\delta x}{x} - \frac{(\delta x)^2}{2x^2} + \ldots\right)$$

Hence the approximate slope

$$\frac{\delta y}{\delta x} = \frac{\ln[1 + (\delta x/x)]}{\delta x}$$

$$= \left(\frac{1}{x} - \frac{(\delta x)}{2x^2} + \ldots\right)$$

Taking the limit as δx tends to zero gives dy/dx. Therefore,

$$\frac{dy}{dx} = \lim_{\delta x \to 0} \left(\frac{1}{x} - \frac{(\delta x)}{2x^2} + \ldots \right)$$

$$= \frac{1}{x}$$

Therefore

$$y = \ln(x)$$

implies

$$\frac{dy}{dx} = \frac{1}{x}$$

Example 5-6-1 Differentiate (a) $3(\ln(x))$ and (b) $\ln(ax)$ where a is any constant.

SOLUTION (a) Let

$$y = 3(\ln(x))$$

$$\frac{dy}{dx} = (3)\left(\frac{1}{x}\right)$$

$$= \frac{3}{x}$$

(b) Let $y = \ln(ax)$ and let $u = ax$. Thus we have

$$y = \ln(u)$$

and

$$\frac{dy}{du} = \frac{1}{u}$$

Since

$$u = ax$$

$$\frac{du}{dx} = a$$

and by the chain rule

$$\frac{dy}{dx} = \frac{dy}{du} \cdot \frac{du}{dx}$$

$$= \left(\frac{1}{u}\right)(a)$$

$$= \frac{a}{ax}$$

$$= \frac{1}{x}$$

Therefore it follows that if

$$y = \ln(ax)$$

where a is a constant, we have

$$\frac{dy}{dx} = \frac{1}{x}$$

5-7 TRIGONOMETRIC FUNCTIONS

Consider $y = \sin(x)$ and let $f(x) = \sin(x)$. This implies that

$$f(x + \delta x) = \sin(x + \delta x)$$

and we can form the approximate slope equation. Therefore,

$$\frac{\delta y}{\delta x} = \frac{\sin(x + \delta x) - \sin(x)}{\delta x}$$

Since

$$\sin A - \sin B = 2 \cos\left(\frac{A + B}{2}\right) \sin\left(\frac{A - B}{2}\right)$$

we have on replacing A by $(x + \delta x)$ and B by (x) that

$$\frac{\delta y}{\delta x} = \frac{\sin(x + \delta x) - \sin(x)}{\delta x}$$

$$= \frac{2 \cos[(2x + \delta x)/2] \sin(\delta x/2)}{\delta x}$$

$$= \cos\left(x + \frac{\delta x}{2}\right) \frac{\sin(\delta x/2)}{\delta x/2}$$

on dividing numerator and denominator by 2. Thus

$$\frac{dy}{dx} = \lim_{\delta x \to 0} \left[\cos\left(x + \frac{\delta x}{2}\right) \frac{\sin(\delta x/2)}{\delta x/2}\right]$$

$$= \cos(x)$$

since (see Table 5-1)

$$\left(\frac{\sin(\delta x/2)}{\delta x/2}\right) \to 1 \qquad \text{as } \delta x \to 0$$

Therefore if

$$y = \sin(x) \qquad \text{then} \qquad \frac{dy}{dx} = \cos(x)$$

We shall leave it to the reader to prove in a similar manner that if

$$y = \cos(x) \qquad \text{then} \qquad \frac{dy}{dx} = -\sin(x)$$

Example 5-7-1 Differentiate with respect to x, (a) $4 \cos(x)$, (b) $\cos(3x)$, and (c) $\sin(4x)$.

Table 5-1 A computer print-out illustrating as $X \to 0$ $\sin(X)/X \to 1$

	X	$\sin(X)$	$\dfrac{\sin(X)}{X}$	
	0.1940	0.1928	0.9937	
	0.1860	0.1849	0.9942	
	0.1780	0.1771	0.9947	
	0.1700	0.1692	0.9952	
	0.1620	0.1613	0.9956	
	0.1540	0.1534	0.9961	$\dfrac{\sin(X)}{X}$
	0.1460	0.1455	0.9965	
X tending to zero	0.1380	0.1376	0.9968	
	0.1300	0.1296	0.9972	tending to one
	0.1220	0.1217	0.9975	
	0.1140	0.1138	0.9978	
	0.1060	0.1058	0.9981	
	0.0980	0.0978	0.9984	
	0.0900	0.0899	0.9987	
	0.0820	0.0819	0.9989	
	0.0740	0.0739	0.9991	

SOLUTION (*a*) Let

$$y = 4\cos(x)$$

$\Rightarrow$

$$\frac{dy}{dx} = -4\sin(x)$$

(*b*) Let $y = \cos(3x)$ and let $u = 3x$. Thus we have

$$y = \cos(u)$$

and

$$\frac{dy}{du} = -\sin(u)$$

Since $u = 3x$ we have $du/dx = 3$ and by the chain rule

$$\frac{dy}{dx} = \frac{dy}{du} \cdot \frac{du}{dx}$$

$$= (-\sin(u))(3)$$

$$= -3\sin(3x)$$

(*c*) Let $y = \sin(4x)$, then let $u = 4x$, so

$$y = \sin(u)$$

and

$$\frac{dy}{du} = \cos(u)$$

Since $u = 4x$ we have $du/dx = 4$ and by the chain rule

$$\frac{dy}{dx} = \frac{dy}{du} \cdot \frac{du}{dx}$$

$$= 4\cos(u)$$

$$= 4\cos(4x)$$

Example 5-7-2 If $y = \cos\theta$ and $x = \sin\theta$ show, by using the chain rule, that $dy/dx = -\tan\theta$.

SOLUTION

$$y = \cos\theta \qquad \text{implies} \qquad \frac{dy}{d\theta} = -\sin\theta$$

and $\qquad x = \sin\theta \qquad \text{implies} \qquad \frac{dx}{d\theta} = \cos\theta$

Using the chain rule

$$\frac{dy}{dx} = \frac{dy}{d\theta} \cdot \frac{d\theta}{dx}$$

$$= (-\sin\theta)\left(\frac{1}{\cos\theta}\right)$$

$$= -\tan\theta$$

Example 5-7-3 Find the value of the slope of the curve

$$y = 3\cos(x) - 4\sin(2x)$$

at $x = 1$.

SOLUTION

$$y = 3\cos(x) - 4\sin(2x)$$

$\Rightarrow \qquad\qquad \frac{dy}{dy} = -3\sin(x) - 8\cos(2x)$

At $x = 1$ we obtain (remembering to set the calculator to *radian mode*)

$$\frac{dy}{dx} = -3\sin(1) - 8\cos(2)$$

$$= -3(0.8415) - 8(-0.4162) \qquad \text{(rounding to 4 decimal places at each stage)}$$

$$= 0.805$$

5-8 THE PRODUCT AND QUOTIENT RULES

Consider two functions of x represented by the equations

$$u = f(x) \qquad \text{and} \qquad v = g(x)$$

If we form the equation

$$y = u \cdot v$$

we have a **product** of two functions of x. Let x be increased by δx. This implies that the values of u and v will both change. Let the change in the value of u be δu, and let the change in the value of v be δv. Then

$$y + \delta y = (u + \delta u)(v + \delta v)$$

$$= u \cdot v + u \cdot \delta v + \delta u \cdot v + \delta u \cdot \delta v$$

This implies that

$$\frac{\delta y}{\delta x} = u \cdot \frac{\delta v}{\delta x} + \frac{\delta u}{\delta x} \cdot v + \frac{\delta u}{\delta x} \cdot \delta v$$

on subtracting $y = u \cdot v$ from both sides and dividing throughout by δx. Let δx tend to zero and we have

$$\lim_{\delta x \to 0} \left(\frac{\delta y}{\delta x} \right) = \frac{dy}{dx}$$

$$\lim_{\delta x \to 0} \left(\frac{\delta u}{\delta x} \right) = \frac{du}{dx}$$

and

$$\lim_{\delta x \to 0} \left(\frac{\delta v}{\delta x} \right) = \frac{dv}{dx}$$

As δx tends to zero, so the changes in u and v will tend to zero. In symbols

$$\text{as} \quad \delta x \to 0 \quad \text{we have} \quad \delta u \to 0 \quad \text{and} \quad \delta v \to 0$$

Thus, for the **product** of two functions of x

$$\frac{dy}{dx} = u \cdot \frac{dv}{dx} + v \cdot \frac{du}{dx}$$

or

$$y' = u \cdot v' + v \cdot u'$$

Example 5-8-1 Differentiate with respect to x the functions $(a)\, x^2 \sin(x)$ and $(b)\, xe^x$.

SOLUTION (a) Let

$$y = x^2 \sin(x)$$

and let

$$u = x^2 \quad \text{and} \quad v = \sin(x)$$

Substituting u and v into $y = x^2 \sin(x)$ gives

$$y = u \cdot v$$

We have the product of two functions of x and we use the **product rule** to obtain the first derivative. Since $y = u \cdot v$,

$$\frac{dy}{dx} = u\frac{dv}{dx} + v\frac{du}{dx}$$

or

$$y' = u \cdot v' + v \cdot u'$$

Since

$$u = x^2 \qquad \text{and} \qquad v = \sin(x)$$

$$u' = 2x \qquad \text{and} \qquad v' = \cos(x)$$

Substituting these functions into the product rule formula we have

$$y' = x^2 \cos(x) + 2x \sin(x)$$

or

$$\frac{dy}{dx} = x^2 \cos(x) + 2x \sin(x)$$

$$= x[x \cos(x) + 2 \sin(x)]$$

(b) Let

$$y = xe^x$$

and let

$$u = x \qquad \text{and} \qquad v = e^x$$

Substituting u and v into the equation $y = xe^x$ gives

$$y = u \cdot v$$

We have as before a product of two functions of x. Since

$$u = x \qquad u' = 1$$

and

$$v = e^x \qquad v' = e^x$$

Substituting these functions into the product rule formula gives

$$y' = xe^x + e^x$$

$$= e^x(x + 1)$$

We shall leave it to the reader to prove the **quotient rule** which states that if u and v represent two functions of x such that

$$y = \frac{u}{v}$$

then

$$\frac{dy}{dx} = \frac{v(du/dx) - u(dv/dx)}{v^2}$$

or

$$y' = \frac{v \cdot u' - u \cdot v'}{v^2}$$

Example 5-8-2 Using the quotient rule, differentiate x^2/e^x.

SOLUTION Let

$$y = x^2/e^x$$

and let

$$u = x^2 \qquad \text{and} \qquad v = e^x$$

Substituting u and v into $y = x^2/e^x$ gives

$$y = u/v$$

We have a **quotient** involving two functions of x and we use

$$\frac{dy}{dx} = \frac{v(du/dx) - u(dv/dx)}{v^2}$$

or

$$y' = \frac{v \cdot u' - u \cdot v'}{v^2}$$

Since

$$u = x^2 \qquad u' = 2x$$

and

$$v = e^x \qquad v' = e^x$$

Therefore we have

$$y' = \frac{v \cdot u' - u \cdot v'}{v^2}$$

$$= \frac{e^x 2x - x^2 e^x}{e^{2x}}$$

and hence

$$\frac{dy}{dx} = \frac{2x - x^2}{e^x}$$

$$= \frac{x(2 - x)}{e^x}$$

$$= e^{-x} x(2 - x)$$

Example 5-8-3 Show, by using the quotient rule, that if $y = \tan\theta$, then $y' = \sec^2\theta$.

SOLUTION Let

$$y = \tan\theta = \frac{\sin\theta}{\cos\theta}$$

Let $u = \sin\theta$ and $v = \cos\theta$ and on substituting into $y = \tan\theta$ we have

$$y = \frac{u}{v}$$

$$\Rightarrow \qquad y' = \frac{v \cdot u' - u \cdot v'}{v^2}$$

Since

$$u = \sin\theta \qquad u' = \cos\theta$$

and

$$v = \cos\theta \qquad v' = -\sin\theta$$

Substituting these functions into

$$y' - \frac{v \cdot u' - u \cdot v'}{v^2}$$

gives

$$y' = \frac{(\cos\theta)(\cos\theta) - (\sin\theta)(-\sin\theta)}{\cos^2\theta}$$

$$= \frac{\cos^2\theta + \sin^2\theta}{\cos^2\theta}$$

$$= \frac{1}{\cos^2\theta} \qquad \text{since } \cos^2\theta + \sin^2\theta = 1$$

$$= \sec^2\theta$$

Hence if

$$y = \tan\theta \qquad \text{then} \qquad \frac{dy}{d\theta} = \sec^2\theta$$

Example 5-8-4 Find the value of the derivative of the function represented by $y = x^2 \cos(3x)$ at the point $x = 2$.

SOLUTION $y = x^2 \cos(3x)$ is a product of two functions, so we use the product rule. Let $y = u \cdot v$ then $y' = u' \cdot v + v' \cdot u$. Let

$$u = x^2 \qquad \Rightarrow \qquad u' = 2x$$

and

$$v = \cos(3x) \qquad \Rightarrow \qquad v' = -3\sin(3x)$$

Then using the product rule

$$y' = 2x \cdot \cos(3x) - x^2 \cdot 3\sin(3x)$$

At $x = 2$

$$y' = 2(2)\cos(6) - 3(2^2)\sin(6)$$

$$= 4(0.9602) - 12(-0.2794)$$

$$= 7.1936$$

The reader should note that we are using *radian* mode in this calculation. It should also be noted that we have accumulated errors by rounding off to 4 decimal places at each stage. If we use 6 decimal place rounding at each stage we arrive at 7.193672. This rounded to 4 decimal places gives 7.1937.

5-9 THE SECOND DERIVATIVE

If we differentiate a function $f(x)$ twice we obtain the second derivative notated

$$f''(x) = \frac{d^2 y}{dx^2}$$

Since the first derivative,

$$\frac{dy}{dx} = f'(x)$$

forms a slope equation of a curve $y = f(x)$, it follows that the second derivative,

$$f''(x) = \frac{d^2 y}{dx^2}$$

forms the slope equation for the curve dy/dx. The second derivative is the **rate of change** of the function dy/dx.

Example 5-9-1
(a) Differentiate twice the function represented by the curve $y = x^3$.
(b) Sketch the graphs of (i) y against x and (ii) dy/dx against x.
(c) Find the value of the slope at $x = 2$ for both curves in part (b).

SOLUTION (a) $y = x^3$ implies

$$\frac{dy}{dx} = 3x^2$$

Differentiating a second time

$$\frac{d^2 y}{dx^2} = 6x$$

(b) Figure 5-4 illustrates the graphs $y = x^3$ and $dy/dx = 3x^2$.
(c) The slope at $x = 2$ on both graphs is given by the respective slope equations. For the graph of $y = x^3$ the **slope** equation is

$$\frac{dy}{dx} = 3x^2$$

and at $x = 2$ we have a gradient of $3(2)^2 = 12$. For the graph of $dy/dx = 6x$ we have a **slope** equation given by

$$\frac{d^2 y}{dx^2} = 6x$$

and at $x = 2$ the gradient is $6(2) = 12$.

Example 5-9-2 If $y = \cos x$, show that

$$\frac{d^2 y}{dx^2} + y = 0$$

SOLUTION $y = \cos x$ implies $dy/dx = -\sin x$ and differentiating a second time gives $d^2 y/dx^2 = -\cos x$. However $y = \cos x$ and $-y = -\cos x$.

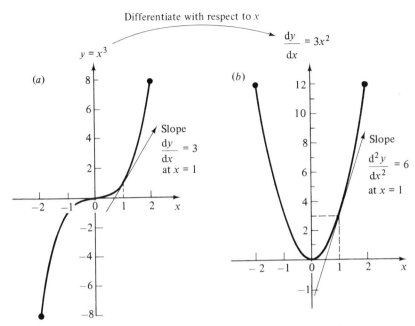

Figure 5-4 (*a*) A graph of $y = x^3$; (*b*) a graph of the slope equation for $\dfrac{dy}{dx} = 3x^2$.

Comparing $-y$ with the second derivative d^2y/dx^2 we can see that

$$\frac{d^2y}{dx^2} = -y = -\cos x$$

and therefore we have

$$\frac{d^2y}{dx^2} + y = 0$$

5-10 APPLICATIONS I

The velocity of a body is defined as the rate of change of position with respect to time. In calculus terms

$$\text{Velocity} = \frac{ds}{dt}$$

where s is a measure of position and t is the time variable. It can be seen that this velocity equation is also a slope equation for the distance–time graph.

The acceleration of a body is defined as the rate of change of its velocity with respect to time. If v represents the body's velocity at time t we have, in calculus terms

$$\text{Acceleration} = \frac{dv}{dt}$$

However,

$$\text{Velocity} = v = \frac{ds}{dt}$$

and on differentiation

$$\frac{dv}{dt} = \frac{d^2 s}{dt^2}$$

It follows that

$$\text{Acceleration} = a = \frac{dv}{dt} = \frac{d^2 s}{dt^2}$$

Example 5-10-1 A body is moving in a straight line with its position, measured in metres, from a fixed point modelled by the equation

$$s = 3t^3 - t$$

Find (a) the velocity equation, (b) the value of the velocity at $t = 3$ s, (c) the acceleration equation, and (d) the magnitude of the acceleration at $t = 3$ s.

SOLUTION

(a)

$$\text{Velocity} = v = \frac{ds}{dt}$$

$$= 9t^2 - 1$$

The velocity equation is given by

$$v = 9t^2 - 1$$

This is a mathematical model describing the relationship between velocity and time. The reader may like to observe that we are restricted to values of t greater than or equal to zero since time cannot have negative values.

(b) At $t = 3$ s,

$$v = 9(3)^2 - 1$$

$$= 80 \, \text{m/s}$$

(c)

$$\text{Acceleration} = \frac{dv}{dt}$$

$$= 18t$$

Therefore a mathematical model describing the relationship between acceleration and time for this body is given by

$$a = 18t$$

(d) At $t = 3$ s,

$$\text{Acceleration} = 18(3)$$

$$= 54 \, \text{m/s}^2$$

Example 5-10-2 A body moving through a liquid has its position from a fixed point given by $s = 12(1 - e^{-t})$, where s is in metres. Assuming that the body moves in a straight horizontal line, find equations for the acceleration and velocity at a time t. Calculate the time at which the velocity of the body is 6 m/s.

SOLUTION Since
$$s = 12(1 - e^{-t})$$

$$\frac{ds}{dt} = 12e^{-t}$$

The velocity equation is
$$v = 12e^{-t}$$

and the acceleration is
$$\frac{dv}{dt} = -12e^{-t}$$

At $v = 6$ m/s we have
$$6 = 12e^{-t}$$

or
$$0.5 = e^{-t}$$

Taking logs we have
$$\ln(0.5) = -t$$

$$-0.693\,15 = -t$$

Hence time at which velocity is 6 m/s is 0.693 15 s.

Example 5-10-3 A body of mass 4 kg is moving through a dense liquid with its position given by $s = 2(1 - e^{-2t})$ where s is its distance in metres from a fixed point and t is the respective time in seconds. Find (a) the velocity equation (b) an equation describing the kinetic energy (KE) at any instant in time, and (c) an equation describing the decelerating force.

SOLUTION
(a)
$$\text{Velocity} = \frac{ds}{dt}$$

$$= 4e^{-2t} \text{ m/s}$$

(b) Since

we have
$$\text{KE} = \tfrac{1}{2}(\text{mass})(\text{velocity})^2$$

$$\text{KE} = \tfrac{1}{2}(4)(4e^{-2t})^2$$

$$= 32e^{-4t} \text{ joules}$$

(c) By Newton's second law we have

$$(\text{mass})(\text{acceleration}) = (\text{accelerating force})$$

Hence we require the acceleration equation

$$\frac{d^2 s}{dt^2} = -8e^{-2t}$$

This is a deceleration and we have the equation for the deceleration force as

$$\text{Deceleration force} = \text{mass}(-8e^{-2t})$$

$$= -32e^{-2t} \text{ newtons}$$

Physically we note that this force opposes motion (the negative sign), and is decaying as time increases.

5-11 APPLICATIONS II

In this section we shall consider using differentiation to find potential differences (p.d.) across electrical components. Consider a series circuit consisting of a resistor, a capacitor and an inductor as shown in Fig. 5-5.

The current flowing is labelled i and is usually a function of time. For example, $i = 3\sin(2t + 1)$ is an equation which describes the relationship between current flowing and time.

The p.d. across the resistor is given by

$$V_R = iR$$

and since current is defined as the rate of change of charge with respect to time we have

$$V_R = R\frac{dq}{dt} \qquad \text{where} \qquad i = \frac{dq}{dt}$$

The p.d. across the inductor is proportional to the rate of change of current with respect to time. That is,

$$V_L = L\frac{di}{dt}$$

Since $i = dq/dt$ we can differentiate both sides to obtain

$$\frac{di}{dt} = \frac{d^2 q}{dt^2}$$

and

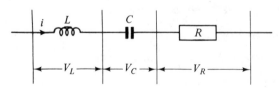

Figure 5-5

$$V_L = L\frac{di}{dt} = L\frac{d^2q}{dt^2}$$

Finally, the p.d. across the capacitor is given by

$$V_C = \frac{q}{C}$$

Example 5-11-1 A circuit consists of an inductor of 10 H (henries) in series with a resistor of 100 Ω (ohms). If the current flowing at time t is given by $i = \sin 3t$, find the p.d. across each component.

SOLUTION The p.d. across the resistor is

$$V_R = iR$$
$$= (\sin 3t)100$$
$$= 100 \sin 3t \text{ volts}$$

The p.d. across the inductor is given by

$$V_L = L\frac{di}{dt}$$
$$= 10 (3 \cos 3t)$$
$$= 30 \cos 3t \text{ volts}$$

Example 5-11-2 A coil has resistance of 5 Ω and inductance of 5 H. Following experimental work it is known that the current flowing through the coil is given by $i = 2 - 2e^{-t}$. Find an equation which describes the p.d. across the coil at a time t.

SOLUTION A coil can be considered as an inductor and a resistor in series. Hence p.d. across the coil is the sum of the p.d.'s across the resistor and the inductor shown in Fig. 5-6.

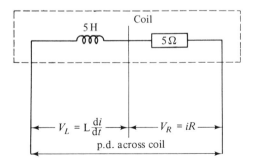

Figure 5-6

The p.d. across the resistor is

$$iR = 5(2 - 2e^{-t})$$

The p.d. across the inductor is

$$L\frac{di}{dt} = 5(2e^{-t})$$

$$= 10e^{-t}$$

Hence p.d. across coil is

$$5(2 - 2e^{-t}) + 10e^{-t} = 10\,\text{V}$$

PROBLEMS

For problems **5-1** to **5-3** differentiate the function represented by $y = f(x)$ from first principles.

5-1 $y = 3x^2$.

5-2 $y = 6x + 2x^3$.

5-3 $y = 4x - 2 + 3x^4$.

*5-4 By expanding $(3 + x^2)^3$ by the binomial theorem or otherwise find the first derivative of the function $f(x) = 3(3 + x^2)^3$.

For problems **5-5** to **5-9** find the slope equation for the curve $y = f(x)$.

5-5 $f(x) = 3x^6$.

5-6 $f(x) = 35 - 6x^3$.

5-7 $f(x) = 48x - 2x^5$.

*5-8 $f(x) = 2x^{-1}$.

*5-9 $f(x) = 3/x^2$.

For problems **5-10** to **5-12** differentiate the function $f(t)$ with respect to t.

5-10 $f(t) = 3t^4 - 2t^3 + t - 6$.

5-11 $f(t) = 6t^{0.5} - 7$.

5-12 $f(t) = -5t - 6t^{1.5}$.

For problems **5-13** to **5-15** find the value of the slope of the curve $y = f(x)$ at the point $x = 3.5$

5-13 $f(x) = 6x^2$.

*5-14 $f(x) = -4x - 5x^{0.5}$.

*5-15 $f(x) = 2x - 3x^{-1}$.

**5-16 Differentiate with respect to t the function represented by $3s = 2t^2 - 3t$. Hence find the value of the slope of the curve at the point $t = 1$.

**5-17 The curve $s = 3t^3$ has two points at which the gradient has a value of 36. Find the cartesian coordinates of these points.

*5-18 Find the position of the point on the curve $y = x^2 + 1$ where the slope has a value zero.

For problems **5-19** to **5-27** find the first derivative of the function defined by $y = f(x)$.

5-19 $y = e^{-x}$.

5-20 $y = e^{3x}$.

5-21 $y = e^{-9x}$.

*5-22 $y = (5.6)e^{-2x}$.

*5-23 $y = 4e^{2x}$.

5-24 $y = \exp(-5x)$.

5-25 $y = \exp(5x)$.

*5-26 $y = 4\exp(8x)$.

*5-27 $y = -6\exp(2x)$.

For problems **5-28** to **5-33** by using the chain rule find dy/dx.

5-28 $y = \exp(x^2 + 100)$.

5-29 $y = \exp(x^3)$.

5-30 $y = \exp(-x^2 + 1)$.

*5-31 $y = \exp(4x - 3x^3)$.

5-32 $y = \exp(x^2 + 3x + 1)$.

*5-33 $y = 4\exp(-2x + 10x^2)$.

5-34 Find the value of the slope of the curve $y = (x^2 - 3x)^{75}$ at $x = 1$.

For problems **5-35** to **5-40** find dy/dx.

5-35 $y = \ln(2x)$.

5-36 $y = \ln(-4x)$.

5-37 $y = \ln(0.7x)$.

5-38 $y = \ln(8x)$

5-39 $y = \ln(5.3x)$.

*5-40 $y = 5[\ln(x)]$.

For problems **5-41** to **5-45** find dy/dx by using the chain rule.

5-41 $y = \ln(x^2)$.

5-42 $y = \ln(3x^2)$.

5-43 $y = \ln(x + 3x^2)$.

*5-44 $y = 5[\ln(4x^{0.5})]$.

*5-45 $y = 6[\ln(5x - 1)]$.

**5-46 By *simplifying* the function $\ln(\exp(x^2))$ show that $dy/dx = 2x$.

****5-47 Is it possible to find the gradient of the curve $y = \ln(x)$ at $x = -1$? Give reasons for your answer.

For problems **5-48** to **5-60** find dy/dx.

5-48 $y = \sin(2x)$.

5-49 $y = \sin(-3x)$.

5-50 $y = \sin(0.4x)$.

*5-51 $y = 4[\sin(3x)]$.

5-52 $y = \cos(-3x)$.

5-53 $y = \cos(5x)$.

5-54 $y = \cos(0.3x)$.

*5-55 $y = 5[\cos(2x)]$.

5-56 $y = \tan(2x)$.

5-57 $y = \tan(-2x)$.

5-58 $y = \tan(0.4x)$.

*5-59 $y = 3[\tan(2x)]$.

5-60 $y = \cos(300x)$.

For problems **5-61** to **5-64** find dy/dx by using the chain rule.

5-61 $y = \cos(x^2)$.

5-62 $y = \sin(x^3)$.

5-63 $y = \tan(x^2 + 1)$.

*5-64 $y = \sin[\cos(x)]$.

For problems **5-65** to **5-68** find the value of the slope on the curve $y = f(x)$ at the point $x = 1$.

5-65 $y = \sin(3x)$.

5-66 $y = \cos(2x)$.

*5-67 $y = \tan(3x)$.

*5-68 $y = \sin(x^2 + 1)$.

**5-69 Find by using the chain rule, when $y = \sin(\theta)$ and $x = \theta^2$, the value of dy/dx at $\theta = \pi$.

For problems **5-70** to **5-75** find dy/dx by using the product rule.

5-70 $y = x \cdot e^x$.

5-71 $y = x \cdot \sin(x)$.

5-72 $y = x^2 \cdot \exp(x)$.

5-73 $y = [\sin(x)][\cos(x)]$.

*5-74 $y = \exp(x) \cdot \sin(x)$.

*5-75 $y = x^3 \sin(2x + 1)$.

For problems **5-76** to **5-80** find dy/dx by using the quotient rule.

5-76 $y = \dfrac{x + 1}{x^2}$.

5-77 $y = \dfrac{x^2 - 3}{x^3 + 2}$.

5-78 $y = \dfrac{\cos(x)}{\sin(x)}$.

5-79 $y = \dfrac{\sin(2x - 1)}{e^{-x}}$.

5-80 $y = \dfrac{\exp(x)}{x^2}$.

*5-81 Evaluate the value of the slope of the curve

$$y = \frac{\cos(2t - 1)}{t^2}$$

at the point $t = 2$.

For problems **5-82** to **5-85** find the second derivative d^2y/dx^2.

5-82 $y = x^2 - 2x$.

5-83 $y = x^3 + \sin(x)$.

**5-84 $y = \tan(x)$.

5-85 $y = \cos(2x)$.

5-86 If $y = -\cos(2x)$ show that $d^2y/dx^2 = -4y$.

**5-87 A body is moving in a straight line with its position, measured in metres, from a fixed point given by $s = t^3$. Find (a) the velocity equation, (b) the value of its velocity at $t = 2$ s, (c) the acceleration equation, and (d) the magnitude of the acceleration at $t = 2$ s.

**5-88 A body of mass 3 kg is moving through a liquid in a straight line with its position given by

$$s = 3.2(1 - e^{-2t}) \text{ metres}$$

Find (a) the velocity and acceleration equations, (b) the acceleration force equation, (c) the value of the acceleration force at $t = 2$ s, and (d) the KE equation and the value of kinetic energy at $t = 3$ s.

***5-89 The position of a body of mass 2 kg is given by

$$s = e^{-t}(\sin(t))$$

where s is the distance in metres from a fixed point and t is the time in seconds. Find an equation which describes the KE of the body at an instant in time. Hence, calculate the decrease in the KE over the first 3.5 s.

**5-90 A circuit consists of an inductor of 5 H in series with a resistor of 50 Ω. If the current flowing at time t seconds is given by

$$i = \cos(4t - 1)$$

find the p.d. across each component.

**5-91 A coil has an inductance of 12 H and a resistance of 10 Ω. If the current flowing through the coil is given by

$$i = 3[1 - \exp(-2t)]$$

find the p.d. across this component.

***5-92 Two resistors of values 100 Ω and 150 Ω are in series with a coil which has an inductance of 20 H and a resistance of 50 Ω. If the current flowing through these resistors is given by

$$i = 4[1 - e^{-t}\sin(t)]$$

find the p.d. equation across each resistor and the coil. Find the total p.d. across the three components at the time value of $t = 1$ s.

Solutions

5-1 $6x$.

5-2 $6 + 6x^2$.

5-3 $4 + 12x^3$.

5-4 $18x(3 + x^2)^2$.

5-5 $\dfrac{dy}{dx} = 18x^5$.

5-6 $\dfrac{dy}{dx} = -18x^2$.

5-7 $\dfrac{dy}{dx} = 48 - 10x^4$.

5-8 $\dfrac{dy}{dx} = -2x^{-2}$.

5-9 $\dfrac{dy}{dx} = -\dfrac{6}{x^3}$.

5-10 $12t^3 - 6t + 1$.

5-11 $3t^{-0.5}$.

5-12 $-5 - 9t^{0.5}$.

5-13 42.

5-14 -5.3363.

5-15 2.2449.

5-16 $\frac{1}{3}$.

5-17 $(2, 24) (-2, -24)$.

5-18 $(0, 1)$.

5-19 $-e^{-x}$.

5-20 $3e^{3x}$.

5-21 $-9e^{-9x}$.

5-22 $-11.2(e^{-2x})$.

5-23 $8e^{2x}$.

5-24 $-5 \exp(-5x)$.

5-25 $5 \exp(5x)$.

5-26 $32 \exp(8x)$.

5-27 $-12 \exp(2x)$.

5-28 $2x \cdot \exp(x^2 + 100)$.

5-29 $3x^2 \cdot \exp(x^3)$.

5-30 $-2x \cdot \exp(-x^2 + 1)$.

5-31 $(4 - 9x^2)[\exp(4x - 3x^3)]$.

5-32 $(2x + 3)[\exp(x^2 + 3x + 1)]$.

5-33 $(-8 + 80x)[\exp(-2x + 10x^2)]$.

5-34 -1.4167×10^{24}.

5-35 $1/x$.

5-36 $1/x$.

5-37 $1/x$.

5-38 $1/x$.

5-39 $1/x$.

5-40 $5/x$.

5-41 $2/x$.

5-42 $2/x$.

5-43 $(1 + 6x)/(x + 3x^2)$.

5-44 $2.5/x$.

5-45 $30/(5x - 1)$.

5-46 [*Hint:* ln is the inverse of exp.]

5-47 [*Hint:* sketch a graph of ln(x).]

5-48 $2 \cos(2x)$.

5-49 $-3\cos(-3x) = -3\cos(3x)$.

5-50 $0.4\cos(0.4x)$.

5-51 $12\cos(3x)$.

5-52 $3\sin(-3x) = -3\sin(3x)$.

5-53 $-5\sin(5x)$.

5-54 $-0.3\sin(0.3x)$.

5-55 $-10\sin(2x)$

5-56 $2\sec^2(2x)$.

5-57 $-2\sec^2(-2x)$.

5-58 $0.4\sec^2(0.4x)$.

5-59 $6\sec^2(2x)$.

5-60 $-300\sin(300x)$.

5-61 $2x[-\sin(x^2)]$.

5-62 $3x^2\cos(x^3)$.

5-63 $2x \cdot \sec^2(x^2 + 1)$.

5-64 $[-\sin(x)][\cos(\cos(x))]$.

5-65 -2.97.

5-66 1.8186.

5-67 3.061.

5-68 -0.8323.

5-69 $(-1)/2\pi$.

5-70 $e^x(1 + x)$.

5-71 $\sin(x) + x \cdot \cos(x)$.

5-72 $xe^x(2 + x)$.

5-73 $\cos^2(x) - \sin^2(x) = \cos(2x)$.

5-74 $e^x[\sin(x) + \cos(x)]$.

5-75 $x^2[3\sin(2x + 1) + 2x\cos(2x + 1)]$.

5-76 $(-x - 2)/x^3$.

5-77 $\dfrac{2x(x^3 + 2) - (x^2 - 3)(3x^2)}{(x^3 + 2)^2}$

5-78 $-\text{cosec}^2(x)$.

5-79 $e^x[2\cos(2x - 1) + \sin(2x - 1)]$.

5-80 $[e^x(x - 2)]/x^3$.

5-81 0.1769.

5-82 2.

5-83 $6x - \sin(x)$.

5-84 $2 \cdot \tan(x) \cdot \sec^2(x)$.

5-85 $-4\cos(2x)$.

5-87

(a) $\dfrac{ds}{dt} = 3t^2$,

(b) $12\,\text{m/s}$,

(c) $\dfrac{d^2 s}{dt^2} = 6t$,

(d) $12 \, \text{m/s}^2$,

5-88

(a) $\dfrac{ds}{dt} = v = 6.4 e^{-2t}$, $\dfrac{dv}{dt} = -12.8 e^{-2t}$.

(b) $F = -38.4 e^{-2t}$.

(c) -0.7033 N, the negative sign indicates it is opposing motion.

(d) $\text{KE} = 61.44 e^{-4t}$, $3.775(10^{-4})$ J.

5-89 $\text{KE} = e^{-2t}[\cos(t) - \sin(t)]^2$, 0.9997 J.

5-90 P.D. across 50 Ω resistor is $50 \cos(4t - 1)$ volts.

P.D. across 5 H inductor is $-20 \sin(4t - 1)$ volts.

5-91 $30 + 42 e^{-2t}$ volts.

5-92 P.D. across 100 Ω resistor is $400[1 - e^{-t} \sin(t)]$.

P.D. across 150 Ω resistor is $600[1 - e^{-t}\sin(t)]$.

P.D. across coil is $\{200 - e^{-t}[120 \sin(t) + 80 \cos(t)]\}$.

P.D. across all three components at $t = 1$ s is 837.3916 V.

MAXIMUM AND MINIMUM VALUES

Objectives After reading this chapter you should be able to:

1. Determine the position of a stationary point.
   (*a*) Define a turning point.
   (*b*) Define a stationary point.
   (*c*) Determine the coordinates of a stationary point.
2. Distinguish between maximum and minimum points.
   (*a*) Define graphically a maximum point.
   (*b*) Define graphically a minimum point.
   (*c*) Determine, by consideration of the slope on either side of the stationary point, the shape of the curve in the region of that point.
   (*d*) Relate the shape of the curve from 2(*c*) to the definitions of maximum and minimum.
   (*e*) Determine the coordinates of the turning points.
   (*f*) Use the second derivative to distinguish between maximum and minimum points.
3. Solve problems involving the concepts of maximum and minimum points.
   (*a*) Determine the overall maximum or the overall minimum value of a function within some specified interval derived from the engineering problem.
   (*b*) Sketch the curve involved in the engineering problem after determining the turning points.

6-1 INTRODUCTION

In engineering it is often the case that we wish to know a maximum size of an object, the minimum cost to produce the required number of goods, or the maximum output from an automatic lathe in a given time period. In all these cases, provided we have established a relationship between the variables involved in the form of an equation, we can use a technique based on the calculus to find the maximum or minimum quantity. The concepts will be developed, as in previous chapters, by using graphs along with examples.

6-2 THE ZERO SLOPE

The zero slope is a gradient on a curve whose value is zero. If we know that there exists a point on a curve at which we have a zero slope, then there are *four* possibilities in terms of the shape of the curve in the neighbourhood of that point. Figure 6-1 illustrates these four shapes.

The points at which the zero slope occurs are called **stationary points**. Again referring to Fig. 6-1, the stationary points in graphs (*a*) and (*b*) are also named **turning points** owing to the change of direction of the curve in each case.

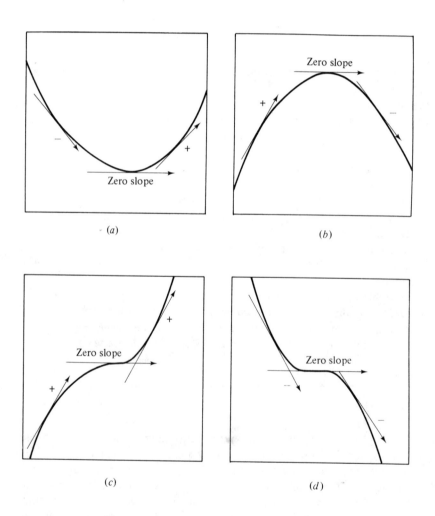

(*a*)

(*b*)

(*c*)

(*d*)

Figure 6-1 + positive slope; − negative slope.

Example 6-2-1 The curve $y = x^2 + 1$ has one stationary point. Find the co-ordinates of this point.

SOLUTION Since the stationary point is one where the gradient has a value of zero, we differentiate $y = x^2 + 1$ to find the slope equation. Thus,

$$\frac{dy}{dx} = 2x$$

and for zero slope we have

$$\frac{dy}{dx} = 0$$

$\Rightarrow$ $\qquad\qquad\qquad 2x = 0$

or $\qquad\qquad\qquad x = 0$

A zero slope occurs at $x = 0$ and we find the y value by substituting into $y = x^2 + 1$ to obtain

$$y = 0^2 + 1$$

$$= 1$$

Therefore the coordinates of the stationary point are $(x, y) = (0, 1)$.

Example 6-2-2 Show that the curve defined by the relationship

$$y = 0.25x^4 + x^3 - 2x^2$$

has three stationary points at $(-4, -32)$, $(0, 0)$, and $(1, -0.75)$.

SOLUTION

$$y = 0.25x^4 + x^3 - 2x^2$$

$\Rightarrow$ $\qquad\qquad \frac{dy}{dx} = x^3 + 3x^2 - 4x$

For stationary points we have

$$\frac{dy}{dx} = 0$$

$\Rightarrow$ $\qquad\qquad x^3 + 3x^2 - 4x = 0$

or $\qquad\qquad x(x^2 + 3x - 4) = 0$

on factorization. Hence

$\qquad\quad x = 0 \qquad$ or $\qquad (x^2 + 3x - 4) = 0$

$\Rightarrow \qquad\quad x = 0 \qquad$ or $\qquad (x + 4)(x - 1) = 0$

Hence $\ x = 0 \qquad$ or $\qquad (x + 4) = 0 \qquad$ or $\qquad (x - 1) = 0$

$\Rightarrow \qquad\quad x = 0 \qquad$ or $\qquad x = -4 \qquad$ or $\qquad x = 1$

We have three stationary points at $x = -4$, $x = 0$, and $x = 1$. To find the coordinates, we substitute these x values into the original equation.

At $x = -4$, $y = 0.25(-4)^4 + 3(-4)^3 - 2(-4)^2$

                     $= -32$

At $x = 0$, $y = 0$

At $x = 1$, $y = -0.75$

Therefore the three stationary points have coordinates $(-4, -32)$, $(0, 0)$, and $(1, -0.75)$.

6-3 TURNING POINTS

It has already been stated that a **turning point** is a special form of stationary point where the curve changes direction. There are two types of turning points. The first type is the turning point which occurs at the bottom of a valley shape in a graph. This is illustrated in Fig. 6-2. and is known as a **minimum point** or simply a **minimum**. The value of y at this point is known as a **minimum value**.

The turning point at the crest of a hill in a graph is the second type and is known as a **maximum point** or a **maximum**. This is illustrated also in Fig. 6-2. The value of y at this point is known as a **maximum value**. The following examples will develop a technique which we shall call the **box** method for determining the shape of the curve in the region of a stationary point and, in particular, a turning point.

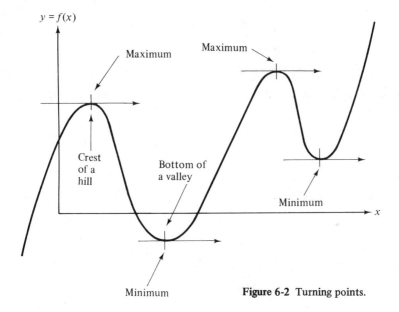

Figure 6-2 Turning points.

Example 6-3-1 Show that the curve $y = x^2 + 3x$ has only one turning point at $(-1.5, -2.25)$ and state its nature.

SOLUTION Differentiation of $y = x^2 + 3x$ gives

$$\frac{dy}{dx} = 2x + 3$$

For a stationary point we have

$$\frac{dy}{dx} = 0$$

$\Rightarrow$ $$2x + 3 = 0$$

or $$x = -1.5$$

Substituting $x = -1.5$ into $y = x^2 + 3x$ gives $y = -2.25$ and the co-ordinates of the stationary point are

$$(x, y) = (-1.5, -2.25)$$

To determine whether this stationary point is a turning point or not, we shall construct a 'box' as shown in Fig. 6-3. This method will also determine the nature of the turning point. By the term 'nature' we are referring to the definitions of **maximum** and **minimum**.

The method is as follows:

1. Choose a value for x on either side of $x = -1.5$, say $x = -1$ and $x = -2$.
2. Calculate the value of the slope at these points.
   At $x = -2$ we have

$$\frac{dy}{dx} = -1 \qquad \text{which is negative}$$

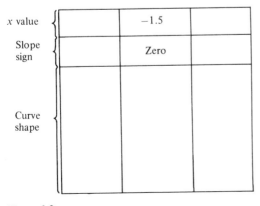

Figure 6-3

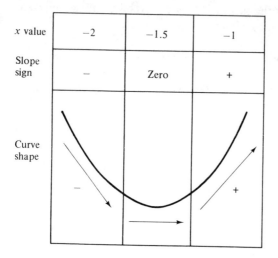

x value	-2	-1.5	-1
Slope sign	$-$	Zero	$+$
Curve shape	$-$		$+$

Figure 6-4

At $x = -1$ we have

$$\frac{dy}{dx} = 1 \qquad \text{which is positive}$$

3. Complete the box as shown in Fig. 6-4 and sketch the curve shape by using the gradient directions.

This curve has a valley shape and hence at $(-1.5, -2.25)$ we have a turning point which is a minimum.

Example 6-3-2 Find the coordinates and nature of any turning points on the graph of the curve defined by

$$y = 3x^4 - 2x^3 + 1$$

SOLUTION Since $y = 3x^4 - 2x^3 + 1$ we have

$$\frac{dy}{dx} = 12x^3 - 6x^2$$

For stationary points

$$\frac{dy}{dx} = 0$$

On factorizing we have

and therefore

$$6x^2(2x - 1) = 0$$

$$x = 0 \qquad \text{or} \qquad x = 0.5$$

which gives the x coordinates of two stationary points.

Using the box method we have to choose values of x on either side of

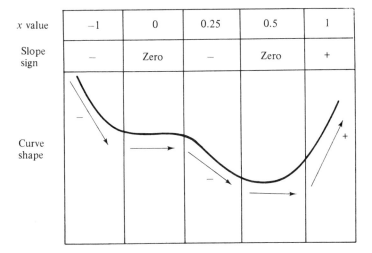

x value	−1	0	0.25	0.5	1
Slope sign	−	Zero	−	Zero	+
Curve shape					

Figure 6-5

each stationary point. For the x coordinate 0, we can choose $x = -1$ and $x = 0.25$, and for the other x coordinate 0.5 we can choose $x = 0.25$ and $x = 1$.

At $x = -1$ we have

$$\frac{dy}{dx} = -18 \qquad \text{which is negative}$$

At $x = 0.25$ we have

$$\frac{dy}{dx} = -0.1875 \qquad \text{which again is negative}$$

At $x = 1$ we have

$$\frac{dy}{dx} = 6 \qquad \text{which is positive}$$

We complete the box, sketching in the slope directions and the curve shape. The curve shape in Fig. 6-5 shows we have only *one* turning point at $(x, y) = (0.5, 0.9375)$ which is a minimum. The other stationary point is known as **a point of inflection**.

Example 6-3-3 Show that the function defined by the relationship $y = -x^2 + 2x + 1$ has a maximum value at $x = 1$. Calculate this maximum value.

SOLUTION

$$y = -x^2 + 2x + 1$$

gives
$$\frac{dy}{dx} = -2x + 2$$

For stationary points
$$\frac{dy}{dx} = 0$$

$\Rightarrow$
$$-2(x-1) = 0$$

or
$$x = 1$$

Using the box method we have at $x = 0$,

$$\frac{dy}{dx} = 2 \qquad > 0$$

and at $x = 2$,

$$\frac{dy}{dx} = -2 \qquad < 0$$

We have at $x = 1$ a maximum. Substituting $x = 1$ into $y = -x^2 + 2x + 1$ gives $y = 2$.

Hence the function defined by the relationship $y = -x^2 + 2x + 1$ has a maximum value at $x = 1$ of $y = 2$.

6-4 THE SECOND-DERIVATIVE METHOD

A second method for determining the nature of the turning point involves the use of the second differential coefficient d^2y/dx^2.

If a turning point is a *minimum*, the slope dy/dx starts with negative values and, as x increases, passes through zero to positive values. This is illustrated once again in Fig. 6-6. The slope dy/dx increases in value as x increases in value. Thus, the rate of change of the slope with respect to x is *positive*. This implies that at the turning point

$$\frac{d}{dx}\left(\frac{dy}{dx}\right) = \frac{d^2y}{dx^2} > 0$$

If a turning point is a *maximum*, the slope dy/dx starts with positive values and, as x increases, passes through zero to negative values. The slope dy/dx decreases as x increases in value. Therefore the rate of change of the slope with respect to x is *negative*. This implies that at the turning point

$$\frac{d}{dx}\left(\frac{dy}{dx}\right) = \frac{d^2y}{dx^2} < 0$$

The maximum point is illustrated once again in Fig. 6-6.

A Summary

1.
$$\frac{d^2y}{dx^2} > 0 \qquad \text{at turning point implies a **minimum**}$$

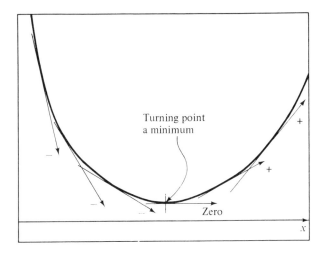

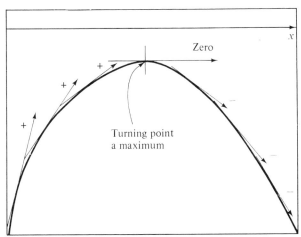

Figure 6-6

2. $\dfrac{d^2y}{dx^2} < 0$ at turning point implies a **maximum**

3. If $\dfrac{d^2y}{dx^2} = 0$ the test *fails* and the box method should be used

Example 6-4-1 Find the coordinates of the turning points on the graph defined by $y = x^3 + 3x^2 - x$. Using the second method determine the nature of these turning points.

SOLUTION
$$y = x^3 + 3x^2 - x$$

gives
$$\frac{dy}{dx} = 3x^2 + 6x - 1$$

For stationary points
$$\frac{dy}{dx} = 0$$

$\Rightarrow$
$$3x^2 + 6x - 1 = 0$$

Solving for x gives,
$$x = \frac{-6 \pm \sqrt{6^2 - (4)(3)(-1)}}{2(3)}$$

and we have $x = 0.1547$ or -2.1547. Since

$$\frac{dy}{dx} = 3x^2 + 6x - 1$$

we have
$$\frac{d^2 y}{dx^2} = 6x + 6$$

At $x = 0.1547$

$$\frac{d^2 y}{dx^2} = 6.9282 > 0 \qquad \text{(positive)}$$

which implies that at this point we have a minimum.
At $x = -2.1547$
$$\frac{d^2 y}{dx^2} = -6.9282 < 0 \qquad \text{(negative)}$$

which implies that at this point we have a maximum.

Hence for $y = x^3 + 3x^2 - x$ we have the turning points defined by Table 6-1.

Table 6-1

Turning point coordinates	Nature
(0.1547, −0.0792)	Minimum
(−2.1547, 6.0792)	Maximum

Example 6-4-2 Find the coordinates and nature of the turning point on the graph of the function defined by the relationship $y = x^2 + 4x + 1$.

SOLUTION Differentiating
$$y = x^2 + 4x + 1$$

gives
$$\frac{dy}{dx} = 2x + 4$$

For stationary points

$$\frac{dy}{dx} = 0$$

$\Rightarrow$ $$2x + 4 = 0$$

or $$x = -2$$

Since we have

$$\frac{dy}{dx} = 2x + 4$$

$$\frac{d^2y}{dx^2} = 2$$

which is positive for all values of x and hence it is positive for $x = -2$ at the stationary point. Therefore at $x = -2$ we have a turning point which is a minimum. The coordinates of this minimum point are

$$(x, y) = (-2, -3)$$

Example 6-4-3 Find the coordinates of the turning point on the graph of the function defined by the equation $y = x^4 + 1$.

SOLUTION Since

$$y = x^4 + 1$$

we have $$\frac{dy}{dx} = 4x^3$$

For stationary points

$$\frac{dy}{dx} = 0$$

$\Rightarrow$ $$4x^3 = 0$$

and we have $$x = 0$$

Since

$$\frac{dy}{dx} = 4x^3$$

we have $$\frac{d^2y}{dx^2} = 12x^2$$

At $x = 0$ we have

$$\frac{d^2y}{dx^2} = 0 \qquad \text{and the test fails}$$

We now turn to the box method. From Fig. 6-7 it can be seen that at $x = 0$ we have a minimum, and the coordinates are $(x, y) = (0, 1)$.

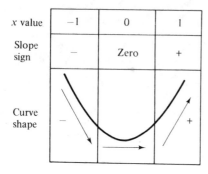

x value	-1	0	1
Slope sign	$-$	Zero	$+$
Curve shape			

Figure 6-7

The following example illustrates the use of the techniques of turning points using the alternative notation.

Example 6-4-4 Find in terms of the coordinates, the turning points associated with the function

$$f(x) = 0.5x^4 - x^3 - x^2$$

By using the second derivative, determine the nature of each turning point.

SOLUTION Since

$$f(x) = 0.5x^4 - x^3 - x^2$$

we have

$$f'(x) = 2x^3 - 3x^2 - 2x$$

For stationary points

$$f'(x) = 0$$

$\Rightarrow$

$$2x^3 - 3x^2 - 2x = 0$$

Hence, on factorization, we have

$$x(2x + 1)(x - 2) = 0$$

This gives

$$x = 0, x = -0.5, \text{ and } x = 2$$

On differentiating a second time we have

$$f''(x) = 6x^2 - 6x - 2$$

On using $x = 0$ we have

$$f''(0) = -2$$

which is negative, implying that at $x = 0$ we have a maximum. Similarly,

$$f''(-0.5) = 2.5$$

which is positive, giving at $x = -0.5$ a minimum, and

$$f''(2) = 10$$

Table 6-2

Turning point coordinates	Nature
$(-0.5, -0.09375)$	Minimum
$(0, 0)$	Maximum
$(2, -4)$	Minimum

which is positive giving, again, a minimum. The turning points for this function are shown in Table 6-2.

6-5 THE OVERALL MINIMUM VALUE

A function may have several minimum values each at a turning point as shown in Fig. 6-2. It is important to realise that the *smallest* value of the function may not occur at one of these points. Figure 6-8 illustrates a function where the *smallest* value is *not* at a turning point. The smallest value of a function is termed the **overall minimum value**.

Example 6-5-1 By finding the coordinates of all stationary points, sketch on plain paper the curve $y = x^3 + x^2$, restricting the x values between -2 and 1.5. Find the overall minimum value of y, stating whether or not it occurs at a turning point.

SOLUTION Since

$$y = x^3 + x^2$$

we have

$$\frac{dy}{dx} = 3x^2 + 2x$$

For stationary points

$$\frac{dy}{dx} = 0$$

$\Rightarrow$

$$3x^2 + 2x = 0$$

or

$$x(3x + 2) = 0$$

Hence $x = 0$ or $x = -\frac{2}{3}$. Substituting these values into the equation $y = x^3 + x^2$ gives

$$\text{at } x = 0 \qquad y = 0$$

and

$$\text{at } x = -\frac{2}{3} \qquad y = 0.1482$$

Thus we have the coordinates of the two stationary points as

$$(x, y) = (0, 0) \qquad \text{and} \qquad (-\tfrac{2}{3}, 0.1482)$$

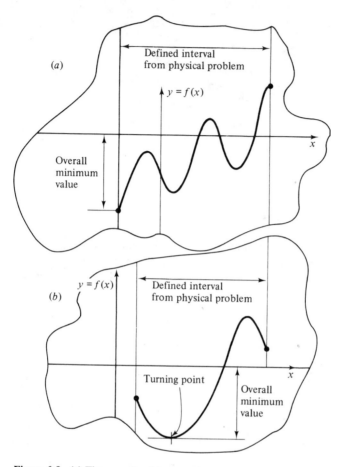

Figure 6-8 (*a*) The overall minimum value *not* at a turning point; (*b*) the overall minimum value at a turning point.

To find the nature of these stationary points, we use the box method. This also helps us to sketch the curve in the regions around the stationary points. Using the curve shape in Fig. 6-9 and calculation of the coordinates of the turning points, we can sketch the curve between −2 and 1.5. It is also useful to calculate the value of y at the extremes. At

$$x = -2 \qquad y = -4$$

and at

$$x = 1.5 \qquad y = 5.625$$

From the sketch in Fig. 6-10, it can be seen that y has the smallest value at $x = -2$. Thus the overall minimum value of y is −4 when restricting the x values to between −2 and 1.5. This restriction occurs many times in practice during measurement of variables. In this case, the overall minimum value was not at a turning point.

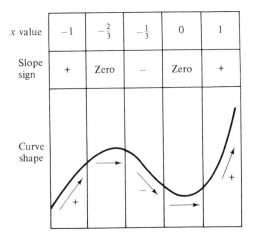

x value	-1	$-\frac{2}{3}$	$-\frac{1}{3}$	0	1
Slope sign	+	Zero	−	Zero	+
Curve shape					

Figure 6-9

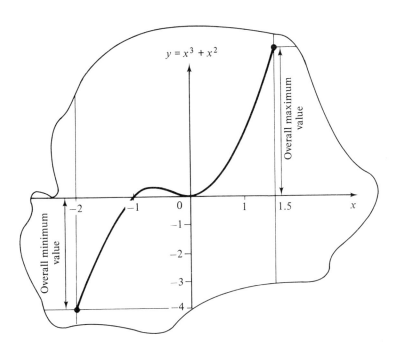

$$y = x^3 + x^2$$

Figure 6-10

6-6 THE OVERALL MAXIMUM VALUE

A similar concept occurs when we have to find the largest value for y over a defined interval. As with the overall minimum value, this may occur at a turning point or at the end of an interval. Figure 6-10 illustrates an **overall maximum** at $x = 1.5$ with a value $y = 5.625$.

> **Example 6-6-1** Find the turning point coordinates on the curve $y = -x^2 + 1$. Sketch the curve between $x = -2$ and $x = 2$ labelling the overall maximum.

SOLUTION

$$y = -x^2 + 1$$

On differentiating

$$\frac{dy}{dx} = -2x$$

For stationary points

$$\frac{dy}{dx} = 0$$

$\Rightarrow$

$$-2x = 0$$

or

$$x = 0$$

At $x = 0, y = 1$. Using the second differential coefficient

$$\frac{d^2 y}{dx^2} = -2$$

we see that this stationary point at $(0, 1)$ is a maximum since $d^2 y/dx^2$ is negative. Figure 6-11 illustrates the curve between $x = -2$ and $x = 2$. The overall maximum in this case is at the turning point and y has an overall maximum value of 1.

6-7 APPLICATIONS I

In Secs 6-5 and 6-6 we defined the overall maximum and minimum values of a curve. It cannot be overstressed that when applying the principles of turning points to practical problems we must be fully aware that overall maximum and minimum values may *not* occur at the turning points. The only way to be certain when finding overall maximum or minimum values is to sketch the curve as in Examples 6-5-1 and 6-6-1.

Attention will now be focused on applications involving geometrical ideas of volumes and areas.

> **Example 6-7-1** A cylinder of radius r metres has a length L metres. If the circumference is equal to $(2 - L)$ find (a) the radius which allows the volume to have a maximum value, and (b) the maximum volume of this cylinder.

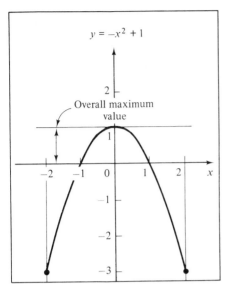

$y = -x^2 + 1$

Overall maximum
value

Figure 6-11

SOLUTION Let V be the volume of the cylinder. By 'maximum' in this example we are referring to the overall maximum value. We have

$$\text{Circumference} = 2\pi r$$

$$= (2 - L)$$

On rearranging we have

$$L = 2 - 2\pi r$$

$$\text{Volume} = V = \pi r^2 L$$

$$= \pi r^2 (2 - 2\pi r)$$

Hence

$$V = 2\pi r^2 - 2\pi^2 r^3$$

(*a*) For stationary points we have $dV/dr = 0$. Hence

$$\frac{dV}{dr} = 4\pi r - 6\pi^2 r^2 = 0$$

or

$$2\pi r(2 - 3\pi r) = 0$$

$\Rightarrow$
$$r = 0 \quad \text{or} \quad r = \frac{2}{3\pi}$$

Since physically a cylinder cannot have a radius $r = 0$, we use the second value

$$r = \frac{2}{3\pi}$$

$$= 0.2122 \, \text{m}$$

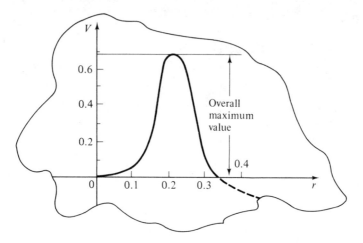

Figure 6-12

Since

$$\frac{dV}{dr} = 4\pi r - 6\pi^2 r^2$$

we have

$$\frac{d^2 V}{dr^2} = 4\pi - 12\pi^2 r$$

$$= 4\pi - 12\pi^2 (0.2122) \qquad \text{on substituting } r = 0.2122$$

$$= -12.57 \qquad \text{which is negative}$$

Thus at $r = 0.2122$ m we have a maximum. Figure 6-12 illustrates the curve $V = 2\pi r^2 - 2\pi^2 r^3$ and shows that this maximum is, indeed, the *overall* maximum volume of the cylinder.

(b) At $r = 0.2122$ m the volume is $0.6602 \, \text{m}^3$.

It should be noted that the radius has restricted values from $r = 0$ m to $r = 0.3183$ m. Both these values can be found by placing $V = 0$ and solving the resulting equation.

Example 6-7-2 A container with a square base is to be used to hold nuclear waste. Maximum permissible volume is $100 \, \text{m}^3$. The cost of lead lining is £60/m².

(a) Find an equation relating the cost of lining the box with the side of the container.

(b) Find the side of the box so that the cost of lining the sides, top, and bottom is kept to a minimum.

SOLUTION Let h be the height of the container and x be the side of the square.

(a)
$$\text{Volume of box} = 100 = hx^2 \tag{6-1}$$

$$\text{Surface area} = \text{top} + \text{bottom} + \text{four sides}$$

$$= x^2 + x^2 + 4hx$$

$$= 2x^2 + 4hx$$

$$\text{Cost of lining} = (\text{surface area})(60)$$

$$C = 120x^2 + 240hx \tag{6-2}$$

From Eq. (6-1) we have

$$h = \frac{100}{x^2}$$

and on substituting this value into Eq. (6-2) we have

$$C = 120x^2 + \frac{24\,000}{x}$$

(b) For stationary points $dC/dx = 0$. Hence

$$\frac{dC}{dx} = 240x - 24\,000x^{-2} = 0$$

or $\qquad\qquad 240x^3 - 24\,000 = 0 \qquad$ on multiplying both sides by x^2

or $\qquad\qquad\qquad x^3 = 100$

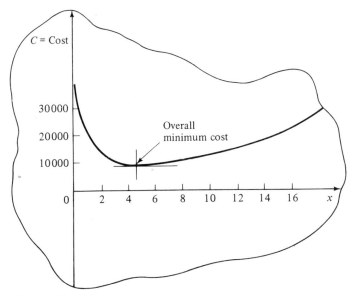

Figure 6-13

Hence $x = 4.6416$ m. Differentiating C a second time gives

$$\frac{d^2 C}{dx^2} = 240 + 48\,000 x^{-3}$$

$$= 720 \qquad \text{on substituting } x = 4.6416$$

Since $d^2 C/dx^2$ is positive we have a turning point which is a minimum.

A sketch of the curve, shown in Fig. 6-13, shows that this minimum is an overall minimum. So the side of the box to keep cost to a minimum is 4.6416 m.

If the value $x = 4.6416$ is substituted into the cost equation, we find that the minimum cost will be £7756.

6-8 APPLICATIONS II

Applications of the theory of turning points will continue in this section with problems from engineering studies. The relationships we shall be concerned with in this section have all been established by experiment or survey work.

Example 6-8-1 A production engineer finds that the costs (in £) of producing x metres of a particular extrusion is given by

$$C = 20x + \frac{200\,000}{x} \qquad (25 \leqslant x \leqslant 200)$$

where C is the cost/day. Find the number of metres to be produced per day so that the production costs are kept down to a minimum. Calculate the minimum cost/day possible with this process.

SOLUTION Since

$$C = 20x + \frac{200\,000}{x}$$

we have

$$\frac{dC}{dx} = 20 - \frac{200\,000}{x^2}$$

For stationary points

$$\frac{dC}{dx} = 0$$

$\Rightarrow$

$$20 - \frac{200\,000}{x^2} = 0$$

Multiplying both sides by x^2 gives

$$20x^2 - 200\,000 = 0$$

$\Rightarrow$

$$x = 100 \text{ m}$$

Differentiating C a second time gives

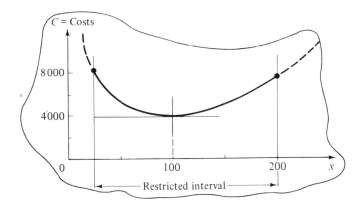

Figure 6-14

Hence

$$\frac{400\,000}{x^3} = \frac{d^2 C}{dx^2}$$

$$\frac{d^2 C}{dx^2} = 4 \times 10^{-1}$$

which is positive, implying that at $x = 100$ we have a minimum. To show that it's an overall minimum, we can sketch the graph as in Fig. 6-14. The smallest cost per day is achieved with a production run of 100 m and this cost is

$$C = 20(100) + \frac{200\,000}{100}$$

$$= £4000$$

Example 6-8-2 Figure 6-15 shows a block of mass 3 kg being pulled along a horizontal rough surface. if the coefficient of friction μ is 0.5 determine (a) the minimum force required just to overcome the frictional resistance in order to move the block in a horizontal straight line, and (b) the angle at which this force has to be applied.

SOLUTION The first stage is to form the relationship between the force F and the angle θ. This will be revision for those readers who have studied engineering science. Resolving the forces horizontally gives

$$F \cos \theta = 0.5N$$

Resolving forces vertically

$$N = 3g - F \sin \theta$$

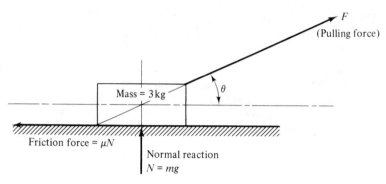

Figure 6-15

Combining the two equations gives

$$F \cos \theta = 1.5g - 0.5F \sin \theta$$

or
$$F = 1.5g/(\cos \theta + 0.5 \sin \theta)$$

The angle θ is physically restricted to between $0°$ and $90°$. Since

$$F = 1.5g(\cos \theta + 0.5 \sin \theta)^{-1}$$

we let
$$u = (\cos \theta + 0.5 \sin \theta)$$

$$\frac{du}{d\theta} = (-\sin \theta + 0.5 \cos \theta)$$

$\Rightarrow$
$$F = 1.5gu^{-1}$$

and
$$\frac{dF}{du} = -1.5gu^{-2}$$

Using the chain rule
$$\frac{dF}{d\theta} = \frac{dF}{du} \cdot \frac{du}{d\theta}$$

we have
$$\frac{dF}{d\theta} = \frac{-1.5g(-\sin \theta + 0.5 \cos \theta)}{\cos \theta + 0.5 \sin \theta}$$

For stationary points
$$\frac{dF}{d\theta} = 0$$

$\Rightarrow$
$$\frac{-1.5g(-\sin \theta + 0.5 \cos \theta)}{\cos \theta + 0.5 \sin \theta} = 0$$

or
$$-\sin \theta + 0.5 \cos \theta = 0$$

or
$$0.5 \cos \theta = \sin \theta$$

and
$$\tan \theta = 0.5$$

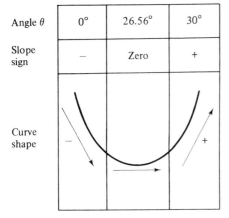

Angle θ	0°	26.56°	30°
Slope sign	—	Zero	+
Curve shape			

Figure 6-16

on dividing both sides by $\cos\theta$. Since we are restricted to the first quadrant $\theta = 26.56°$.

The box method is easier to use in this case than trying to differentiate a second time. From Fig. 6-16 we have a minimum at $\theta = 26.56°$. Checking that this will give an *overall* minimum value is left to the reader.

The minimum force is

$$F_{min} = \frac{1.5g}{\cos(26.56°) + 0.5\,\sin(26.56°)}$$

$$= 13.16 \text{ newtons} \qquad \text{at } 26.56°$$

Example 6-8-3 The power in kilowatts developed by a wind-driven machine was measured and the relationship

$$P = -x^4 + 8x^2$$

where x is the diameter of the fan in metres, is fitted to experimental results.
(a) Find the size of fan required for this machine to develop maximum power.
(b) Calculate the maximum power output from the machine.
(c) Sketch the graph illustrating the relationship between power and the diameter of the fan.

SOLUTION
(a) $\qquad\qquad\qquad\qquad P = -x^4 + 8x^2$

gives $\qquad\qquad\qquad\qquad \dfrac{dP}{dx} = -4x^3 + 16x$

For stationary points

$$\frac{\mathrm{d}P}{\mathrm{d}x} = 0$$

$$\Rightarrow \qquad\qquad -4x^3 + 16x = 0$$

or $\qquad\qquad -4x(x^2 - 4) = 0$

which gives $x = 0, x = 2$ or $x = -2$.

Since physically the diameter of the blade cannot be zero or a negative value, we neglect $x = 0$ and $x = -2$.

Differentiating a second time gives

$$\frac{\mathrm{d}^2 P}{\mathrm{d}x^2} = -12x^2 + 16$$

At $x = 2$ we have

$$\frac{\mathrm{d}^2 P}{\mathrm{d}x^2} = -32 < 0$$

and we have a maximum point. Hence the size of the fan for maximum power would appear to be $x = 2\,\mathrm{m}$.

(b) At $x = 2$

$$P = -(2)^4 + 8(2)^2$$

$$= -16 + 32$$

$$= 16\,\mathrm{kW}$$

Maximum power output with this machine is predicted to be 16 kW.

(c) Figure 6-17 illustrates the relationship between power and the diameter of the fan. From the graph it can be seen that the maximum power output of 16 kW is in fact an overall maximum value.

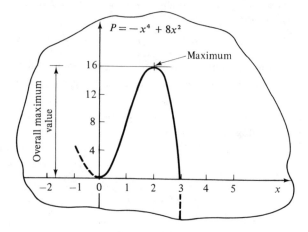

Figure 6-17

PROBLEMS

Find the positions, in terms of the coordinates, of the zero slopes for the curves in **6-1** to **6-10**.

6-1 $y = x^2 + 3$.

6-2 $y = 4x^2 - 3$.

6-3 $y = 2x^2 + 3x - 1$.

6-4 $y = 6x^2 - 2x - 2$.

6-5 $s = t^3 - 3t^2$.

6-6 $s = t^3 - 4t$.

6-7 $V = 4t^3 + 3t^2 - 5t + 1$.

6-8 $V = 2s^4 - 3s^2$.

**6-9 $y = t \exp(-6t)$.

**6-10 $y = t + \cos(2t)$ for $0 \leqslant t \leqslant 2\pi$.

Find the positions of all stationary points for the curves in **6-11** to **6-20**.

6-11 $y = 3x^2$.

6-12 $y = x^3 + 3x^2 - 3x$.

6-13 $s = \exp(t)$.

**6-14 $s = -t \exp(-t)$.

6-15 $V = 0.5t^2 + t - 3$.

6-16 $V = -6x^3 + 3x^2$.

6-17 $A = \cos(t)$ for $0 \leqslant t \leqslant 2\pi$.

6-18 $y = 3 \sin(2t)$ for $0 \leqslant t \leqslant \pi$.

6-19 $y = 8 + \sin(x)$ for $0 \leqslant x \leqslant 2\pi$.

**6-20 $y = 3e^{-2x} \sin(4x)$ for $0 \leqslant x \leqslant \pi/4$.

For the curves in **6-21** to **6-30** find all the possible turning points in terms of the coordinates and the nature of each point.

6-21 $y = 0.8x^2$.

6-22 $y = -3x^3 + 4x^2$.

6-23 $s = -6x^3 + 5x$.

**6-24 $s = t \exp(-6t)$.

**6-25 $s = e^{-t} \sin(t)$ for $0 \leqslant t \leqslant 2\pi$.

6-26 $V = -3t^2 - 4t + 1$.

**6-27 $V = e^{-2t} \cos(2t)$ for $0 \leqslant t \leqslant \pi$.

6-28 $y = 100.2 \sin(x)$ for $-\pi \leqslant t \leqslant \pi$.

**6-29 $W = e^{-t} \sin(0.5t)$ for $0 \leqslant t \leqslant \pi$.

6-30 $s = -t^4 + 3t^2$.

6-31 A cylinder of radius r has its circumference related to its length L by the formula

$$C = 3 - L.$$

(a) Find the radius r such that the volume attains a maximum value.

(b) Calculate the maximum volume.

(c) Show by sketching the curve that the maximum volume calculated in (b) is in fact an overall maximum.

6-32 Calculate the maximum area of a rectangular field which can be enclosed by 1000 m of fencing.

6-33 A square container is to have a maximum volume of $1000 \, \text{m}^3$. The cost of painting the container on all sides and top and bottom is £3.00/m^2.

    (a) Find an expression relating the cost of painting to the side of the square container.

    (b) Find the side of the square so that the painting cost is a minimum.

**6-34 A container consists of a cylinder with a hemispherical top. The dimensions of the cylinder are L metres in length and r metres in radius. Find these dimensions so that the material costs can be kept to a minimum assuming that the volume of this closed container is $1000 \, \text{m}^3$.

6-35 The length and circumference of a cylinder added together give $12 \, \text{m}$. Find the maximum volume permissible under this condition.

6-36 A stone is thrown vertically upwards. The height reached is given by the relationship

$$s = 130t - \tfrac{1}{2}gt^2$$

Taking g to be $9.81 \, \text{m/s}^2$ find the maximum possible height gained by the stone.

6-37 A body moving in a straight line has its velocity v given by the equation.

$$v = -t^4 + 1$$

Find the overall maximum velocity attained.

6-38 A manager finds that the costs (in £) of running his business are related to the time that the factories are in production by the equation

$$C = 10t + \frac{1000}{t}$$

where C is the cost and t is the time in hours. Find the number of hours that the factory must be in production if the cost is to be kept to a minimum. Find this minimum cost.

6-39 A boat is moving through water at a velocity given by

$$v = -3t^4 + 9t^2$$

where t is the time in seconds. Find the maximum velocity and the time at which this speed is reached.

**6-40 A block of mass 6 kg lies on a rough horizontal plane. A force F is applied to the block at an angle θ to the horizontal. If the coefficient of friction between the surfaces is 0.4 find (a) the minimum force required just to overcome the frictional resistance in order to move the block in a horizontal straight line, and (b) the angle at which this force has to be applied.

Solutions

6-1 (0, 3).

6-2 (0, − 3).

6-3 (− 0.75, − 2.125).

6-4 (0.1667, − 2.167).

6-5 (0, 0), (2, − 4).

6-6 (1.1547, − 3.0792), (− 1.1547, 3.0792).

6-7 (−0.9422, 5.0285), (0.4422, −0.2785).

6-8 (0, 0), (0.8660, − 1.125), (− 0.866, − 1.125).

6-9 (0.1667, 0.0613).

6-10 (0.2618, 1.1278), (1.309, 0.4430).

6-11 (0, 0).

6-12 (-2.142, 10.6569), (0.4142, -0.65685).

6-13 No stationary points.

6-14 (1, -0.3679).

6-15 (-1, -3.5).

6-16 (0, 0), (0.3333, 0.1111).

6-17 (0, 1), (3.1416, -1), (6.2832, 1).

6-18 (0.7854, 3), (2.3562, -3).

6-19 (1.5708, 9), (4.7124, 7).

6-20 (0.2768, 1.5426).

6-21 (0, 0) minimum.

6-22 (0.8889, 1.0535) maximum, (0, 0) minimum.

6-23 (-0.5270, -1.7568) minimum, (0.5270, 1.7568) maximum.

6-24 (0.1667, 0.06131) maximum.

6-25 (0.7854, 0.3224) maximum, (3.9270, -0.0139) minimum.

6-26 (-0.6667, 2.3333) maximum.

6-27 (1.1781, 0.0947) maximum, (2.7489, 0.0041) minimum.

6-28 (1.5708, 100.2) maximum, (-1.5708, -100.2) minimum.

6-29 (0.9273, 0.1769) maximum.

6-30 (-1.2247, 2.25) maximum, (1.2247, 2.25) maximum, (0, 0) minimum.

6-31 Radius = 0.3183 m, maximum volume = 0.3183 m^3.

6-32 Maximum rectangular area is 62 500 m^2.

6-33 $\text{Cost} = 6x^2 + \dfrac{12\,000}{x}$

where x is the side of the square bottom. Minimum cost is £1800 with a side $x = 10$ m.

6-34 Radius = 5.759 m, length = 5.759 m.

6-35 Maximum volume = 20.372 m^3.

6-36 Maximum possible height is 861.37 m at a time of 13.252 s.

6-37 Overall maximum velocity is 1 m/s.

6-38 Number of hours to minimize costs is 10. Minimum costs are £200.

6-39 Maximum velocity is 6.75 m/s at a time of 1.2247 s.

6-40 Minimum force is 21.86 N at 21.8°.

SEVEN

INTEGRATION

Objectives After reading this chapter you should be able to:

1. Integrate simple functions using the principle of reverse differentiation.
   (*a*) Define integration with respect to a given slope equation.
   (*b*) Use a standard table of integrals.
   (*c*) Integrate trigonometric functions.
   (*d*) Integrate exponential functions.
   (*e*) Integrate functions by substitution.

7-1 INTRODUCTION

Consider the functions defined by the equation

$$y = x^4 + C$$

where C is a constant. On differentiation, this becomes

$$\frac{dy}{dx} = 4x^3$$

and we have a slope equation. If we now reverse this process and start with the slope equation

$$\frac{dy}{dx} = 4x^3$$

we obtain

$$y = x^4 + C$$

where C is an *arbitrary* constant. This reverse differentiation process is called **integration** and is illustrated in Fig. 7-1.

In symbols we write,

if $\qquad \dfrac{dy}{dx} = 4x^3 \qquad$ then $\qquad y = \int (4x^3)dx$

where the $\int$ sign informs us to integrate the function $4x^3$ with respect to x.

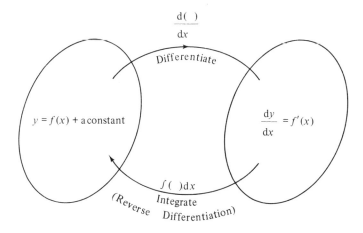

Figure 7-1 Integration as the reverse of differentiation.

In general,

if $\qquad \dfrac{dy}{dx} = f'(x) \qquad$ then $\qquad y = \displaystyle\int f'(x)\,dx$

$$= f(x) + C$$

where C is an arbitrary constant. Table A-5 in the appendix gives a list of standard integrals which will be referred to throughout the chapters using integration.

Example 7-1-1 Find

$$(a) \int (x^4 + 3x^2)\,dx, \quad (b) \int 4\,dx \quad \text{and} \quad (c) \int x^{-2}\,dx.$$

SOLUTION (a) Let

$$y = \int (x^4 + 3x^2)\,dx$$

$\Rightarrow \qquad\qquad \dfrac{dy}{dx} = (x^4 + 3x^2)$

and using reverse differentiation we have by Table A-5 in the appendix,

$$\int ax^n\,dx = \frac{ax^{n+1}}{n+1} + C$$

which implies that

$$y = x^5/5 + x^3 + C$$

or $\qquad y = 0.2x^5 + x^3 + C \qquad$ (C is an arbitrary constant)

(b) Let

$$y = \int 4 \, dx$$

$\Rightarrow$

$$\frac{dy}{dx} = 4 = 4x^0 \qquad \text{since } x^0 = 1$$

Hence

$$y = 4x + C \qquad (C \text{ is an arbitrary constant})$$

(c) Let

$$y = \int x^{-2} \, dx$$

$\Rightarrow$

$$\frac{dy}{dx} = x^{-2}$$

Hence

$$y = -x^{-1} + C \qquad (C \text{ is an arbitrary constant})$$

It is advisable for the reader to check the integration by differentiating the function y. The original slope equation should be obtained.

In most engineering applications, we restrict the interval of the function. Under these circumstances, we require **definite integration**. The reader is familiar with this concept and so we shall content ourselves by demonstrating the technique with an example.

Example 7-1-2 Evaluate

$$\int_1^2 (2x + 1) \, dx$$

SOLUTION Let

$$y = \int (2x + 1) \, dx$$

$\Rightarrow$

$$\frac{dy}{dx} = (2x + 1)$$

Hence

$$y = x^2 + x + C \qquad (C \text{ is an arbitrary constant})$$

If we now consider the limits we have

$$y = (x^2 + x + C)]_1^2$$
$$= (2^2 + 2 + C) - (1^2 + 1 + C)$$
$$= (6 + C) - (2 + C)$$

Thus

$$y = 4$$

The constant C is not normally written down when evaluating these integrals and so

$$y = \int_1^2 (2x + 1) \, dx$$
$$= (x^2 + x)]_1^2$$

Hence on substituting the limits we have

$$y = (2^2 + 2) - (1^2 + 1)$$

$$= 4$$

7-2 STANDARD INTEGRALS

Consider $y = \sin x + C$ where C is an arbitrary constant. On differentiating with respect to x, we have

$$\frac{dy}{dx} = \cos x$$

Thus, $dy/dx = \cos x$ implies that

$$y = \int (\cos x)dx$$

$$= \sin x + C$$

If $y = \cos x + C$ where C is an arbitrary constant then we have

$$\frac{dy}{dx} = -\sin x$$

Thus, $dy/dx = -\sin x$ implies that

$$y = \int (-\sin x)dx$$

$$= \cos x + C$$

Example 7-2-1 Find

$$\int (-\sin x + 3\cos x)dx$$

SOLUTION Let

$$y = \int (-\sin x + 3\cos x)dx$$

$$= \int (-\sin x)dx + \int (3\cos x)dx$$

$$= \cos x + 3\sin x + C \qquad \text{where } C \text{ is an arbitrary constant}$$

If $y = \tan x + C$ where C is an arbitrary constant, then

$$\frac{dy}{dx} = \sec^2 x$$

Therefore, $dy/dx = \sec^2 x$ implies that

$$y = \int (\sec^2 x)dx$$

$$= \tan x + C$$

Example 7-2-2 Find
$$\int (\sec^2 x + \sin x - 4 \cos x)dx$$

SOLUTION Let
$$y = \int (\sec^2 x + \sin x - 4 \cos x)dx$$

$$\Rightarrow \quad \frac{dy}{dx} = (\sec^2 x + \sin x - 4 \cos x)$$

$$= [\sec^2 x - (-\sin x) - 4 \cos x]$$

Hence $y = \tan x - \cos x - 4 \sin x + C$ (C is an arbitrary constant),

Example 7-2-3 Evaluate the following trigonometric integrals by using the standard form:
$$(a) \int_0^1 - \sin(x)dx \qquad (b) \int_{0.5}^{1.5} \cos(x)dx$$

SOLUTION (a) Since
$$\int -\sin(x) = \cos(x) + C$$
we have
$$\int_0^1 -\sin(x)dx = [\cos(x)]_0^1$$
$$= \cos(1) - \cos(0) \qquad \text{(remember, } x \text{ is in radians)}$$
$$= -0.4597$$

(b) Since
$$\int \cos(x)dx = \sin(x) + C$$
we have
$$\int_{0.5}^{1.5} \cos(x) = [\sin(x)]_{0.5}^{1.5}$$
$$= \sin(1.5) - \sin(0.5)$$
$$= 0.5181$$

If $y = \exp(x) + C$ where C is an arbitrary constant, then,
$$\frac{dy}{dx} = \exp(x)$$

Therefore, $dy/dx = \exp(x)$ implies that
$$y = \int [\exp(x)] dx$$
$$= \exp(x) + C$$

Also if $y = \ln(x) + C$ then
$$\frac{dy}{dx} = \frac{1}{x}$$

Therefore, $dy/dx = 1/x$ implies that

$$y = \int \frac{1}{x} dx$$

$$= \ln(x) + C$$

Example 7-2-4 Find

$$\int \frac{4}{x} dx$$

SOLUTION Let

$$y = \int \frac{4}{x} dx$$

then

$$\frac{dy}{dx} = \frac{4}{x}$$

$\Rightarrow$

$$y = 4 \ln(x) + C \qquad (C \text{ is a constant})$$

Let $C = \ln(k)$ where k is a constant. Then using the theory of logarithms, we have

$$y = 4 \ln(x) + C$$

$$= 4 \ln(x) + \ln(k)$$

$$= \ln(x^4) + \ln(k)$$

or

$$y = \ln(kx^4)$$

The reader can check the solution of Example 7-2-4 by using the chain rule when differentiating.

Example 7-2-5 Evaluate

$$\int_0^1 (\sin x + e^x) dx$$

SOLUTION Let

$$y = \int_0^1 (\sin x + e^x) dx$$

$$= (-\cos x + e^x)]_0^1$$

$$= [-\cos(1) + e^1] - [-\cos(0) + e^0]$$

$$= 2.1780$$

Thus the value of

$$\int_0^1 (\sin x + e^x) dx = 2.1780 \qquad \text{to 4 decimal places}$$

The reader should note that all calculations should be carried out in *radian* mode.

7-3 INTEGRATION BY CHANGE OF VARIABLE

Integration by change of variable enables a function to be transformed into a standard integral form. For example, consider

$$y = \int \cos(3x)\,dx$$

The standard integral involving cosine is

$$y = \int \cos(u)\,du$$

or

$$y = \sin(u) + C$$

By comparing the standard integral with the one to be solved we see that

$$u = 3x$$

$\Rightarrow$

$$\frac{du}{dx} = 3$$

or

$$\frac{du}{3} = dx$$

Therefore,

$$y = \int \cos(3x)\,dx$$

$$= \int \cos(u)\,\frac{du}{3}$$

$$= \tfrac{1}{3} \int \cos(u)\,du$$

$$= \tfrac{1}{3} \sin(u) + C$$

or

$$y = \tfrac{1}{3} \sin(3x) + C \qquad \text{on replacing } u \text{ by } 3x$$

Example 7-3-1 Find

$$(a) \int \sin(4x)\,dx, \quad (b) \int \exp(3x)\,dx \quad \text{and} \quad (c) \int \frac{1}{(6x+1)}\,dx$$

SOLUTION (a) Let

$$y = \int \sin(4x)\,dx$$

and let

$$u = 4x$$

$$\frac{du}{dx} = 4$$

or
$$\frac{du}{4} = dx$$

On substituting into the original integral we have

$$y = \int \sin(u)\frac{du}{4}$$

$$= \tfrac{1}{4} \int \sin(u)\,du$$

$$= \tfrac{1}{4}[-\cos(u)] + C$$

Hence on replacing u by $4x$ we have

$$y = -\tfrac{1}{4}\cos(4x) + C \qquad (C \text{ is an arbitrary constant})$$

(b) Let
$$y = \int \exp(3x)\,dx$$

and let
$$u = 3x$$

then
$$\frac{du}{dx} = 3$$

or
$$\frac{du}{3} = dx$$

Hence

$$y = \int \exp(u)\frac{du}{3}$$

$$= \tfrac{1}{3} \int \exp(u)\,du$$

$$= \tfrac{1}{3}\exp(u) + C$$

Replacing u by $3x$ gives
$$y = \int \exp(3x)\,dx = \tfrac{1}{3}\exp(3x) + C$$

(c) Let
$$y = \int \frac{1}{(6x+1)}\,dx$$

and let
$$u = 6x + 1$$

$$\frac{du}{dx} = 6$$

or
$$\frac{du}{6} = dx$$

Hence
$$y = \int \frac{1}{u} \frac{du}{6}$$

$$= \tfrac{1}{6} \ln(u) + C$$

On replacing u by $6x + 1$ we have

$$y = \tfrac{1}{6} \ln(6x + 1) + C \qquad (C \text{ is an arbitrary constant})$$

It is left to the reader to show that an alternative form for the solution is

$$y = \ln[k(6x + 1)^{1/6}] \qquad \text{where } k \text{ is a constant dependent on } C$$

The method of substituting a new variable allows us to develop some useful formulae for integration. Consider

$$y = \int \sin(ax) dx \qquad \text{where } a \text{ is a constant}$$

Let $u = ax$ then
$$\frac{du}{dx} = a$$

or
$$\frac{du}{a} = dx$$

Thus,
$$y = \int \sin(ax) dx$$

$$= \frac{1}{a} \sin(u) du$$

$$= \frac{1}{a}[-\cos(u)] + C$$

Replacing u by ax gives

$$y = \int \sin(ax) dx = -\frac{1}{a} \cos(ax) + C \qquad (C \text{ is an arbitrary constant})$$

It will be left to the reader to prove by the same technique that

$$\int \cos(ax) dx = \frac{1}{a} \sin(ax) + C$$

$$\int \exp(ax) dx = \frac{1}{a} \exp(ax) + C$$

$$\int \sec^2(ax)\,dx = \frac{1}{a}\tan(ax) + C$$

All these results can be checked by differentiation as well as by the integration method.

Example 7-3-2 Find

$$(a) \int \sec^2(10x)\,dx \quad \text{and} \quad (b) \int \cos(12x)\,dx$$

SOLUTION (a) Let

$$y = \int \sec^2(10x)\,dx$$

Since

$$\int \sec^2(ax)\,dx = \frac{1}{a}\tan(ax) + C$$

We replace a by 10 to give

$$y = \int \sec^2(10x)\,dx = 0.1\tan(10x) + C$$

(b) Since

$$\int \cos(ax)\,dx = \frac{1}{a}\sin(ax) + C$$

we replace a by 12. Hence

$$\int \cos(12x)\,dx = \frac{1}{12}\sin(12x) + C$$

Example 7-3-3 Evaluate

$$(a) \int_0^1 \cos(3t)\,dt \quad \text{and} \quad (b) \int_{-1}^1 \sin(2t)\,dt$$

SOLUTION (a) Let

$$y = \int \cos(3t)\,dt$$

then let

$$u = 3t$$

$\Rightarrow$

$$\frac{du}{dt} = 3$$

or

$$\frac{du}{3} = dt$$

On substituting

$$y = \int \cos(u)\frac{du}{3}$$

$$= \tfrac{1}{3} \sin(u) + C$$

$$= \tfrac{1}{3} \sin(3x) + C$$

Hence

$$\int_0^1 \cos(3t) = [\tfrac{1}{3} \sin(3x)]_0^1$$

$$= \tfrac{1}{3}[\sin(3) - \sin(0)]$$

$$= 0.0470$$

(b) By Example 7-3-1(c) we have

$$\int \sin(ax)dx = -\frac{1}{a} \cos(ax) + C$$

and on replacing a by 2 we have

$$\int_{-1}^1 \sin(2x) = [-\tfrac{1}{2} \cos(2x)]_{-1}^1$$

$$= -0.5[\cos(2) - \cos(-2)]$$

$$= -0.5(0)$$

$$= 0$$

Example 7-3-4 By using the substitution $u = \sin(x)$ evaluate

$$\int_0^{\pi/4} \cos(x) \sin^2(x)dx$$

SOLUTION (a) Let

$$u = \sin(x)$$

then

$$\frac{du}{dx} = \cos(x)$$

or

$$du = \cos(x)dx$$

Let

$$y = \int \cos(x) \sin^2(x)dx$$

⇒

$$y = \int u^2 du$$

on substituting $u = \sin(x)$ and $du = \cos(x)dx$. Hence

$$y = \frac{u^3}{3} + C$$

$$= \frac{\sin^3(x)}{3} + C$$

Therefore

$$\int_0^{\pi/4} \cos(x) \sin^2(x)dx = [\tfrac{1}{3} \sin^3(x)]_0^{\pi/4}$$

$$= \tfrac{1}{3}[\sin^3(\pi/4) - \sin^3(0)]$$

$$= 0.1178$$

7-4 TRANSFORMATION OF INTEGRATION LIMITS

When we use a substitute variable in definite integration we can use a procedure of changing the limits of integration. Example 7-4-1 will illustrate the method.

Example 7-4-1 Evaluate the integral

$$\int_1^3 (x+2)^4 \, dx$$

by using the substitution $u = (x+2)$.

SOLUTION Let

$$y = \int_1^3 (x+2)^4 \, dx$$

then let

$$u = x + 2$$

This implies that

when $x = 1$ $u = 1 + 2 = 3$

when $x = 3$ $u = 3 + 2 = 5$

and $du = dx$

Therefore, on substitution,

$$y = \int_1^3 (x+2)^4 \, dx = \int_3^5 u^4 \, du$$

where the limits of integration have been changed. Hence

$$y = \int_3^5 u^4 \, du$$

$$= \left. \frac{u^5}{5} \right|_3^5$$

$$= \tfrac{1}{5}(5^5 - 3^5)$$

$$= 576.4$$

The reader should notice that, as we have changed the limits of integration, there is no need to change back to the x variable.

PROBLEMS

For problems **7-1** to **7-3** find the indefinite integral.

7-1 $\int (5x^4 + 4x^3)dx$.

7-2 $\int (3 + x^{1.5})dx$.

7-3 $\int (x^{-3} + 6x^{-5} + 5)dx$.

For problems **7-4** to **7-6** evaluate the definite integral.

7-4 $\int_{-2}^{-1} (3x^2 + 1)dx$.

7-5 $\int_1^2 (x - 2x^{-2})dx$.

7-6 $\int_1^3 (x^{2.5})dx$.

For problems **7-7** to **7-10** find the indefinite integral associated with the sine function.

7-7 $\int \sin(2x)dx$.

7-8 $\int - \sin(5x)dx$.

*****7-9** $\int 2 \sin(-2x)dx$.

******7-10** $\int \sin(2)dx$.

For problems **7-11** to **7-15** find the indefinite integral associated with the cosine function.

7-11 $\int \cos(2x)dx$.

******7-12** $\int \cos(3)dx$.

*****7-13** $\int 4 \cos(4x)dx$.

*****7-14** $\int 3 \cos(2x)dx$.

7-15 $\int \cos(0.4x)dx$.

For problems **7-16** to **7-24** find the value of the definite integral.

7-16 $\int_\pi^{2\pi} \sin(x)dx$

7-17 $\int_0^{\pi/3} \cos(x)dx$.

7-18 $\int_0^{\pi/12} \sin(3x)dx$.

7-19 $\int_{\pi/2}^\pi \cos(5x)dx$.

7-20 $\int_{-1}^0 4 \sin(x)dx$.

*****7-21** $\int_0^1 - 3 \sin(2x)dx$.

7-22 $\int_0^{\pi/2} 3 \cos(2x)dx$.

7-23 $\int_{\pi/2}^\pi - 2 \sin(x)dx$.

7-24 $\int_{-\pi/2}^0 \cos(2x)dx$.

For problems **7-25** to **7-30** find the indefinite integral.

7-25 $\int \sec^2(2x)dx$.

*****7-26** $\int 3 \sec^2(x)dx$.

*****7-27** $\int 4 \sec^2(2x)dx$.

*****7-28** $\int - 3 \sec^2(x)dx$.

******7-29** $\int 4 \sec^2(3)dx$.

*****7-30** $\int 3 \sec^2(-3x)dx$.

For problems **7-31** to **7-33** find the value of the definite integral.

7-31 $\int_0^{0.5} \sec^2(x)dx$.

******7-32** $\int_0^1 \sec^2(4)dx$.

7-33 $\int_0^{0.5} \sec^2(4x)dx$.

For problems **7-34** to **7-40** find the indefinite integral associated with the exponential function.

7-34 $\int e^x dx$.

7-35 $\int e^{2x}dx$.

7-36 $\int e^{-4x}dx$.

7-37 $\int \exp(5x)dx$.

7-38 $\int \exp(-3x)dx$.

*7-39 $\int 4 \exp(4x)dx$.

*7-40 $\int 16 \exp(4x)dx$.

For problems 7-41 to 7-43 find the value of the definite integral.

7-41 $\int_0^1 \exp(2x)dx$.

7-42 $\int_1^2 3 \exp(1.5x)dx$.

7-43 $\int_0^1 -2 \exp(0.5x)dx$.

For problems 7-44 to 7-50 find the indefinite integral.

7-44 $\int (4/x)dx$.

7-45 $\int (-6/x)dx$.

7-46 $\int (9/x)dx$.

*7-47 $\int (1/2x)dx$.

*7-48 $\int (1/4x)dx$.

7-49 $\int (2/x + 3/x)dx$.

**7-50 $\int \left(\dfrac{3x + 2x^2}{x^2} \right) dx$

*7-51 The slope equation

$$\frac{dy}{dx} = 3x$$

is associated with a set of functions. Find that set of functions.

For problems 7-52 to 7-56 using a suitable substitution evaluate the definite integral.

*7-52 $\int_0^1 \exp(t + 1)dt$.

*7-53 $\int_1^2 \exp(-t + 1)dt$.

7-54 $\int_0^1 3 \exp(3t - 2)dt$.

7-55 $\displaystyle\int_9^{24} \frac{1}{(x-4)} dx$

*7-56 $\displaystyle\int_{200}^{300} \frac{10}{(x-45)} dx$

**7-57 By using the substitution $u = x^4$, evaluate

$$\int_0^1 4x^3 \cdot \cos(x^4)dx.$$

**7-58 By using a suitable substitution find

$$\int 4x \cdot \exp(2x^2)dx.$$

**7-59 Evaluate

$$\int_1^2 \sin^2(x)dx$$

by using the trigonometric substitution

$$\sin^2(x) = \frac{1 - \cos(2x)}{2}.$$

***7-60 Evaluate

$$\int_{1}^{3} \cos(2x) \cdot \sin(3x) \, dx$$

by using the formulae in Sec. 2-5.

Solutions

In all the solutions C or k will be used to denote the *arbitrary* constant if this is necessary.

7-1 $x^5 + x^4 + C$.

7-2 $3x + \frac{2}{5} x^{2.5} + C$.

7-3 $-0.5x^{-2} - 1.5x^{-4} + 5x + C$.

7-4 8.

7-5 0.5.

7-6 13.0758.

7-7 $-0.5 \cos(2x) + C$.

7-8 $0.2 \cos(5x) + C$.

7-9 $\cos(-2x) = \cos(2x)$.

7-10 $0.9093x + C$.

7-11 $0.5 \sin(2x) + C$.

7-12 $-0.99x + C$.

7-13 $\sin(4x) + C$.

7-14 $1.5 \sin(2x) + C$.

7-15 $2.5 \sin(0.4x) + C$.

7-16 -2.

7-17 0.866.

7-18 0.0976.

7-19 -0.2.

7-20 -1.8388.

7-21 -2.1242.

7-22 0.

7-23 -2.

7-24 0.

7-25 $0.5 \tan(2x) + C$.

7-26 $3 \tan(x) + C$.

7-27 $2 \tan(2x) + C$.

7-28 $-3 \tan(x) + C$.

7-29 $4.0813x + C$

7-30 $-\tan(-3x) + C$.

7-31 0.5463.

7-32 2.3406.

7-33 -0.5463.

7-34 $e^x + C$.

7-35 $\dfrac{e^{2x}}{2} + C$.

7-36 $-0.25e^{-4x} + C$.

7-37 $0.2 \exp(5x) + C$.

7-38 $-\frac{1}{3} \exp(-3x) + C$.

7-39 $\exp(4x) + C$.

7-40 $4 \exp(4x) + C$.

7-41 3.1945.

7-42 31.2077.

7-43 -2.5949.

7-44 $\ln(kx^4)$.

7-45 $\ln(kx^{-6})$.

7-46 $\ln(kx^9)$.

7-47 $\ln(kx^{0.5})$.

7-48 $\ln(kx^{0.25})$.

7-49 $\ln(kx^5)$.

7-50 $\ln(x^3) + 2x + C$.

7-51 $y = \dfrac{3x^2}{2} + C$.

7-52 4.6708.

7-53 0.6321.

7-54 2.5830.

7-55 1.3863.

7-56 4.9784.

7-57 0.8415.

7-58 $\exp(2x^2) + C$.

7-59 0.9165.

7-60 0.8695.

APPLICATIONS OF INTERGRATION THEORY

Objectives After reading this chapter you should be able to:

1. Determine the areas under graphs of functions.
   (*a*) Determine the area between the curve, the *x* axis and given ordinates.
   (*b*) Determine the area between two curves which intersect.
   (*c*) Establish the limits of integration involved in calculating areas.
   (*d*) Apply the theory of integration to velocity–time graphs.
2. Determine the volume of revolution if a given area is revolved about the *x* axis.
   (*a*) Form an incremental volume.
   (*b*) Sketch the form of the volume of revolution for a given area.
   (*c*) State the limits of the variable defining the given volume.
   (*d*) Determine the volume of revolution by definite integration.

8-1 INTRODUCTION

Consider a body travelling in a straight line with its velocity given by

$$v = 3e^{-t}$$

where t is the time in seconds. A sketch of the curve is shown in Fig. 8-1. The time interval has been restricted from 0 to 4 s. By finding the area under the curve, we are able to estimate the distance travelled by the body in 4 s. We shall employ a numerical method, in the first instance, called the **mid-ordinate rule** and divide the area into strips of equal width. The height of each strip is governed by the curve as shown in Fig. 8-2. The area under the curve, above the t axis and between the ordinates $t = 0$ and $t = 4$, can be approximated by the eight strips. The area of each strip is base × height. The height of each strip is calculated by using the midpoint along its base, as shown in the figure. Table 8-1 shows the results of the calculations for the eight strips.

Using this method we have

$$\text{Area under curve} = (\text{base})(\Sigma \text{ mid-ordinates})$$

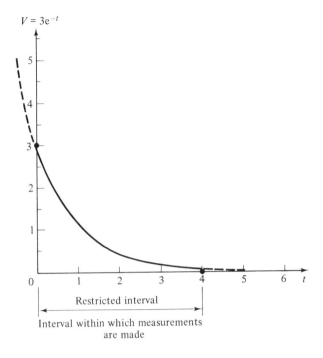

Figure 8-1

Table 8-1

t midpoint	Height mid-ordinate	Area = base × height	
0.25	2.3364	1.1682	
0.75	1.4171	0.7086	
1.25	0.8595	0.4298	
1.75	0.5213	0.2607	
2.25	0.3162	0.1581	
2.75	0.1918	0.0959	
3.25	0.1163	0.0582	
3.75	0.0706	0.0353	
	Total area =	2.9148	
	=	2.915	to 3 decimal places

In practice, we carry out the calculations on a computer or an electronic calculator. Hence, by calculator we have

$$\Sigma \text{ mid-ordinates} = 5.8292$$

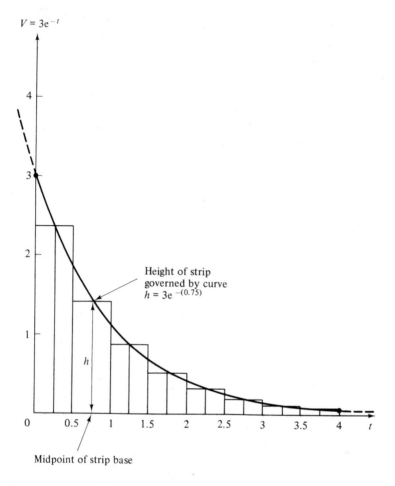

Figure 8-2 Area under curve split into eight strips of equal width. This area represents distance travelled by the body.

and hence

$$\text{Area} = (0.5)(5.8292)$$

$$= 2.9146$$

$$= 2.915 \qquad \text{to 3 decimal places}$$

By increasing the number of strips, the area by the mid-ordinate rule will tend to the *exact* value under the curve. This is illustrated in the print-out from a computer programmed to reduce the base and thereby increase the number of strips.

RUN

THIS PROGRAM EVALUATES THE AREA UNDER THE CURVE $V = 3 * EXP(-T)$, ABOVE THE T AXIS AND BETWEEN THE ORDINATES $T = 0$ AND $T = 4$.

THE PROGRAM IS BASED ON THE MID-ORDINATE RULE.

NUMBER OF STRIPS	WIDTH OF STRIP	AREA UNDER CURVE
1	4.000000	1.653768
2	2.000000	2.505999
4	1.000000	2.825830
8	0.500000	2.914598
16	0.250000	2.937398
32	0.125000	2.943137
64	0.062500	2.944574
128	0.031250	2.944933
256	0.015625	2.945023
512	0.007813	2.945046
1024	0.003906	2.945051

FINISHED

Using 1024 strips, the approximate area under the curve $v = 3e^{-t}$ is 2.945 05 to 5 decimal places. In the computer print-out, it can be seen that as the number of strips increases, the base or width of strip decreases. The *greater* the number of strips, the *smaller* the strip width and the **approximate area** tends to the **exact area** under the curve. We can find the exact area by using **definite integration** and, as we shall see, Example 8-2-2 gives the area by this method as 2.945 05 to 5 decimal places, which agrees with the mid-ordinate method when using 1024 strips.

8-2 AREAS BY DEFINITE INTEGRATION

Consider a function represented by the curve $y = f(x)$ where the values of x have been restricted by the experiment or the engineering problem. In the first place, we make a further assumption by only considering functions which have graphs above the x axis and thereby the y values are **positive**. This is illustrated in Fig. 8-3. To find the area below this curve $y = f(x)$, above the x axis and between the lines $x = a$ and $x = b$, we choose a strip with a width of δx. The height of the strip is, as in the numerical method of Sec. 8-1, governed by the curve. Therefore,

$$\text{Area of strip} = y(\delta x)$$

and by adding all these elemental strips together we obtain the *approximate* area under the curve between the ordinates $x = a$ and $x = b$. That is,

$$\text{Approximate area under curve} = \sum_{x=a}^{x=b} y(\delta x)$$

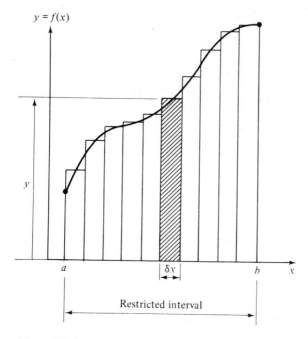

Figure 8-3 Area under curve split into strips of width δx, height y governed by the curve $y = f(x)$. The values of y are all above the x axis in this case, i.e., the values of y are positive.

With the numerical method, reduction in the width of the strip increases the number of strips and the approximate area tends to the *exact* area under the curve.

Therefore, let δx tend to zero, thus decreasing the width of the strip, and we have

$$\lim_{\delta x \to 0} \sum_{x=a}^{x=b} y(\delta x) = \text{exact area}$$

Let the exact area under the curve be A. Let the area of the elemental strip be δA. Hence

$$\delta A = y(\delta x)$$

and on dividing both sides by δx we have

$$\frac{\delta A}{\delta x} = y$$

Now, taking limits, we can reduce the width of the strip δx, allowing the height y to remain constant. Thus,

$$\lim_{\delta x \to 0} \left(\frac{\delta A}{\delta x} \right) = \lim_{\delta x \to 0} (y)$$

$$\Rightarrow \qquad \frac{dA}{dx} = y$$

Since we have a slope equation, by the integration chapter, we have

$$A = \int y \, dx$$

and since we have a restricted interval

$$A = \int_a^b y \, dx$$

Therefore,

$$\text{Area under curve} = A = \lim_{\delta x \to 0} \sum_{x=a}^{x=b} y(\delta x) = \int_a^b y \, dx$$

Example 8-2-1 Find the area under curve $y = x^2$, above the x axis and between the ordinates $x = 1$ and $x = 2$.

SOLUTION Figure 8-4 illustrates that the curve is above the x axis and therefore we only have positive values of y.

$$\text{Area of strip} = y \cdot \delta x$$

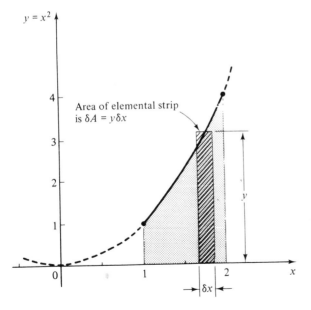

Figure 8-4.

Hence
$$\delta A = y \cdot \delta x$$

or
$$\frac{\delta A}{\delta x} = y$$

On taking limits as $\delta x \to 0$ we have

$$\frac{dA}{dx} = y$$

a *slope* equation. By the integration chapter,

$$\lim_{\delta x \to 0} \left(\sum_{x=1}^{x=2} y\delta x \right) = A = \int_1^2 y\,dx = \int_1^2 x^2\,dx$$

$$= (x^3/3)_1^2$$

$$= \left(\frac{2^3}{3} - \frac{1^3}{3} \right)$$

Hence

Area under curve $= 2.3333$

Example 8-2-2 Find the distance travelled by a body moving in a straight line after a period of 4 s has elapsed if its velocity is given by $v = 3e^{-t}$ where t is the time in seconds, and v is in m/s.

SOLUTION The area under the velocity–time curve represents the distance travelled by the body. This function is shown in Fig. 8-1 along with the restricted time interval from 0 to 4 s. The values of the function are all positive and the area is given by

$$A = \int_0^4 v\,dt$$

$$= \int_0^4 3e^{-t}\,dt$$

$$= (-3e^{-t})_0^4$$

Hence area under curve, representing distance travelled between 0 and 4 s, is given by

$$(-3e^{-t})_0^4 = -3(e^{-4} - e^0)$$

$$= 2.945\,05 \text{ m}$$

It has been stressed that when using

$$A = \int_a^b y\,dx$$

y must *always* have positive values between a and b. If the value of y is negative at any point, we must be careful when attempting to find areas between the

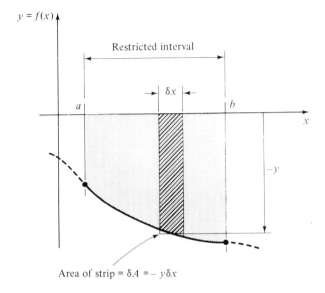

Area of strip = $\delta A = -y\,\delta x$

Figure 8-5

curve and the x axis. Let us consider the case where $y = f(x)$ is negative through-out the interval as shown in Fig. 8-5.

The strip shown as an area

$$\delta A = -y(\delta x)$$

the negative sign appearing since we have defined on graphs the upwards direction as positive. The opposite direction, downwards, is negative. Therefore, on divid-ing both sides of

$$\delta A = -y(\delta x)$$

by δx, we have

$$\frac{\delta A}{\delta x} = -y$$

and on taking limits,

$$\lim_{\delta x \to 0} \left(\frac{\delta A}{\delta x} \right) = \frac{dA}{dx} = -y$$

Therefore, for curves below the x axis, the area between the curve, the axis and the ordinates a and b is given by

$$A = \int_a^b -y\,dx$$

$$= -\int_a^b y\,dx$$

Example 8-2-3 Find the area between the curve $y = -x^2 + 1$, the x axis, and the lines $x = 1$ and $x = 3$.

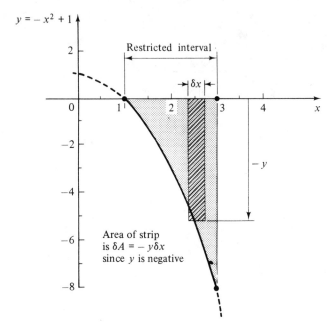

Figure 8-6

SOLUTION Figure 8-6 illustrates the curve with an elemental strip. Since y is negative throughout the interval, we have

$$\text{Area between curve and } x \text{ axis} = -\int_a^b y\, dx$$

$$= -\int_1^3 (-x^2 + 1)\, dx$$

$$= (x^3/3 - x)_1^3$$

$$= \left(\frac{3^3}{3} - 3\right) - \left(\frac{1^3}{3} - 1\right)$$

$$= 6.6667$$

Example 8-2-4 Find the area between the curves $y = x$ and $y = x^2/4$.

SOLUTION A sketch of the two graphs is shown in Fig. 8-7. The points of intersection of the two curves indicate the limits of the integration. To find the x coordinate of intersection we have

$$x = x^2/4$$

or

$$\frac{x^2}{4} - x = 0$$

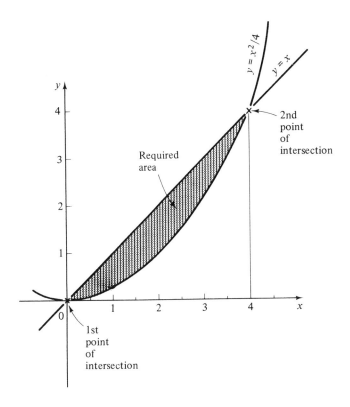

Figure 8-7

Factorization gives

$$x\left(\frac{x}{4} - 1\right) = 0$$

which implies

$$x = 0 \qquad \text{or} \qquad \frac{x}{4} - 1 = 0$$

Hence $x = 0$ or $x = 4$ are the x coordinates of the points of intersection and these are the limits of the integration.

Area *under* the straight line $y = x$, above the x axis, and between $x = 0$ and $x = 4$, is given by

$$A_1 = \int_0^4 y \, dx$$

$$= \int_0^4 x \, dx$$

$$= \left(\frac{x^2}{2}\right)_0^4$$

hence $$A_1 = 8$$

Area *under* curve $y = x^2/4$, above the x axis, and between the ordinates $x = 0$ and $x = 4$ is given by

$$A_2 = \int_0^4 y\,dx$$

$$= \int_0^4 \frac{x^2}{4}\,dx$$

$$= \left(\frac{x^3}{12}\right)_0^4$$

$$= \left(\frac{4^3}{12} - \frac{0^3}{12}\right)$$

hence $$A_2 = 5\tfrac{1}{3}$$

Area between curves $= A_1 - A_2$

$$= (\text{area under } y = x) - (\text{area under } y = x^2/4)$$

$$= 8 - 5\tfrac{1}{3}$$

$$= 2\tfrac{2}{3}$$

8-3 VOLUMES OF REVOLUTION

Consider the rectangular area shown in Fig. 8-8, and allow it to revolve about the x axis. In completing one revolution, this area forms a cylinder of radius y. Other areas form different shapes as illustrated in Example 8-3-1.

Example 8-3-1 The area under the curve $y = x^2 + 1$, above the x axis and between the lines $x = 0$ and $x = 2$, is revolved about the x axis. Sketch the resulting figure if the area completes one revolution.

SOLUTION The shape of the curve $y = x^2 + 1$ is sketched. This curve is the outline of the volume of revolution illustrated in Fig. 8-9.

8-4 VOLUMES OF REVOLUTION BY DEFINITE INTEGRATION

Section 8.3 showed that if an area is revolved about the x axis, a three-dimensional figure is formed. Consider the area which lies under the curve $y = f(x)$, above the x axis and between the ordinates $x = a$ and $x = b$. Consider a small rectangular strip, width δx and height $y = f(x)$. If we revolve this strip about the x axis, we form an elemental disc of radius y, illustrated in Fig. 8-10. The volume of a disc is given by

(Area of face)(thickness)

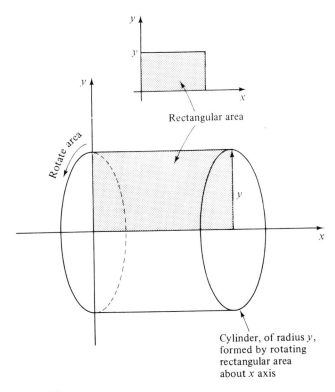

Rectangular area

Cylinder, of radius y, formed by rotating rectangular area about x axis

Figure 8-8

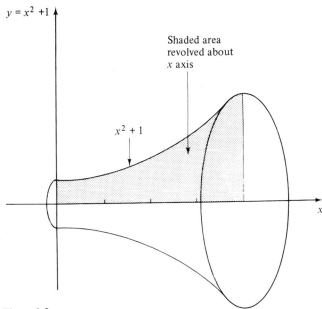

$y = x^2 + 1$

Shaded area revolved about x axis

$x^2 + 1$

Figure 8-9

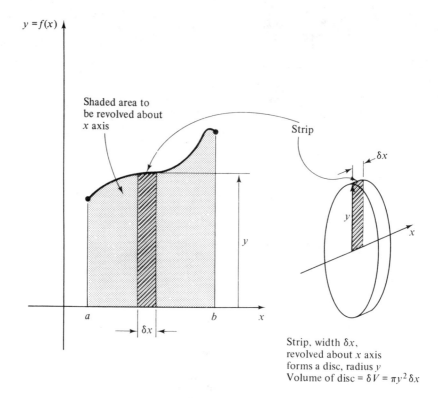

Figure 8-10

Therefore, volume of elemental disc is

$$\pi(\text{radius})^2(\text{thickness}) = \pi y^2 \delta x$$

If we add these small discs together, we form the **approximate volume of revolution.** Therefore,

$$\text{Approximate volume of revolution} = \sum_{x=a}^{x=b} (\pi y^2 \,\delta x)$$

As the width of the elemental strip *decreases*, the thickness of the elemental disc *decreases*, the number of discs *increases* and the approximate volume tends to the *exact* volume of revolution. Therefore

$$\text{Exact volume} = \lim_{\delta x \to 0} \sum_{x=a}^{x=b} (\pi y^2 \,\delta x)$$

Let V be the exact volume of revolution about the x axis. Let δV be the volume of the elemental disc. Therefore,

$$\delta V = \pi y^2 \delta x$$

or

$$\frac{\delta V}{\delta x} = \pi y^2$$

Taking limits as δx tends to zero we have

$$\frac{dV}{dx} = \pi y^2$$

and we have a slope equation for the volume of revolution. Using reverse differentiation we have

$$V = \int_a^b \pi y^2 \, dx$$

Thus,

$$V = \lim_{\delta x \to 0} \sum_{x=a}^{x=b} (\pi y^2 \delta x)$$

$$= \int_a^b \pi y^2 \, dx$$

Example 8-4-1 The area between the curve $y = e^{-2x}$, the x axis and the lines $x = 0$ and $x = 1$, is revolved about the x axis. Calculate the volume of revolution.

SOLUTION Figure 8-11 shows the area to be revolved along with an elemental strip of width δx. The strip is revolved about the x axis to form the elemental disc with radius $y = e^{-2x}$. Hence

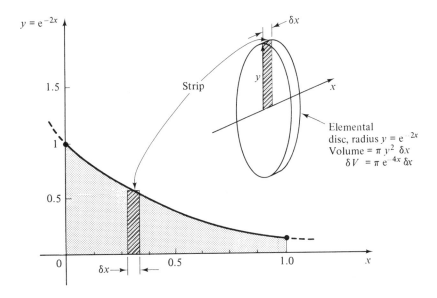

$y = e^{-2x}$

1.5

Strip

δx

y

x

Elemental
disc, radius $y = e^{-2x}$
Volume $= \pi y^2 \delta x$
$\delta V = \pi e^{-4x} \delta x$

1

0.5

0   0.5   1.0 x

δx

Figure 8-11

$$\text{Volume of elemental disc} = \delta V = \pi y^2 \delta x$$

$$= \pi (e^{-2x})^2 \delta x$$

$$\Rightarrow \qquad \frac{\delta V}{\delta x} = \pi e^{-4x}$$

Hence, on taking limits as δx tends to zero, we have

$$\text{Volume of revolution} = V = \int_0^1 \pi e^{-4x} \, dx$$

$$= \left(\frac{\pi}{-4} e^{-4x} \right)_0^1$$

$$= -\frac{\pi}{4} (e^{-4} - e^0)$$

$$= 0.7710 \qquad \text{to 4 decimal places}$$

Example 8-4-2 The area between the curve $y = x^2 - 1$, the x axis and the line $x = 3$ is revolved, once, around the x axis. Calculate the volume of revolution.

SOLUTION A sketch of the area in Fig. 8-12 illustrates that the curve crosses the x axis at $x = 1$. As before, consider an elemental strip of width δx revolved once about the x axis. Therefore

$$\text{Volume of disc} = \pi y^2 \delta x$$

$$\delta V = \pi (x^2 - 1)^2 \delta x$$

$$\frac{\delta V}{\delta x} = \pi (x^4 - 2x^2 + 1)$$

Allowing the disc thickness to become very small, we have as δx tends to zero

$$\frac{dV}{dx} = \pi (x^4 + 2x^2 + 1)$$

and therefore

$$V = \int_1^3 \pi (x^4 - 2x^2 + 1) \, dx$$

$$= \pi \left[\left(\frac{x^5}{5} - \frac{2x^3}{3} + x \right) \right]_1^3$$

$$= \pi \left[\left(\frac{(3)^5}{5} - \frac{2(3)^3}{3} + 3 \right) - \left(\frac{(1)^5}{5} - \frac{2(1)^3}{3} + 1 \right) \right]$$

$$= 103.88$$

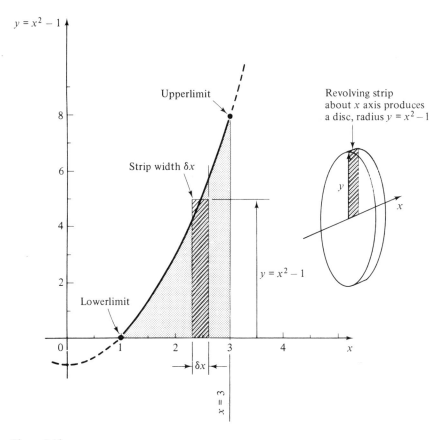

Figure 8-12

Example 8-4-3 The area under the curve $y = \sin(x)$ and above the x axis between $x = 0$ and $x = \pi$ is revolved once about the x axis. Calculate the volume generated.

SOLUTION It will be left to the reader to sketch the curve in this example. By using

$$\text{Volume of revolution} = \int_a^b \pi y^2 \, dx$$

we have

$$V = \int_0^\pi \pi [\sin(x)]^2 \, dx$$

$$= \int_0^\pi \pi \sin^2(x) \, dx$$

By Chapter 2 we have

and on substituting

$$\cos^2(x) - \sin^2(x) = \cos(2x)$$

this becomes

$$\cos^2(x) = 1 - \sin^2(x)$$

Hence

$$\cos(2x) = 1 - 2\sin^2(x)$$

$$\sin^2(x) = \tfrac{1}{2}[1 - \cos(2x)]$$

can be substituted into the required integral to give

$$V = \int_0^\pi \pi[\sin^2(x)]\,dx$$

$$= \int_0^\pi \frac{\pi}{2}[1 - \cos(2x)]\,dx$$

$$= \frac{\pi}{2}\left[\left(x - \frac{\sin(2x)}{2}\right)\right]_0^\pi$$

$$= \frac{\pi}{2}\left[\left(\pi - \frac{\sin(2\pi)}{2}\right) - \left(0 - \frac{\sin(0)}{2}\right)\right]$$

$$= \frac{\pi^2}{2} = 4.935$$

Hence, volume generated by revolving the area under the curve $y = \sin(x)$, above the x axis between $x = 0$ and $x = \pi$, is 4.935.

PROBLEMS

For the problems **8-1** to **8-3** find the area between the curve $y = f(x)$, the x axis and the ordinates $x = 1$ and $x = 2$.

8-1 $f(x) = x^2 + 3$.

8-2 $f(x) = 2x + x^2$.

8-3 $f(x) = 3 + 2x^3$.

For problems **8-4** to **8-6** find the area between the curve $y = f(x)$, the x axis and the ordinates $x = -2$ and $x = -1$.

8-4 $f(x) = 3.5x^2 - x$.

8-5 $f(x) = -x^3 + 1$.

8-6 $f(x) = 3x^2 + 2$.

For problems **8-7** to **8-10** find the area between the curve $y = f(x)$, the x axis and the ordinates $x = 0$ and $x = 1$.

*8-7 $f(x) = -x^4$.

*8-8 $f(x) = -3x^2 - 1$.

*8-9 $f(x) = -10x^3 + x - 10$.

*8-10 $f(x) = -2x^{0.2}$.

For problems **8-11** to **8-14** find the area between the curve $y = f(x)$ and the x axis, assuming a restricted interval $0 \leqslant x \leqslant \pi/2$.

8-11 $f(x) = \sin(x)$.

8-12 $f(x) = \cos(x)$.

*8-13 $f(x) = \sin(2x)$.

**8-14 $f(x) = 3\sin(x) + 1$.

For problems **8-15** to **8-20** find the area between the curve $y = f(x)$, the x axis and the ordinates $x = 0$ and $x = 1$.

8-15 $f(x) = e^x$.

8-16 $f(x) = \exp(3x)$.

*8-17 $f(x) = e^{-2x}$.

**8-18 $f(x) = 3x + e^x$.

**8-19 $f(x) = \sec^2(0.5x)$.

**8-20 $f(x) = 3\sin(0.5x)$.

For problems **8-21** to **8-23** find the area between the curve $y = f(x)$, the x axis and the ordinates $x = 1$ and $x = 2$.

8-21 $f(x) = \dfrac{1}{x}$.

*8-22 $f(x) = \dfrac{1}{x + 1}$.

**8-23 $f(x) = \dfrac{2x}{x^2 + 3}$.

**8-24 A body travelling in a straight line has its velocity defined by

$$v = 0.5t^2 + 3t + 1$$

Find (a) the initial velocity, (b) the distance travelled in the first 3 s, and (c) the distance travelled in the second 3 s, i.e. $t = 3$ to $t = 6$.

***8-25 A body travels in a straight line for 10 s. Its velocity is given by the equation

$$v = e^{-2t} + 1.2$$

and has been measured in m/s. Evaluate the distance travelled in the 10 s. If the body travelled in the same straight line for a further 10 s, find, using the same model for its velocity, the extra distance covered.

*8-26 Find the area between the curves $y = x$ and $y = 0.25x^2$.

**8-27 The current flowing in a capacitive circuit is given by $i = e^{-t}$ amperes. Sketch the graph of current against time and hence find the area between the curve, the t axis and the ordinates $t = 0$ and $t = 2.5$ s. Describe this result in terms of electrical engineering science.

For problems **8-28** to **8-30** find the volume generated by revolving about the x axis the area between the curve $y = f(x)$, the x axis and the ordinates $x = 0$ and $x = 2$.

8-28 $f(x) = x + 1$.

8-29 $f(x) = x - 3$.

8-30 $f(x) = -x^2$.

For the problems **8-31** to **8-34** evaluate the volume of revolution when the area between the curve $y = f(x)$, the x axis and the ordinates $x = 1$ and $x = 2$ is revolved once about the x axis.

8-31 $f(x) = e^{2x}$.

8-32 $f(x) = e^{-x}$.

8-33 $f(x) = 4.5e^x$.

8-34 $f(x) = -3e^{-2x}$.

***8-35** The force exerted on a body moving in a straight line is modelled by the equation

$$F = 3\cos(2s)$$

where s is the distance moved. Evaluate the work done when the body has moved a total distance of 1.5 m. Assume that the force is measured in newtons.

****8-36** Sketch the curve

$$y = x^2 + \frac{2}{x}$$

for x values between $x = 1$ and $x = 2$. Allow the curve to revolve around the x axis for one revolution and sketch the resulting volume of revolution. Find the value of the resulting volume of revolution.

****8-37** The area between the curve $3\sin(t)$, the t axis and the ordinates $t = 0$ and $t = 1$, is allowed to revolve around the t axis once. Find the volume of the figure formed by this process.

***8-38** The curve $y = e^{-t}$ is revolved about the t axis once. If the volume of revolution is 1.0 (units)^3, find the possible restriction on the upper value of t. It may be assumed that the lower limit is 0.

Solutions

8-1 $5\frac{1}{3}$.

8-2 $5\frac{1}{3}$.

8-3 10.5.

8-4 $9\frac{2}{3}$.

8-5 4.75.

8-6 9.

8-7 0.2.

8-8 2.

8-9 12.

8-10 $1\frac{2}{3}$.

8-11 1.

8-12 1.

8-13 1.

8-14 4.5708.

8-15 1.7183.

8-16 6.3618.

8-17 0.4323.

8-18 3.2183.

8-19 1.0926.

8-20 0.7345.

8-21 0.6931.

8-22 0.4055.

8-23 0.5596.

8-24 (a) 1 m/s, (b) 21 m, (c) 75 m.

8-25 12.5 m, 11.5 m.

8-26 $2\frac{2}{3}$.

8-27 0.9179.

8-28 27.2271.

8-29 27.2271.

8-30 20.1062.

8-31 2298.36.

8-32 0.1838.

8-33 1501.66.

8-34 0.1271.

8-35 0.2117 J.

8-36 44.6106.

8-37 7.71.

8-38 0.506 153.

FIRST MOMENTS OF AREA

Objectives After reading this chapter you should be able to:

1. Determine first moments of area and the centroids of simple plane shapes.
   (*a*) Sketch a given area under a known function.
   (*b*) Sketch a typical incremental area whose centroid is known.
   (*c*) Determine the first moment of the incremental area about both the x and y axes.
   (*d*) Sum the first moments between given limits by definite integration.
   (*e*) Determine the given area between limits.
   (*f*) Define the centroid of a plane shape.
   (*g*) Calculate the coordinates of the centroid.
2. Determine the centroid of plane shapes by using the theorem of Pappus.
   (*a*) Determine the centroid of a semicircle.
   (*b*) Determine the centroid of a rectangle.
   (*c*) Determine the centroid of a circle.
3. Determine the centroid of a triangle.
4. Determine the centroid of a sector of a circle.

9-1 INTRODUCTION

In mechanics, the concept of a moment of a force is used very frequently. We shall develop from this concept a method of finding first moments of other quantities with reference to the cartesian coordinate system.

In all the work that follows, we shall assume a simple *plane* shape with a *uniform* thickness. Consider Fig. 9-1 in which the area between the curve $y = f(x)$, the x axis and the ordinates $x = a$ and $x = b$ is the area of a plate of thickness w. Consider, as was the case in the last chapter, this area being split into rectangular strips of width δx and height y, which is governed by the curve. The centre of gravity of this rectangular strip acts at the coordinates $(x, y/2)$ as shown in the figure. In general, the centre of gravity, or centroid, is the point through which the weight of the plate acts.

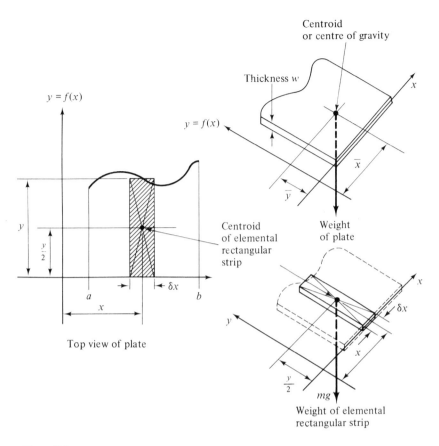

Figure 9-1

Let the mass of this rectangular strip be m. Let the **moment of force** of this rectangular strip about the y axis be

$$\delta M_y = (\text{force})(\text{distance})$$

$$= (mg)(x)$$

However,

$$\text{Mass} = (\text{density})(\text{volume})$$

$$m = \rho \cdot w(\text{area})$$

or

$$m = \rho \cdot w(y \cdot \delta x)$$

Using substitution, we have

$$\delta M_y = (\rho \cdot w \cdot y \cdot \delta x)g \cdot x$$

Dividing throughout by δx, and letting $\delta x \rightarrow 0$, gives

$$\frac{dM_y}{dx} = \rho \cdot w \cdot g \cdot y \cdot x$$

which is a slope equation for the function M_y, the **first moment of force** about the y axis. It depends on a knowledge of the density and thickness of the plate.

As we have a slope equation by Chapter 7, we can use reverse differentiation to give

$$M_y = \rho \cdot w \cdot g \int_a^b yx \, dx$$

As the total weight of the plate acts through its centre of gravity which we label $(\bar{x}, \bar{y})$, we can use the principle of moments to obtain

$$M_y = (\text{total mass})(g)(\bar{x})$$

$$= (\text{density})(\text{total volume})(g)(\bar{x})$$

$$= (\text{density})(\text{total area})(w)(g)(\bar{x})$$

Hence

$$M_y = \rho \cdot w \cdot g \cdot \int_a^b (yx) \, dx = \rho \cdot w \cdot g \cdot (\text{total area})(\bar{x})$$

This implies, on dividing both sides by $\rho \cdot w \cdot g$ that

$$(\text{Total area})(\bar{x}) = \int_a^b (yx) \, dx$$

The quantity

$$\int_a^b (yx) \, dx$$

is the **first moment of area** about the y axis and is usually denoted by A_y. Thus,

$$A_y = \int_a^b (yx) \, dx = (\text{total area})(\bar{x})$$

From Chapter 8 we have

$$\text{Area} = \int_a^b (y) \, dx$$

Therefore

$$\int_a^b (yx) \, dx = \left(\int_a^b (y) \, dx \right)(\bar{x})$$

or

$$\bar{x} = \frac{\int_a^b (yx) \, dx}{\int_a^b y \, dx}$$

The argument can be repeated for moments about the x axis. Let

$$\delta M_x = (y/2)(mg)$$

be the **first moment of force** about the x axis. On substituting

$$m = \rho \cdot w \cdot y \cdot \delta x$$

as before we have that

$$\delta M_x = (\rho \cdot w \cdot y \cdot \delta x)(g)(y/2)$$

Hence

$$\frac{\delta M_x}{\delta x} = (\rho \cdot w \cdot g)\left(\frac{y^2}{2}\right)$$

Taking the limit as δx tends to zero we have

$$\frac{dM_x}{dx} = (\rho \cdot w \cdot g)\left(\frac{y^2}{2}\right)$$

$$\Rightarrow \qquad M_x = \rho \cdot w \cdot g \cdot \int_a^b \frac{y^2}{2} \, dx$$

Hence using the argument that

$$M_x = (\text{total mass})(g)(\bar{y})$$

we have

$$\int_a^b \frac{y^2}{2} \, dx = (\text{total area})(\bar{y})$$

The quantity

$$\int_a^b \frac{y^2}{2} \, dx$$

is the **first moment of area** about the x axis and is denoted by A_x. Thus,

$$A_x = (\text{total area})(\bar{y}) = \int_a^b \frac{y^2}{2} \, dx$$

or

$$\bar{y} = \frac{\int_a^b \frac{y^2}{2} \, dx}{\int_a^b y \, dx}$$

We have shown that it is possible to calculate the coordinates of the centre of gravity of a plate with a *plane area* and *uniform thickness*. If we consider the thickness as being *very small*, then we call the point denoted by $(\bar{x}, \bar{y})$ the **centre of area** or **centroid**.

Example 9-1-1 Find the position of the centroid of the plane area formed by the curve $y = x^2$, the x axis and the ordinates $x = 1$ and $x = 2$.

SOLUTION A sketch of the curve $y = x^2$ is shown in Fig. 9-2. We have that the first moment of area about the y axis is given by

$$A_y = \int_a^b (xy) \, dx$$

$$= \int_1^2 x^3 \, dx$$

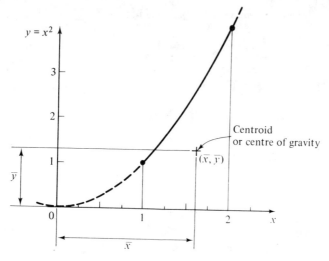

Figure 9-2

$$= \left[\frac{x^4}{4}\right]_1^2$$

$$= 3.75$$

The area under the curve, above the x axis and between the ordinates, is given by

$$\int_1^2 y\, dx = \int_1^2 x^2\, dx$$

$$= \left[\frac{x^3}{3}\right]_1^2$$

$$= 2.333\,33$$

Hence

$$\bar{x} = \frac{A_y}{\text{area}}$$

$$= \frac{3.750\,00}{2.333\,33}$$

$$= 1.6071$$

The first moment of area about the x axis is given by

$$A_x = \int_1^2 \frac{y^2}{2}\, dx$$

$$= 0.5 \int_1^2 x^4\, dx$$

$$= 0.5\left(\frac{x^5}{5}\right)\Bigg]_1^2$$

$$= 3.1$$

Hence we have

$$\bar{y} = \frac{A_x}{\text{area}}$$

$$= \frac{3.100\,00}{2.333\,33}$$

$$= 1.3286$$

Position of centroid is given by $(\bar{x}, \bar{y}) = (1.6071, 1.3286)$.

9-2 THE THEOREM OF PAPPUS

We saw in Chapter 8 that if we revolved a plane area about the x axis then we formed a **volume of revolution**. The theorem of Pappus states that if such a plane area is revolved about an axis which does not intersect this area, then

Volume of revolution = (area)(distance travelled by centroid)

In the theorem of Pappus, we only allow the area to rotate *once* around the axis.

Example 9-2-1 Find the position of the centroid of a semicircle with respect to its base.

SOLUTION Position the semicircle so that its base lies on the x axis and so that it is symmetrical about the y axis as shown in Fig. 9-3. Let the coordinates of the centroid be $(\bar{x}, \bar{y})$.

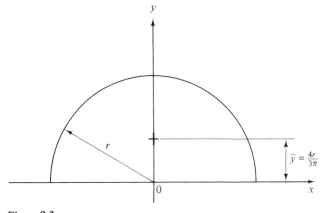

Figure 9-3

From Fig. 9-3, it is obvious that $\bar{x}$ is zero as there is an *equal* amount of area either side of the line $x = 0$. Hence consider revolving the semicircle about the x axis to form a sphere of radius r.

Volume of sphere $= \frac{4}{3}\pi r^3 =$ (area)(distance travelled by centroid)

$$= \frac{\pi r^2}{2} \cdot 2\pi(\bar{y})$$

which implies that

$$\bar{y} = \frac{4r}{3\pi}$$

Hence the centroid of a semicircle with radius r with respect to the base is given by

$$(\bar{x}, \bar{y}) = \left(0, \frac{4r}{3\pi}\right)$$

We will now investigate, with the help of the theorem of Pappus, the centroid of a plane figure in the form of a triangle. Example 9-2-2 illustrates the use of the theorem and the cartesian coordinate system.

Example 9-2-2 A right-angled triangle is positioned in a cartesian coordinate system so that the 90° angle is at the origin and one side lies along each of the axes. Find the position of the centroid with respect to the x and y axes.

SOLUTION Figure 9-4 shows the right-angled triangle in the cartesian system. It is very important that the reader defines quantities in respect of any prob-

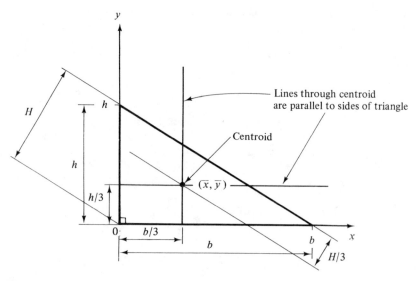

Figure 9-4

lem. In this case, we define the length of the sides of this triangle as h, the height, and b, the base.

Initially, we shall consider the triangle revolving around the y axis. Therefore, by the theorem of Pappus we have that

Volume of revolution = (area)(distance travelled by the centroid)

The volume of revolution is in the form of a *cone*. A cone has a volume of $\frac{1}{3}\pi r^2 h$ where r is the base radius. In this case, $r = b$ and we have a

$$\text{Volume of revolution} = \tfrac{1}{3}\pi b^2 h$$

$$\text{Area of triangle} = \tfrac{1}{2} \cdot \text{base} \cdot \text{height}$$

$$= \tfrac{1}{2} \cdot b \cdot h$$

Hence using the theorem of Pappus we have

$$\tfrac{1}{3}\pi b^2 h = (\tfrac{1}{2}bh)(2\pi\bar{x})$$

This implies that the x coordinate of the centroid is $\bar{x} = b/3$.

Consider the volume of revolution when the triangle is revolved about the x axis. Again we form a *cone*, but this time the radius of the base is h and the height of the cone is b. The volume of revolution is the volume of the cone which is $\frac{1}{3}\pi h^2 b$. Hence using the theorem of Pappus we have

$$\tfrac{1}{3}\pi h^2 b = (\tfrac{1}{2}hb)(2\pi\bar{y})$$

This implies that the y coordinate of the centroid is $\bar{y} = h/3$.

The position of the centroid of this right-angled triangle is given by

$$(\bar{x},\bar{y}) = \left(\frac{b}{3}, \frac{h}{3}\right)$$

9-3 THE CENTROID OF A TRIANGLE

We shall now consider the problem of finding the centroid of any triangular plate. The triangle under consideration is positioned so that one of its sides lies along the y axis in the cartesian system. This is illustrated in Fig. 9-5.

By the theorem of Pappus

Volume of revolution = (area)(distance travelled by centroid)

Hence, if we revolve the triangle about the y axis, we require the volume of revolution generated.

The triangle AOC will produce a cone of radius b and height 0A. This has a volume.

$$\tfrac{1}{3}\pi b^2 (0A)$$

Similarly, the triangle BOC will produce a volume of revolution equal to

$$\tfrac{1}{3}\pi b^2 (0B)$$

If these two volumes are subtracted from each other, we have the required volume of revolution produced by revolving triangle ABC about the y axis. Therefore,

$$\text{Volume of revolution for triangle } ABC = \tfrac{1}{3}\pi b^2(0A) - \tfrac{1}{3}\pi b^2(0B)$$

$$= \tfrac{1}{3}\pi b^2(0A - 0B)$$

$$= \tfrac{1}{3}\pi b^2(AB)$$

Hence, using the theorem of Pappus, we have

$$\tfrac{1}{3}\pi b^2(AB) = (\text{area of triangle } ABC)(2\pi\bar{x})$$

$$= [\tfrac{1}{2}b(AB)](2\pi\bar{x})$$

which gives

$$\bar{x} = \frac{b}{3}$$

As we chose any side of the triangle to be placed along the y axis, it follows that the centroid will lie on a line parallel to the side and at a distance of one-third the perpendicular height from it. Figure 9-5 illustrates the position of the centroid with respect to the sides.

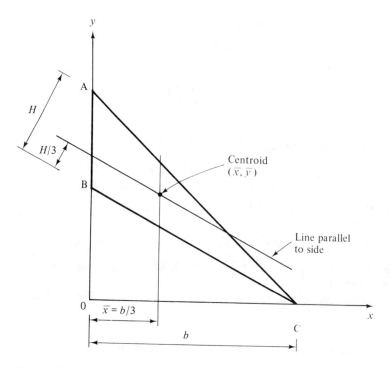

Figure 9-5

Example 9-3-1 Find the position of the centroid of a triangular plate whose sides are 6 m, 4 m and 3 m in length.

SOLUTION As the centroid of a triangle lies on a line one-third of the perpendicular height from a side, we calculate the distance of this line from *two* sides. Where these lines intersect will be the position of the centroid.

We can obtain the perpendicular height of the apex of the triangle from any particular side by using the area relationship:

$$\text{Area of triangle} = \sqrt{s(s-a)(s-b)(s-c)} = \tfrac{1}{2} \cdot \text{base} \cdot \text{height}$$

where, in this case

$$s = (6+4+3)/2$$

$$= 6.5$$

Hence

$$\text{Area} = \sqrt{6.5(6.5-6)(6.5-4)(6.5-3)}$$

$$= 5.3327 \, \text{m}^2$$

Hence for the 6 m side, the apex will be at a perpendicular height of h metres given by

$$\tfrac{1}{2}(6)(h) = 5.3327$$

$$\Rightarrow \qquad h = 1.7776 \, \text{m}$$

Hence the centroid lies on a line at a distance 0.5925 m from the side and parallel to it.

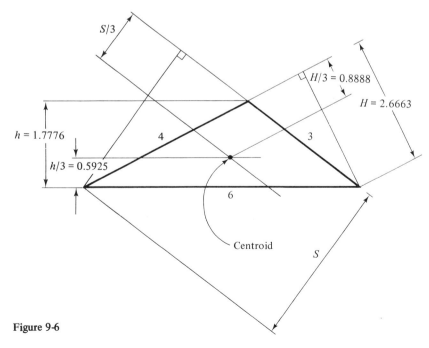

Figure 9-6

Consider the 4 m side. We have by using the area formula that

$$\tfrac{1}{2}(4)(H) = 5.3327$$

$$\Rightarrow \qquad H = 2.6663 \text{ m}$$

which is the perpendicular height from the 4 m side to the corner opposite this side. Hence the centroid lies on a line at a distance 0.8888 m away from the 4 m side and parallel to it.

Figure 9-6 illustrates the two lines, one parallel to the 6 m side and the other to the 4 m side. Where these lines intersect is the position of the centroid.

9-4 THE CENTROID OF A SECTOR OF A CIRCLE

Consider a sector of a circle of angle 2α. Let the sector be positioned so that its centreline lies along the x axis. Consider a small elemental sector of angle $\delta\theta$, as shown in Fig. 9-7. The area of this element is given by $\tfrac{1}{2}r^2(\delta\theta)$, where r is the radius. Let δA be this elemental area, which can be considered to be a triangle. Hence

$$\delta A = \tfrac{1}{2}r^2(\delta\theta)$$

$$\Rightarrow \qquad \frac{\delta A}{\delta\theta} = \tfrac{1}{2}r^2$$

Let $\delta\theta \to 0$ and we have

$$\frac{\mathrm{d}A}{\mathrm{d}\theta} = \tfrac{1}{2}r^2$$

which is the slope equation for the function area A. Therefore, applying reverse differentiation, we have

$$A = \int_{-\alpha}^{\alpha} \tfrac{1}{2}r^2 \; \mathrm{d}\theta$$

and since $\tfrac{1}{2}r^2$ is *constant* it can be brought outside the integral sign to give

$$A = \tfrac{1}{2}r^2 \int_{-\alpha}^{\alpha} \mathrm{d}\theta$$

$$= \tfrac{1}{2}r^2 (\theta)]_{-\alpha}^{\alpha}$$

$$= \tfrac{1}{2}r^2 [\alpha - (-\alpha)]$$

$$= \alpha r^2$$

Area of **sector** is αr^2

The centroid of a triangle lies one-third along the perpendicular height from a side. Thus, the centroid of this triangular element lies at two-thirds of the radius from the origin. The first moment of area about the y axis for the element is $x(\tfrac{1}{2}r^2\delta\theta)$. By projecting the length $\tfrac{2}{3}r$ onto the x axis we have

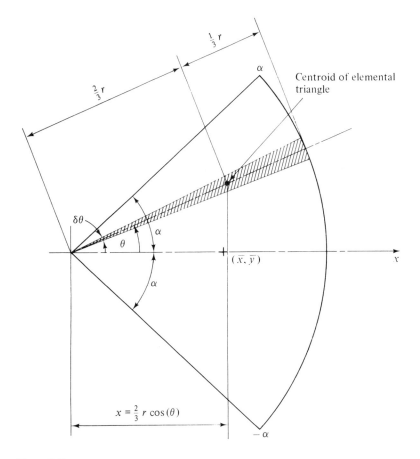

Figure 9-7

$$x = \tfrac{2}{3}r(\cos\theta)$$

Let this first moment of area for the element be δA_y. Hence

$$\delta A_y = \tfrac{1}{3}r^3 \cos\theta \cdot \delta\theta$$

on substituting $x = \tfrac{2}{3}r(\cos\theta)$. Therefore, dividing both sides by $\delta\theta$ and taking limits as $\delta\theta \to 0$, we have

$$\lim_{\delta\theta \to 0}\left(\frac{\delta A_y}{\delta\theta}\right) = \frac{\mathrm{d}A_y}{\mathrm{d}\theta} = \tfrac{1}{3}r^3 \cos\theta$$

which is a slope equation for the function A_y. Therefore, using integration, we have

$$A_y = \int_{-\alpha}^{\alpha} \tfrac{1}{3}r^3 \cos\theta \cdot \mathrm{d}\theta$$

$$= [\tfrac{1}{3}r^3 \sin\theta]_{-\alpha}^{\alpha}$$

$$= \tfrac{1}{3}r^3 [\sin(\alpha) - \sin(-\alpha)]$$

$$= \tfrac{2}{3}r^3 \sin(\alpha)$$

Therefore, we have the **first moment of area** of a **sector** of a circle about the y axis as

$$A_y = \tfrac{2}{3}r^3 \sin(\alpha)$$

By Sec. 9-1 the centroid position $\bar{x}$ is given by A_y/area. Hence

$$\bar{x} = \frac{\tfrac{2}{3}r^3 \sin(\alpha)}{\alpha r^2}$$

$$= \tfrac{2}{3}r \cdot \frac{\sin(\alpha)}{\alpha}$$

In all problems involving the sector of a circle, it is important that the centreline of the figure is placed along the x axis.

Example 9-4-1 Find the position of the centroid of a sector of a circle of radius 2 m and angle 60°.

SOLUTION The centroid lies along the centreline of the sector. Thus, placing this centreline along the x axis gives $\bar{y} = 0$. The x coordinate of the centroid is given by

$$\bar{x} = \tfrac{2}{3}r \cdot \frac{\sin(\alpha)}{\alpha}$$

where α is half of the sector angle. In this case $\alpha = 30°$. Hence

$$\bar{x} = \tfrac{2}{3}r \cdot \frac{\sin(\pi/6)}{\pi/6}$$

The reader should note that we *must* use radians for α. Therefore, the position of the centroid for a 60° sector from a 2 m radius circle is given by

$$(\bar{x}, \bar{y}) = (1.2732, 0)$$

when placing its centreline along the x axis.

PROBLEMS

For problems 9-1 to 9-5 find the position of the centroid of the plane area defined by the curve $y = f(x)$, the x axis and the ordinates $x = 1$ and $x = 2$.

9-1 $f(x) = x^3$.

9-2 $f(x) = x^2 + 1$.

9-3 $f(x) = 2x^3 - 1$.

9-4 $f(x) = x + x^3$.

9-5 $f(x) = 1 + 2x + x^2$.

9-6 Find the position of the centroid of a semicircular thin plate of radius 3 m.

For problems **9-7** to **9-10** find the position of the centroid of the triangular plate with sides a, b, and c.

9-7 $a = 4$ m, $b = 5$ m, $c = 3$ m.

9-8 $a = 10$ m, $b = 12$ m, $c = 8$ m.

9-9 $a = 2.5$ m, $b = 4$ m, $c = 3$ m.

9-10 $a = 8$ m, $b = 3.5$ m, $c = 6$ m.

A sector with radius r and angle α is positioned so that it is symmetrical about the x axis. For problems **9-11** to **9-15** find the cartesian coordinates of its centroid.

*9-11 $r = 1$ m, $\alpha = 30°$.

*9-12 $r = 2$ m, $\alpha = 60°$.

9-13 $r = 1.5$ m, $\alpha = 1$ rad.

9-14 $r = 0.7$ m, $\alpha = 1.4$ rad.

9-15 $r = 0.05$ m, $\alpha = 1.6$ rad.

**9-16 Show that the position of the centroid of a triangle is at the intersection of the lines which bisect the angles.

**9-17 Find the position of the centroid for the area bounded by the curve $y = \sin(x)$ and the x axis, $(0 \leqslant x \leqslant \pi)$.

***9-18 Find the position of the centroid of the area bounded by the curves $y = x^{0.5}$ and $y = x^2$.

*9-19 Consider the semicircle of radius r and positioned as shown in Fig. 9-3 with respect to the cartesian axes. Show by using integration and the equation $y^2 + x^2 = r^2$ that the y coordinate of the centroid is

$$\frac{4r}{3\pi}$$

Solutions

In solutions **9-7** to **9-10** the lines are assumed parallel to the respective edges.

9-1 (1.6533, 2.4190).

9-2 (1.575, 1.78).

9-3 (1.6769, 4.5055).

9-4 (1.6254, 3.1311).

9-5 (1.5658, 3.3316).

9-6 (0, 1.2732).

9-7 The centroid is at the intersection of two lines, one 1 m from the 4 m edge and the other 0.8 m from the 5 m edge.

9-8 The centroid is at the intersection of two lines, one 2.6458 m from the 10 m edge and the other 2.204 79 m from the 12 m edge.

9-9 The centroid is at the intersection of two lines, one 0.998 74 m from the 2.5 m edge and the other 0.6242 m from the 4 m edge.

9-10 The centroid is at the intersection of two lines, one 0.811 15 m from the 8 m edge and the other 1.854 m from the 3.5 m edge.

9-11 (0.6366, 0).

9-12 (1.1027, 0).

9-13 (0.8415, 0).

9-14 (0.3285, 0).

9-15 (0.0208, 0).

9-17 ($\pi/2$, $\pi/8$).

9-18 (0.45, 0.45).

SECOND MOMENTS OF AREA

Objectives After reading this chapter you should be able to:

1. Determine the second moments of area for standard sections.
   (*a*) Sketch the incremental area in its correct position.
   (*b*) Define the second moment of area.
   (*c*) Determine the second moment of area for the incremental area.
   (*d*) Determine the second moment of area by using definite integration.
   (*e*) Determine the second moment of area of a rectangle about an edge.
   (*f*) Determine the second moment of area of a triangle about one edge.
   (*g*) Determine the second moment of area of a semicircle and a circle about a diameter.
   (*h*) Determine the second moment of area of a circle about its polar axis.
2. Use the parallel-axes theorem.
   (*a*) State the parallel-axes theorem.
   (*b*) Determine the second moment of area about an axis through the centroid parallel to an axis about which the second moment of area is known.
   (*c*) Determine the second moment of area about an axis parallel to the axis through the centroid about which the second moment of area is known.
   (*d*) Calculate the second moment of area of a composite figure.
3. Determine the polar moments of area for standard sections.
   (*a*) State the perpendicular-axes theorem.
   (*b*) Calculate the second moment of area about an axis perpendicular to an axis about which the second moment of area is known.

10-1 INTRODUCTION

Consider a rectangular plate of uniform thickness w and width b. Position this plate so that its major area lies in the xy plane with the edge of length b running along the x axis from the origin, as shown in Fig. 10-1.

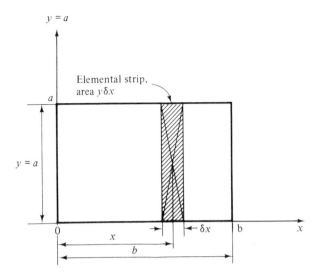

Figure 10-1

Consider an elemental strip of width δx and height y. If this strip is allowed to rotate about the y axis with an angular velocity of ω, then we have a body possessing **rotational kinetic energy**. Let the rotational kinetic energy of the strip be $\delta(\text{KE})$. Hence from engineering science we have

$$\delta(\text{KE}) = \tfrac{1}{2}(\text{mass})(\text{velocity})^2$$

$$= \tfrac{1}{2}(\text{mass})(\omega x)^2$$

since

$$\text{Velocity} = (\text{angular velocity})(\text{radius of rotation})$$

$$= \omega \cdot x$$

However,

$$\text{Mass} = (\text{density})(\text{volume})$$

$$= \rho \cdot w \cdot (\text{area of strip})$$

$$= \rho \cdot w \cdot y \cdot \delta x$$

where ρ is the density and w is the thickness of the plate. Therefore

$$\delta(\text{KE}) = \tfrac{1}{2}(\text{mass})(\omega^2 x^2)$$

$$= \tfrac{1}{2}(\rho \cdot w)(y \cdot \delta x)(\omega^2 x^2)$$

$$= \tfrac{1}{2}(\rho \cdot w \cdot \omega^2)(x^2 y \delta x)$$

On dividing both sides by δx and allowing the strip width δx to tend to zero, we have

$$\lim_{\delta x \to 0} \left(\frac{\delta(\text{KE})}{\delta x} \right) = \frac{d(\text{KE})}{dx} = \tfrac{1}{2}(\rho \cdot w \cdot \omega^2) x^2 y$$

which is a slope equation. Hence by reverse differentiation we have

$$(\text{KE}) = \tfrac{1}{2}(\rho \cdot w \cdot \omega^2) \int_0^b (x^2 y)\, dx$$

The quantity

$$\int_0^b (x^2 y)\, dx$$

is called the second moment of area about the y axis – in this case, about the edge of the rectangular plate with one side of length b.

Example 10-1-1 Find the second moment of area of a rectangular plate whose sides are of length a and b about an axis along one edge of the plate.

SOLUTION If we position the rectangular plate as in Fig. 10-1, then the second moment of area about the edge of length a is given by (since $y = a$)

$$\int_0^b (x^2 a)\, dx = \left[\frac{x^3}{3} \cdot a \right]_0^b$$

$$= \left(\frac{b^3}{3} - \frac{0^3}{3} \right) \cdot a = \frac{a \cdot b^3}{3}$$

$$= \frac{A \cdot b^2}{3} \ (\text{units})^4 \qquad \text{where } A \text{ is the area } a \cdot b$$

Example 10-1-1 illustrated that the second moment of area of the rectangular plate of sides of length a and b, about one edge, in that case the edge a, was $a \cdot b^3/3$. This standard result along with others to be developed in this chapter will be brought together in Table A-6 within the appendix.

In general

$$\int_a^b x^2 y\, dx = \lim_{\delta x \to 0} \sum_{x=a}^{x=b} x^2 y\, \delta x$$

where $x^2 y \cdot \delta x$ is the **second moment of area** of the **elemental strip** about y axis. We also notice that

$$x^2 y\, \delta x \qquad \text{can be written as} \qquad x^2 (\text{area of strip})$$

Example 10-1-2 Find the second moment of area of a rectangle with sides a and b about an axis parallel to side a and through the centroid.

SOLUTION Let the rectangle be positioned on the xy plane so that the y axis passes through the centroid and is parallel to the side a, as shown in Fig. 10-2.

Let an element of width δx be parallel to the y axis. Let δI_y be the second moment of area of the element about the y axis. Hence

$$\delta I_y = (x^2)(\text{area of element})$$

$$= (x^2)(y \cdot \delta x)$$

On dividing both sides by δx, and letting $\delta x \to 0$, we have

$$\lim_{\delta x \to 0} \left(\frac{\delta I_y}{\delta x} \right) = \frac{dI_y}{dx} = x^2 y$$

which is a slope equation for the function I_y, the **second moment of area** of the rectangle about the y axis. Hence on reverse differentiation we have

$$I_y = \int_{-b/2}^{b/2} x^2 a \, dx \qquad \text{since } y = a \text{ in this case}$$

Hence

$$I_y = \left[\frac{ax^3}{3} \right]_{-b/2}^{b/2}$$

$$= \left(\frac{(b/2)^3}{3} - \frac{(-b/2)^3}{3} \right) \cdot a$$

$$= \frac{b^3 a}{12}$$

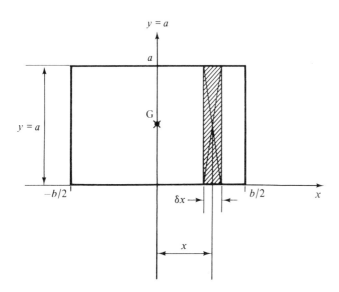

Figure 10-2

Hence the **second moment of area** of a **rectangle** about an axis through its centroid and parallel to edge a is given by

$$I_y = \frac{b^3 a}{12}$$

10-2 THE SECOND MOMENT OF AREA OF A TRIANGLE

Consider a triangle ABC with one edge positioned along the y axis, as shown in Fig. 10-3. Let δx be the width of this strip and k be its height. If we wish to find the second moment of area of this strip about one edge, we use

$$x^2 (\text{area of strip})$$

The strip can be considered to be a rectangle and hence the area of the strip is

$$k \cdot \delta x$$

The length k can be found by using **similar triangles**; that is

$$\frac{H}{b} = \frac{H-x}{k}$$

$\Rightarrow$
$$k = \left(\frac{H-x}{H}\right)(b)$$

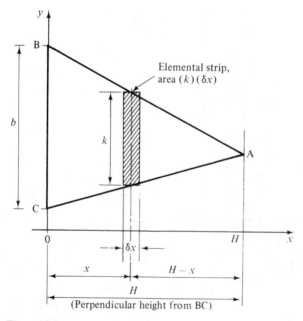

Figure 10-3

Hence the second moment of area of the triangle about the edge BC is given by

$$\sum_{x=0}^{x=H} x^2 \text{(area of strip)} = \sum_{x=0}^{x=H} x^2 \left(\frac{H-x}{H}\right) b \cdot \delta x$$

This implies as $\delta x \to 0$ that we have

$$\lim_{\delta x \to 0} \sum_{x=0}^{x=H} x^2 \cdot \frac{H-x}{H} \cdot b \cdot \delta x = \int_0^H \left[x^2 \left(\frac{H-x}{H}\right) b \right] dx$$

$$= \frac{b}{H} \int_0^H (x^2 H - x^3) dx$$

$$= \frac{b}{H} \left(\frac{x^3}{3} H - \frac{x^4}{4} \right) \Bigg|_0^H$$

$$= \frac{bH^3}{12}$$

Therefore the **second movement of area** of a **triangle** about one edge is

$$\frac{(\text{Length of edge})(\text{perpendicular height})^3}{12} = \frac{bH^3}{12}$$

Example 10-2-1 Find the second movement of area of a triangle with sides 3 m, 4.5 m, and 7 m about each edge in turn.

SOLUTION The second moment of area of a triangle about an edge is given by

$$\frac{(\text{Length of edge})(\text{perpendicular height})^3}{12}$$

To find the perpendicular height from each edge to the respective apex, we use the formulae for area:

$$\text{Area of a triangle} = \tfrac{1}{2}(\text{base})(\text{height})$$

$$= \sqrt{s(s-a)(s-b)(s-c)}$$

$$= \sqrt{7.25(7.25-3)(7.25-4.5)(7.25-7)}$$

$$= 4.6026 \, \text{m}^2$$

This relationship enables us to calculate the perpendicular height of the triangle from each side.

Thus, for the 3 m side, we have a perpendicular height of 3.0684 m and on using the second moment of area formula we have

$$\text{Second moment of area about 3 m edge} = \frac{(3)(3.0684)^3}{12}$$

$$= 7.2223 \, \text{m}^4$$

For the 4.5 m side, we have a perpendicular height of 2.0456 m, and hence

$$\text{Second moment of area about 4.5 m edge} = \frac{(4.5)(2.0456)^3}{12}$$

$$= 3.2098 \, \text{m}^4$$

For the 7 m, we have a perpendicular height of 1.3150 m. Hence we have

$$\text{Second moment of area about 7 m side} = \frac{(7)(1.3150)^3}{12}$$

$$= 1.3265 \, \text{m}^4$$

10-3 SECOND MOMENTS OF AREAS OF CIRCLES

Consider a circle of radius r being positioned so that its centre lies at the origin of the cartesian coordinate system. Figure 10-4 illustrates this positioning and shows an element in the form of a circular hoop of mean radius x and thickness δx.

The second moment of area of this element about the z axis, which passes along the polar axis of the circle, is given by

$$x^2 (\text{area of element}) = x^2 (2\pi \cdot x \cdot \delta x)$$

$$= 2\pi \cdot x^3 \cdot \delta x$$

Summation of these elements gives

$$\sum_{x=0}^{x=r} 2\pi \cdot x^3 \cdot \delta x$$

On letting $\delta x \to 0$ we have

$$\lim_{\delta x \to 0} \sum_{x=0}^{x=r} 2\pi \cdot x^3 \cdot \delta x = \int_0^r 2\pi x^3 \, dx$$

$$= 2\pi \left(\frac{x^4}{4} \right) \Bigg]_0^r$$

$$= 2\pi \left(\frac{r^4}{4} - \frac{0^4}{4} \right)$$

$$= 2\pi \frac{r^4}{4}$$

$$= \pi \frac{r^4}{2}$$

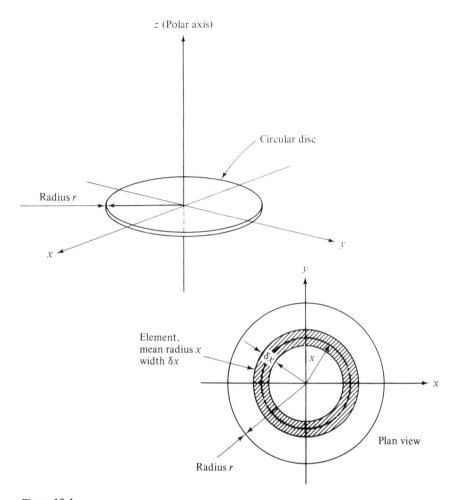

Figure 10-4

Let A be the total area (i.e. $A = \pi r^2$) and, hence, the second moment of area of a circle about its polar axis is

$$\pi \frac{r^4}{2} = A \cdot \frac{r^2}{2}$$

The quantity

$$r^2/2 = k^2$$

where k is the **radius of gyration**.

Example 10-3-1 Find the second moment of area of a circle of radius 3 m about its polar axis and calculate the radius of gyration.

SOLUTION Second moment of area of a circle about its polar axis is given by $A \cdot r^2/2$ where A is the area and r is the radius (3 m). Thus

$$A \cdot \frac{r^2}{2} = \pi(3^2)\frac{(3)^2}{2}$$

$$= 127.2345 \text{ m}^4$$

For the radius of gyration, we have

$$k^2 = r^2/2$$

$$= 3^2/2$$

$$= 4.5$$

Hence k, the radius of gyration, is 2.1213 m.

Consider a semicircle with its diameter along the x axis and its centre at the origin of the cartesian coordinate system. Figure 10-5 illustrates this positioning with an elemental area of mean radius x and width δx.

The second moment of area of the element about the polar axis, that is the z axis, is given by

$$(x^2)(\text{area of element})$$

The area of the element is $\pi \cdot x \cdot \delta x$ and we have on summation that the total second moment of area of elements about the polar axis is

$$\sum_{x=0}^{x=r} x^2 (\pi \cdot x \cdot \delta x) = \sum_{x=0}^{x=r} \pi \cdot x^3 \cdot \delta x$$

Therefore, on taking the limit as $\delta x \to 0$, we have

$$\lim_{\delta x \to 0} \sum_{x=0}^{x=r} \pi x^3 \cdot \delta x = \int_0^r \pi \cdot x^3 \, dx$$

$$= \pi \cdot \left(\frac{x^4}{4}\right)\Big]_0^r$$

$$= \pi \cdot \frac{r^4}{4}$$

Hence **second moment of area** of a semicircle about its *polar* axis is given by

$$\pi \cdot \frac{r^4}{4} = A \cdot \frac{r^2}{2}$$

where A is the area and $A = \pi \cdot r^2/2$.

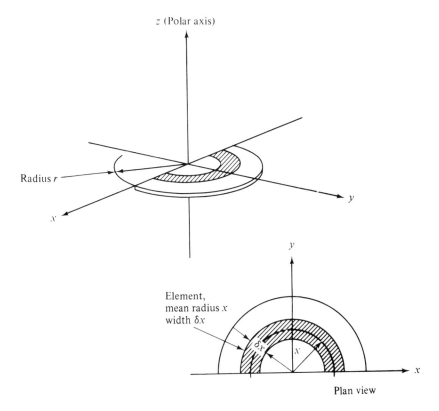

Figure 10-5

Example 10-3-2 Find the radius of gyration of a semicircle of radius 3 m about its polar axis. State the value of the second moment of area about the same axis.

SOLUTION The second moment of area is given by $A \cdot k^2$ where A is the area of the semicircle and k the radius of gyration. Therefore

$$Ak^2 = A \cdot \frac{r^2}{2} \qquad \text{(about the } polar \text{ axis)}$$

$$= 4.5A$$

This implies that $k^2 = 4.5$ and that

$$k = 2.1213 \, \text{m}$$

The second moment of area about the polar axis is

$$A \cdot \frac{r^2}{2} = \frac{\pi \cdot r^4}{4}$$

$$= 63.6172 \, \text{m}^4$$

The next example, Example 10-3-3, contains some trigonometric manipulation and some difficult integration by substitution. The reader may, on his first reading of this chapter, omit this example and note only the result.

Example 10-3-3 Find the second moment of area of the semicircle, radius r, shown in Fig. 10-6 about the y axis.

SOLUTION Consider a rectangular strip of width δx and height y, which is governed by the curve. The circle has an equation with respect to cartesian coordinates given by

$$x^2 + y^2 = r^2$$

From this, we can obtain an equation for y, that is,

$$y = \sqrt{r^2 - x^2}$$

The second moment of area of the rectangular strip about the y axis is given by

$$x^2 (\text{area of strip}) = x^2 (y \cdot \delta x)$$

$$= x^2 (\sqrt{r^2 - x^2})(\delta x)$$

Let δI_y be the second moment of area about the y axis for the rectangular strip. Then,

$$\delta I_y = x^2 (\sqrt{r^2 - x^2})(\delta x)$$

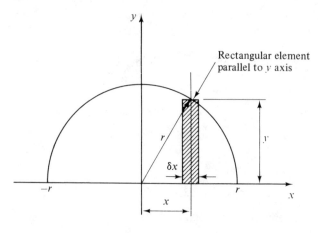

Figure 10-6 Semicircle: by Pythagoras' theorem, $r^2 = x^2 + y^2$, so $y = \sqrt{r^2 - x^2}$.

and on dividing both sides by δx and letting $\delta x \to 0$ we have

$$\frac{dI_y}{dx} = x^2 (\sqrt{r^2 - x^2})$$

Hence, as we have a slope equation, we can integrate to find I_y, the second moment of area about the y axis. Therefore

$$I_y = \int_{-r}^{r} x^2 \sqrt{r^2 - x^2} \cdot dx$$

This integral can be solved by substitution. Let

$$x = r \cdot \cos(\theta)$$

$$\frac{dx}{d\theta} = -r \cdot \sin(\theta)$$

or

$$dx = -r \cdot \sin(\theta) \cdot d\theta$$

We change the limits as well:
At $x = r$, we have

$$r = r \cdot \cos(\theta)$$

or

$$1 = \cos(\theta)$$

or

$$\theta = 0$$

At $x = -r$, we have

$$-r = r \cdot \cos(\theta)$$

or

$$-1 = \cos(\theta)$$

or

$$\theta = \pi$$

Hence the integral

$$I_y = \int_{-r}^{r} x^2 \sqrt{r^2 - x^2} \cdot dx$$

becomes

$$I_y = \int_{\pi}^{0} r^2 \cos^2(\theta) \sqrt{r^2 - r^2 \cos^2(\theta)} \cdot [-r \cdot \sin(\theta)] \, d\theta$$

$$= \int_{\pi}^{0} -r^3 \cos^2(\theta) \sqrt{r^2 [1 - \cos^2(\theta)]} \cdot \sin(\theta) d\theta$$

$$= \int_{\pi}^{0} -r^3 \cos^2(\theta) \sqrt{r^2 \sin^2(\theta)} \cdot \sin(\theta) \, d\theta$$

$$= \int_{\pi}^{0} -r^4 \cos^2(\theta) \cdot \sin^2(\theta) \, d\theta$$

Since $\sin(2\theta) = 2\cos(\theta)\sin(\theta)$ we have

$$\cos^2(\theta) \cdot \sin^2(\theta) = \tfrac{1}{4}\sin^2(2\theta)$$

and since $\cos(2A) = 1 - 2\sin^2(A)$ we have on replacing A by 2θ that

$$\cos(4\theta) = 1 - 2\sin^2(2\theta)$$

or

$$\sin^2(2\theta) = \frac{1 - \cos(4\theta)}{2}$$

Hence

$$\sin^2(\theta) \cdot \cos^2(\theta) = \tfrac{1}{4}\sin^2(2\theta)$$

$$= \frac{1}{4}\left(\frac{1 - \cos(4\theta)}{2}\right)$$

$$= \tfrac{1}{8}[1 - \cos(4\theta)]$$

Substituting this into the integral gives

$$I_y = \int_\pi^0 -r^4 \cdot \left(\frac{1 - \cos(4\theta)}{8}\right) d\theta$$

$$= \frac{-r^4}{8}\int_\pi^0 [1 - \cos(4\theta)]\, d\theta$$

$$= \frac{-r^4}{8}\left(\theta - \frac{\sin(4\theta)}{4}\right)\bigg]_\pi^0$$

$$= \frac{\pi r^4}{8}$$

Therefore, the second moment of area of a semicircle about the y axis is $\pi r^4/8$.

Example 10-3-3 developed a useful result for a semicircle which we shall use later in the section on the perpendicular-axes theorem.

10-4 RELATIONSHIP BETWEEN SECOND MOMENT OF AREA AND MOMENT OF INERTIA

The **moment of inertia** of a continuous body is defined as Mk^2 where M is its total mass and k is the radius of gyration. Hence, if I denotes the moment of inertia, we can transpose

$$I = Mk^2$$

to give

$$k^2 = \frac{I}{M}$$

Thus since

$$\text{Second moment of area} = Ak^2$$

we have

$$\text{Second moment of area} = A\left(\frac{I}{M}\right)$$

from which we can obtain the moment of inertia.

Example 10-4-1 A circular disc of radius 0.5 m is rotating about its polar axis at 30 rad/s. If this disc has a total mass of 1.2 kg, find the moment of inertia about the polar axis. Hence evaluate the kinetic energy of rotation.

SOLUTION For a circular disc, the second moment of area about the polar axis is given by

$$A \cdot \frac{r^2}{2} = A \cdot \frac{0.5^2}{2}$$

$$= A \cdot k^2$$

Hence the radius of gyration squared is $k^2 = 0.125$. Thus the moment of inertia about the polar axis is

$$Mk^2 = 1.2(0.125)$$

$$= 0.15 \text{ kg m}^2$$

Rotational kinetic energy is given by $\frac{1}{2}I\omega^2$ and hence

$$\text{Rotational KE} = \frac{1}{2}(0.15)(30)^2$$

$$= 67.5 \text{ joules}$$

10-5 THE PERPENDICULAR-AXES THEOREM

When calculating the second moment of area about a *polar* axis, usually the z axis, we require the distance from the axis to the elemental area in terms of a radius, denoted r. Figure 10-7 illustrates a plane figure in the xy plane with an elemental area, distance r from the z axis.

By Pythagoras we have

$$r^2 = x^2 + y^2$$

and hence the second moment of area of the element about the z axis is given by

$$r^2 (\text{area of element}) = (x^2 + y^2)(\text{area of element})$$

Let the area of the element be δA. Then the second moment of area about the z axis of the element is given by

$$r^2 \cdot \delta A = x^2 \cdot \delta A + y^2 \cdot \delta A$$

Summing both sides and allowing the area of the element to tend to zero gives

$$\lim_{\delta A \to 0} \sum r^2 \delta A = \lim_{\delta A \to 0} \sum x^2 \delta A + \lim_{\delta A \to 0} \sum y^2 \delta A$$

which implies that

$$\begin{matrix} \text{Second moment of} \\ \text{area about } z \text{ axis} \end{matrix} = \begin{matrix} \text{Second moment of} \\ \text{area about } x \text{ axis} \end{matrix} + \begin{matrix} \text{Second moment of} \\ \text{area about } y \text{ axis} \end{matrix}$$

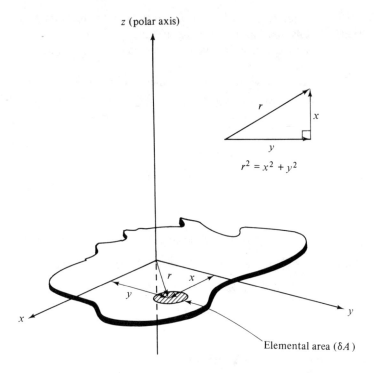

Figure 10-7

In symbols

$$I_z = I_x + I_y$$

Example 10-5-1 Find the second moment of area of a circle, radius r, about its diameter.

SOLUTION From Sec. 10-3 we have the second moment of area of a circle about the polar axis, z axis, given by

$$\frac{\pi \cdot r^4}{2} = I_z$$

Hence by the **perpendicular-axes theorem** we have

$$I_z = I_x + I_y$$

$$= 2(\text{second moment of area about diameter of circle})$$

Hence

$$I_z = \frac{\pi (r)^4}{2} = 2(I_{\text{dia}})$$

$$\Rightarrow \qquad \frac{\pi (r)^4}{4} = I_{\text{dia}}$$

Example 10-5-2 Find the second moment of area of a rectangular plate, 2 m × 3 m, about an axis perpendicular to the plate and passing through one of the corners.

SOLUTION Let the edge of the plate with a 2 m length lie along the x axis and the 3 m length along the y axis. Let one corner be positioned at the origin. Figure 10-8 illustrates the plate in this position.

By Sec. 10-1 we have that the second moment of area about an edge a for a rectangular plate $a \times b$ is given by $A \cdot b^2/3$, where A is the area of the plate. Hence

$$I_x = \frac{(6)(2)^2}{3} = 8 \, \text{m}^4$$

$$I_y = \frac{(6)(3)^2}{3} = 18 \, \text{m}^4$$

By the perpendicular-axes theorem we have

$$I_z = I_x + I_y$$

$$= 8 + 18$$

$$= 26 \, \text{m}^4$$

Therefore the second moment of area of this rectangular plate about a polar axis through one corner is $26 \, \text{m}^4$.

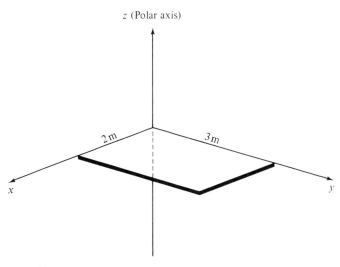

z (Polar axis)

2 m

3 m

x

y'

Figure 10-8

Example 10-5-3 Find the second moment of area of a semicircle positioned as shown in Fig. 10-6 about the base or diameter.

SOLUTION From the perpendicular-axes theorem, we have

$$I_z = I_y + I_x$$

and we have from Example 10-3-3 that

$$I_y = \frac{\pi r^4}{8}$$

and from Sec. 10-3 that

$$I_z = \frac{\pi r^4}{4}$$

Hence

$$I_z = I_y + I_x$$

$$\Rightarrow \qquad \frac{\pi r^4}{4} = \frac{\pi r^4}{8} + I_x$$

or

$$I_x = \frac{\pi r^4}{4} - \frac{\pi r^4}{8}$$

$$= \frac{\pi r^4}{8}$$

Therefore the second moment of area of a semicircle about a diameter is $\pi r^4/8$, precisely half that for a circle.

10-6 THE PARALLEL-AXES THEOREM

Consider the area shown in Fig. 10-9. Let G be the centroid of the area A. Let the axis passing through the centroid be on the y axis. Let CC′ be the axis through the centroid and $I_{CC'}$ be the second moment of area of this area A about CC′. Let BB′ be *any* parallel to the axis CC′ and let $I_{BB'}$ be the second moment of area of area A about BB′.

Consider a rectangular element of height y and width δx. Let $\delta I_{BB'}$ be the second moment of area of this element about BB′. Then we have

$$\delta I_{BB'} = (x + b)^2 (\text{area of element})$$

$$= (x + b)^2 (y \cdot \delta x)$$

On dividing both sides by δx, and letting $\delta x \to 0$, we have

$$\lim_{\delta x \to 0} \left(\frac{\delta I_{BB'}}{\delta x} \right) = \frac{d I_{BB'}}{dx} = (x + b)^2 (y)$$

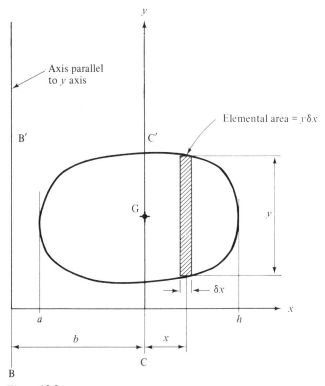

Figure 10-9

which is a slope equation for the function $I_{BB'}$. Hence using reverse differentiation we have

$$I_{BB'} = \int_a^h (x+b)^2 (y \cdot dx)$$

$$= \int_a^h (x^2 + 2xb + b^2)(y \cdot dx)$$

$$= \int_a^h (x^2 y + 2xby + b^2 y) dx$$

$$= \int_a^h x^2 y \cdot dx + \int_a^h 2bxy \cdot dx + \int_a^h b^2 y \cdot dx$$

$$= \int_a^h x^2 y \cdot dx + 2b \int_a^h xy \cdot dx + b^2 \int_a^h y \cdot dx$$

Since $\int_a^h xy \cdot dx$ is the first moment of area about CC', the axis through the centroid we have

$$\int_a^h xy \cdot dx = (\text{area})(\bar{x})$$

But $\bar{x} = 0$ since x coordinate of the centroid is zero. Therefore

$$(\text{area})(\bar{x}) = 0 \qquad \Rightarrow \qquad \int_a^h xy \cdot dx = 0$$

Hence we have

$$I_{BB'} = \int_a^h x^2 y \cdot dx + b^2 \int_a^h y \cdot dx$$

and since $\int_a^h y \cdot dx$ is the area of the Fig. 10-9, we have

$$I_{BB'} = \int_a^h x^2 y \cdot dx + b^2 \cdot A$$

or

$$I_{BB'} = I_{CC'} + b^2 \cdot A$$

Example 10-6-1 A T section is shown in Fig. 10-10. Calculate the second moment of area of the figure about the axis XX'.

SOLUTION The area shown in Fig. 10-10 can be considered as two rectangles.

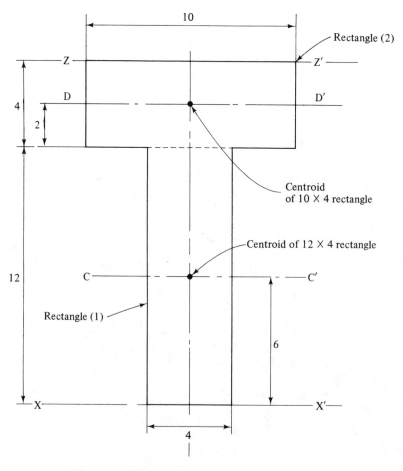

Figure 10-10 A T section (dimensions in centimetres).

Consider rectangle (1):

$$\text{Area} = 12 \times 4 = 48 \text{ cm}^2$$

$$I_{CC'} = 48\left(\frac{12^2}{12}\right) = 576 \text{ cm}^4 \qquad \text{by Example 10-1-2}$$

Hence by the parallel-axes theorem we have

$$I_{XX'} = I_{CC'} + A \cdot b^2$$

$$\Rightarrow \qquad I_{XX'} = 576 + (48)(6^2)$$

$$= 2304 \text{ cm}^4$$

Consider rectangle (2):

$$\text{Area} = 10 \times 4 = 40 \text{ cm}^2$$

$$I_{DD'} = 40\left(\frac{4^2}{12}\right) = 53\tfrac{1}{3} \text{ cm}^4$$

Hence by the parallel-axes theorem we have

$$I_{XX'} = I_{DD'} + A \cdot b^2$$

$$= 53\tfrac{1}{3} + (40)(14^2)$$

$$= 7893\tfrac{1}{3} \text{ cm}^4$$

Hence for the *composite* figure we have that the

Second moment of area about XX' is $7893\tfrac{1}{3} + 2304 = 10\,197\tfrac{1}{3} \text{ cm}^4$

Example 10-6-2 Find by using the parallel-axes theorem the second moment of area for the area shown in Fig. 10-10 about the ZZ' axis.

SOLUTION Again consider the two rectangles. For rectangle (1) we have

$$I_{CC'} = \frac{(4)(12)^3}{12}$$

$$= 576 \text{ cm}^4$$

Hence by the parallel-axes theorem we have

$$I_{ZZ'} = I_{CC'} + Ad^2$$

$$= 576 + 48(10)^2$$

$$= 5376 \text{ cm}^4$$

For rectangle (2) we use

$$I_{ZZ'} = \frac{a \cdot b^3}{3}$$

$$= \frac{(10)(4)^3}{3}$$

$$= 213\tfrac{1}{3} \text{ cm}^4$$

Therefore, for the composite figure we have

$$I_{zz'} = 5376 + 213\tfrac{1}{3}$$

$$= 5589\tfrac{1}{3} \text{ cm}^4$$

PROBLEMS

For problems **10-1** to **10-5** find the second moment of area of a thin rectangular plate with sides a and b about the edge a.

10-1 $a = 2$ m, $b = 4$ m.

10-2 $a = 3$ m, $b = 1$ m.

10-3 $a = 4.5$ m, $b = 1.2$ m.

10-4 $a = 5$ m, $b = 1.6$ m.

10-5 $a = 2.6$ m, $b = 3.7$ m.

For problems **10-6** to **10-10** find the second moment of area of a thin rectangular plate with sides a and b about an axis parallel to the side a and through the centroid.

10-6 $a = 2$ m, $b = 4$ m.

10-7 $a = 3$ m, $b = 1$ m.

10-8 $a = 4.5$ m, $b = 1.2$ m.

10-9 $a = 5$ m, $b = 1.6$ m.

10-10 $a = 2.6$ m, $b = 3.7$ m.

For problems **10-11** to **10-14** find the second moment of area of a triangle whose sides are a, b, and c, about the edge b.

10-11 $a = 2$ m, $b = 3$ m, $c = 4$ m.

10-12 $a = 1.5$ m, $b = 2.3$ m, $c = 2.5$ m.

10-13 $a = 3$ m, $b = 4$ m, $c = 5$ m.

10-14 $a = 0.5$ m, $b = 0.7$ m, $c = 0.9$ m.

For problems **10-15** to **10-18** find the second moment of area of a circle of radius r metres about its polar axis.

10-15 $r = 1.5$ m.

10-16 $r = 2.0$ m.

10-17 $r = 4.9$ m.

10-18 $r = 100$ m.

For problems **10-19** and **10-20** find the radius of gyration for a disc of radius r metres spinning about its polar axis.

10-19 $r = 1.5$ m.

10-20 $r = 4.9$ m.

For problems **10-21** and **10-22** find the radius of gyration of semicircle of radius r metres spinning about its polar axis.

10-21 $r = 1.5$ m.

10-22 $r = 4.9$ m.

*10-23 A circular disc of radius 0.3 m is rotating about its polar axis at 40 rad/s. If this disc has a total mass of 1.4 kg, find the moment of inertia about the polar axis. Hence evaluate the kinetic energy of rotation.

For problems **10-24** and **10-25** evaluate the second moment of area of a circle of radius r metres about its diameter by using the perpendicular-axes theorem.

10-24 $r = 1.5$ m.

10-25 $r = 4.9$ m.

*10-26 Find the second moment of area of a rectangular plate with dimensions 4 m and 3 m, about an axis perpendicular to the plate and passing through one of the corners.

For problems **10-27** to **10-30** find the second moment of area of the given composite figure about the axis XX′. The composite figures are shown in Fig. 10-11.

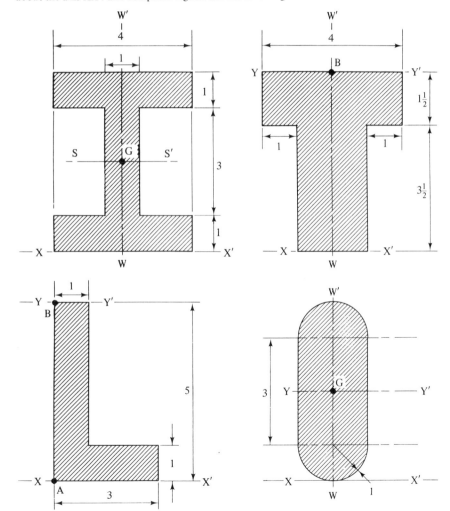

Figure 10-11 Sections for use in problems (dimensions in centimetres).

**10-27 The I section.

**10-28 The T section.

**10-29 The L section.

***10-30 The section with semicircular ends.

****10-31 Prove that the second moment of area of a semicircle about a diameter is $\pi r^4 /8$.

**10-32 Find the second moment of area of the L shape in Fig. 10-11 about an axis through the point A and perpendicular to the plane of the figure.

**10-33 Calculate the second moment of area of the L shape in Fig. 10-11 about the axis YY'.

**10-34 Calculate the second moment of area of the L shape in Fig. 10-11 about an axis through the point B and perpendicular to the plane of the figure.

For problems **10-35** to **10-37** find the second moment of area for the I section shown in Fig. 10-11 about the given axis.

**10-35 Axis WW'.

**10-36 Axis SS'.

**10-37 An axis through the point G and perpendicular to the plane of the figure.

For problems **10-38** to **10-40** find the second moment of area for the T section shown in Fig. 10-11 about the given axis.

**10-38 Axis WW'.

**10-39 Axis YY'.

**10-40 An axis through the point B perpendicular to the plane of the figure.

For problems **10-41** to **10-43** calculate the second moment of area for the area with semicircular ends shown in Fig. 10-11 about the given axis.

***10-41 Axis WW'.

***10-42 Axis YY'.

***10-43 Axis through the point G perpendicular to the plane of the figure.

Solutions

10-1 $42.6667 \, m^4$.

10-2 $1 \, m^4$.

10-3 $2.592 \, m^4$.

10-4 $6.8267 \, m^4$.

10-5 $43.8993 \, m^4$.

10-6 $10.6667 \, m^4$.

10-7 $0.25 \, m^4$.

10-8 $0.648 \, m^4$.

10-9 $1.7067 \, m^4$.

10-10 $10.9748 \, m^4$.

10-11 $1.8155 \, m^4$.

10-12 $0.6133 \, m^4$.

10-13 $9 \, m^4$.

10-14 $0.00718 \, m^4$.

10-15 7.9522 m^4.

10-16 25.1327 m^4.

10-17 905.5328 m^4.

10-18 157 079 632.7 m^4.

10-19 1.0607 m.

10-20 3.4648 m.

10-21 1.0607 m.

10-22 3.4648 m.

10-23 0.063, 50.4 J.

10-24 3.9761 m^4.

10-25 452.7664 m^4.

10-26 100 m^4.

10-27 103.67 cm^4.

10-28 138.08 cm^4.

10-29 42.33 cm^4.

10-30 73.49 cm^4.

10-31 No entry for this in manuscript

10-32 52.67 cm^4.

10-33 82.33 cm^4.

10-34 92.67 cm^4.

10-35 10.9167 cm^4.

10-36 34.9167 cm^4.

10-37 45.8334 cm^4.

10-38 10.33 cm^4.

10-39 85.58 cm^4.

10-40 95.92 cm^4.

10-41 2.7854 cm^4.

10-42 16.354 cm^4.

10-43 19.1394 cm^4.

FIRST-ORDER DIFFERENTIAL EQUATIONS

Objectives After reading this chapter you should be able to:

1. Determine and sketch a family of curves given its derivative.
   (*a*) Define a family of curves.
   (*b*) Find the differential equation associated with the family of curves.
   (*c*) Determine a particular curve belonging to a family given the coordinates of one point on that curve.
2. Solve first-order equations of the type $dy/dx = f(x)$.
   (*a*) Find the general solution to the differential equation $dy/dx = f(x)$ and relate it to the concept of a family of curves.
   (*b*) Define a boundary condition.
   (*c*) Find a particular solution to the differential equation $dy/dx = f(x)$ given a boundary condition.
3. Solve first-order equations of the type $dQ/dt = kQ$ where k is a constant.
   (*a*) Find the general solution to the differential equation $dQ/dt = kQ$ and relate it to the concept of a family of curves.
   (*b*) Find a particular solution to differential equations of the form $dQ/dt = kQ$ given a boundary condition.
   (*c*) Verify the solution of the differential equation $dQ/dt = kQ$ with a boundary condition by using the principles of differentiation.
4. Derive differential equations of the form $dQ/dt = kQ$ from suitable rate-of-change problems.
   (*a*) Derive differential equations of the form $dQ/dt = kQ$ from engineering problems.
   (*b*) Solve the equations derived as in 4(*a*).

11-1 INTRODUCTION

In Chapter 7 we found by using indefinite integration that an arbitrary constant always appears. For example, if
$$y = \int 2x \, dx$$

then
$$y = x^2 + C$$

where C is an arbitrary constant. The constant C, being arbitrary, can take on any value. We do not know the value of the constant at this point, and as a result we have an infinite number of curves defined by

$$y = x^2 + C$$

Figure 11-1 illustrates some of these curves with $C = -1.5, 0, 1,$ and 3.

11-2 A FAMILY OF CURVES

The set of curves which are defined by the relationship

$$y = f(x) + C$$

where C is an arbitrary constant is called a **family of curves**. Figure 11-1 illustrates one family defined by the relationship $y = x^2 + C$.

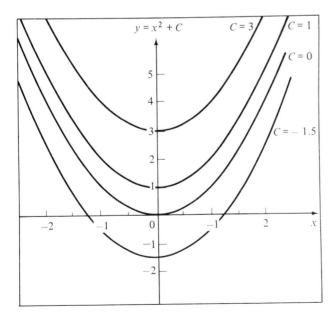

Figure 11-1

Example 11-2-1 Plot four curves from the family defined by $y = x^3 + C$.

SOLUTION Any four different values for the constant C must be chosen. Choosing

$$C = 0 \qquad \text{produces} \qquad y = x^3$$
$$C = 1 \qquad\qquad\qquad\qquad y = x^3 + 1$$
$$C = -1 \qquad\qquad\qquad\qquad y = x^3 - 1$$
and $$C = 2 \qquad\qquad\qquad\qquad y = x^3 + 2$$

Figure 11-2 illustrates the graphs of these curves for the chosen values of C.

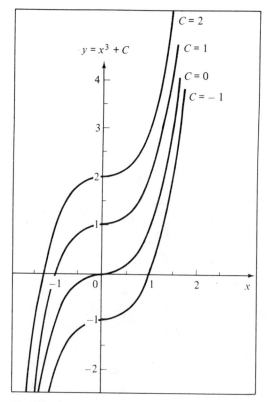

Figure 11-2

It was shown in Example 11-2-1 that if we require a particular curve in the family then we must know the constant C. This constant can be calculated if at least one point, through which the curve passes, is known.

Example 11-2-2 A family of curves is defined by $y = 2x^3 + C$. Find the particular curve which passes through the point with cartesian coordinates $(-1, 2)$.

SOLUTION Since the curve passes through the point $(-1, 2)$, we substitute $x = -1$ and $y = 2$ into the equation

$$y = 2x^3 + C$$

to obtain

$$2 = 2(-1)^3 + C$$

$$\Rightarrow \qquad C = 4$$

Hence the particular curve is defined by

$$y = 2x^3 + 4$$

A very important property of the *family* of curves is that the slope equation is the same for each particular curve. Consider

$$y = x^2 + C$$

Differentiate with respect to x to obtain

$$\frac{dy}{dx} = 2x$$

We have shown that for the *family* of curves defined by

$$y = x^2 + C$$

we have the slope equation

$$\frac{dy}{dx} = 2x$$

Example 11-2-3 Find the slope equation for the family of curves defined by (a) $y = x^3 + C$ and (b) $y = 3\exp(-x) + C$.

SOLUTION (a) $y = x^3 + C$ implies that $dy/dx = 3x^2$ and hence the slope equation is

$$\frac{dy}{dx} = 3x^2$$

(b) $y = 3\exp(-x) + C$ implies that $dy/dx = -3\exp(-x)$ and hence the slope equation is

$$\frac{dy}{dx} = -3\exp(-x)$$

11-3 DIFFERENTIAL EQUATIONS

The slope equation found by differentiation belongs to a group of **first-order differential equations**, since the first derivative dy/dx appears and higher differential coefficients do not. Examples of first-order differential equations are

$$\frac{dy}{dx} = 3x^2$$

and

$$\frac{dy}{dx} = 4y$$

Within the first-order group of differential equations we shall be considering two types:

(1) $$\frac{dy}{dx} = f(x)$$

(2) $$\frac{dy}{dx} = ky \qquad \text{where } k \text{ is a constant}$$

Differential equations of both types can be formed by mathematical modelling of the physical world. It is usual to form the differential equation from known physical laws which have been derived from experimental data. Having formed the differential equation, we can obtain further information by obtaining solutions.

11-4 DIFFERENTIAL EQUATIONS OF THE FORM $dy/dx = f(x)$

The solutions to a differential equation are themselves equations relating variables. Consider the first type

$$\frac{dy}{dx} = f(x)$$

We can rearrange this equation to form

$$\int dy = \int f(x)\, dx$$

$\Rightarrow$
$$y = \int f(x)\, dx$$

This type of integral without limits produces an arbitrary constant C. Thus, by solving the differential equation

$$\frac{dy}{dx} = f(x)$$

we find a **family of curves**. This family of curves is called the **general solution** to the differential equation.

Example 11-4-1 Find the general solution to the differential equation $dy/dx = x$.

SOLUTION Since

$$\frac{dy}{dx} = x \qquad \text{is in the form} \qquad \frac{dy}{dx} = f(x)$$

we have the integral equation

$$\int dy = \int x\, dx$$

$\Rightarrow$
$$y = \frac{x^2}{2} + C$$

where C is an arbitrary constant. The reader should check all solutions to differential equations by using the principles of differentiation. In this case,

$$y = \frac{x^2}{2} + C$$

on differentiation with respect to x becomes

$$\frac{dy}{dx} = x$$

which is the original differential equation. Hence, the general solution to

$$\frac{dy}{dx} = x$$

is
$$y = \frac{x^2}{2} + C \qquad (C \text{ is an arbitrary constant})$$

Example 11-4-2 Find the general solution to the differential equations

(a) $\dfrac{dy}{dx} = 30x^5$,

(b) $\dfrac{dy}{dx} = x^2 + 3x + 4$, and

(c) $\dfrac{dy}{dx} = x^{-2}$.

SOLUTION All the differential equations are in the standard form

$$\frac{dy}{dx} = f(x)$$

(a) $$\frac{dy}{dx} = 30x^5$$

$\Rightarrow$ $$\int dy = \int 30x^5\, dx$$

$\Rightarrow$ $$y = 5x^6 + C \qquad \text{where } C \text{ is an arbitrary constant}$$

(b) $\quad \dfrac{dy}{dx} = x^2 + 3x + 4$

$\Rightarrow \quad \displaystyle\int dy = \int (x^2 + 3x + 4)\,dx$

$\Rightarrow \quad y = \dfrac{x^3}{3} + \dfrac{3x^2}{2} + 4x + C \qquad$ where C is an arbitrary constant

(c) $\quad \dfrac{dy}{dx} = x^{-2} \qquad (x \neq 0)$

$\Rightarrow \quad \displaystyle\int dy = \int x^{-2}\,dx$

$\Rightarrow \quad y = \dfrac{x^{-1}}{-1} + C$

$\qquad y = -\dfrac{1}{x} + C \qquad$ where C is an arbitrary constant

Example 11-4-3 Find the general solution of the differential equations

(a) $3\dfrac{dy}{dx} = 2x$, and

(b) $4x\dfrac{dy}{dx} = x^2 + 3x$.

SOLUTION (a) Transforming the equation

$$3\dfrac{dy}{dx} = 2x$$

into the standard form

$$\dfrac{dy}{dx} = f(x)$$

we have

$$\dfrac{dy}{dx} = \tfrac{2}{3}x$$

$\Rightarrow \qquad \displaystyle\int dy = \int \tfrac{2}{3}x\,dx$

$\Rightarrow \qquad y = \tfrac{2}{6}x^2 + C$

$\qquad y = \dfrac{x^2}{3} + C \qquad$ where C is an arbitrary constant

(b) As in (a), we transform the equation

$$4x\dfrac{dy}{dx} = x^2 + 3x$$

into the standard form to obtain

$$\frac{dy}{dx} = \frac{x}{4} + \frac{3}{4}$$

$$\Rightarrow \quad \int dy = \int (0.25x + 0.75)\,dx$$

$$\Rightarrow \quad y = 0.25\frac{x^2}{2} + 0.75x + C$$

$$y = 0.125x^2 + 0.75x + C \qquad \text{where } C \text{ is an arbitrary constant}$$

The reader can check the general solutions by differentiation.

11-5 BOUNDARY CONDITIONS

Solving a differential equation in the first instance produces a general solution which is a family of curves. To the engineer or scientist, the solution will only be useful if one curve from the family could be found. In Sec. 11-2 it was demonstrated that one particular curve could be found if at least one point on the curve is known. The coordinates of this point are usually known as the **boundary** condition to the problem and can, in most cases, be found from the experimental or physical situation. For example, if we wish to examine experimentally a body moving in a straight line and we wish to measure the distance travelled for some known time, then it is obvious that any relationship between these variables involves the curve passing through the point $(0,0)$. That is to say, the body will travel zero metres in zero seconds.

If a particular curve from the family is found which suits the boundary conditions, then this is known as a **particular solution** to the differential equation.

Example 11-5-1 Find a particular solution of the differential equation

$$\frac{dy}{dx} = 3x^2$$

with a boundary condition $(1, 3)$.

SOLUTION The differential equation is of the form

$$\frac{dy}{dx} = f(x)$$

and hence

$$\frac{dy}{dx} = 3x^2$$

$$\int dy = \int 3x^2\,dx$$

$$y = x^3 + C \qquad \text{where } C \text{ is a constant}$$

This equation is the general solution and hence defines a *family* of curves. If we now use the boundary condition we can find one of these curves and hence the *particular* solution.

This is a similar process to the one carried out in Example 11-2-2. We substitute the boundary condition $(1,3)$, $y = 3$ at $x = 1$, into the general equation

$$y = x^3 + C$$

Therefore

$$3 = 1^3 + C$$

$\Rightarrow$

$$C = 2$$

Hence we have the particular solution

$$y = x^3 + 2$$

Example 11-5-2 Solve the differential equation

$$\frac{dy}{dt} = 5t^4 + 0.6t^2$$

with the boundary conditions (a) $v = 1$ at $t = 0$ and (b) $v = -3$ at $t = 1$.

SOLUTION The differential equation

$$\frac{dv}{dt} = 5t^4 + 0.6t^2$$

is in the standard form

$$\frac{dy}{dx} = f(x)$$

with y replaced by v and x replaced by t. Hence the general solution is given by

$$\int dv = \int (5t^4 + 0.6t^2)\, dt$$

$\Rightarrow$

$$v = t^5 + 0.2t^3 + C \qquad \text{where } C \text{ is a constant}$$

(a) Using the boundary conditions $v = 1$ at $t = 0$, we have, on substituting into the general solution, that $C = 1$. A particular solution is given by

$$v = t^5 + 0.2t^3 + 1$$

(b) Using the boundary condition $v = -3$ at $t = 1$ we have, on substituting into the general equation, $C = -4.2$. Thus a particular solution in this case is

$$v = t^5 + 0.2t^3 - 4.2$$

Both these particular solutions can be checked by using the principles of differentiation.

Example 11-5-3 An experiment measuring the velocity of a body moving in a straight line produced experimental results to which the curve $V = at^b$ was fitted. The constants a and b were found to be $a = 2$ and $b = 1.5$.

(a) Form a differential equation involving the position s of the body from a fixed datum.

(b) By solving the differential equation, find a relationship between position and time. In the experiment, the boundary condition is given by $(t, s) = (0, 0)$.

SOLUTION

(a)
$$V = 2t^{1.5}$$

$\Rightarrow$
$$\frac{ds}{dt} = 2t^{1.5}$$

since velocity is the rate of change of position and hence $V = ds/dt$.

(b) Since the differential equation

$$\frac{ds}{dt} = 2t^{1.5}$$

is in the form

$$\frac{dy}{dx} = f(x)$$

with y replaced by s and x replaced by t, we have

$$\int ds = \int 2t^{1.5} dt$$

$$= 2 \int t^{1.5} dt$$

$\Rightarrow$
$$s = \frac{2t^{2.5}}{2.5} + C$$

$$= 0.8t^{2.5} + C \qquad \text{where } C \text{ is a constant}$$

This is the general solution to the differential equation, and to find the particular solution we substitute the boundary condition, $s = 0$ at $t = 0$, into it to obtain $C = 0$.

Thus we have the particular solution and the relationship between position and time as

$$s = 0.8t^{2.5} + 0$$

or
$$s = 0.8t^{2.5}$$

11-6 DIFFERENTIAL EQUATIONS OF THE FORM $dQ/dt = kQ$

The second type of differential equation under consideration is of the standard form

$$\frac{dQ}{dt} = kQ \qquad \text{where } k \text{ is a constant}$$

This type of equation has a general solution

$$Q = Ae^{kt}$$

or

$$Q = A \exp(kt) \qquad \text{where } A \text{ is the arbitrary constant}$$

The above equation can be shown to be the solution to the differential equation

$$\frac{dQ}{dt} = kQ$$

by using the principles of differentiation. Consider

$$Q = Ae^{kt}$$

On differentiation we have

$$\frac{dQ}{dt} = kAe^{kt}$$

$$= k(Ae^{kt})$$

$$= kQ$$

since $Q = Ae^{kt}$. Therefore

$$\frac{dQ}{dt} = kQ$$

has a general solution

$$Q = Ae^{kt} \qquad \text{where } A \text{ is an arbitrary constant}$$

In the following two examples we show how to use this standard form to obtain solutions of the second type of differential equations.

Example 11-6-1 Find the general solution for each differential equation listed below:

(a) $\dfrac{dy}{dx} = 8y$, and

(b) $\dfrac{dy}{dx} = -2y$

SOLUTION Both the differential equations are in the standard form

$$\frac{dQ}{dt} = kQ$$

with Q replaced by y and t replaced by x.
(a) Compare

$$\frac{dy}{dx} = 8y$$

with the standard form

$$\frac{dQ}{dt} = kQ$$

and we see that $k = 8$. Hence the general solution is given by

$$y = Ae^{8x}$$

or $\qquad\qquad y = A\exp(8x)$

(b) Compare $\qquad\qquad \frac{dy}{dx} = -2y$

with the standard form and we find $k = -2$. Hence we have a general solution

$$y = Ae^{-2x}$$

or $\qquad\qquad y = A\exp(-2x) \qquad A$ is an arbitrary constant

Example 11-6-2 By using the general solution of

$$\frac{dQ}{dt} = kQ$$

find general solutions for

(a) $\dfrac{1}{V}\dfrac{dV}{dt} = 2$ and

(b) $\dfrac{1}{3V^2}\dfrac{dV}{dt} = \dfrac{1}{V}$.

SOLUTION (a) The differential equation

$$\frac{1}{V}\frac{dV}{dt} = 2$$

has to be transformed into the standard form

$$\frac{dQ}{dt} = kQ$$

On multiplying both sides by V we have

$$\frac{dV}{dt} = 2V$$

Hence $k = 2$ and the general solution is

$$V = Ae^{2t}$$

or $\qquad V = A\exp(2t) \qquad$ where A is the arbitrary constant

(b) As before, we transform the differential equation

$$\frac{1}{3V^2}\frac{dV}{dt} = \frac{1}{V}$$

into the standard form by multiplying both sides by $3V^2$. We have

$$\frac{dV}{dt} = 3V$$

which implies that $k = 3$. Hence the general solution is

$$V = Ae^{3t}$$

or $\quad\quad V = A\exp(3t)\quad\quad$ with A an arbitrary constant

11-7 PARTICULAR SOLUTIONS

Having found the general solution for the second type of first-order differential equations, we can find a **particular solution** by the same method as described in Sec. 11-5.

Example 11-7-1 Solve the differential equation

$$\frac{dy}{dx} = 3y$$

given $y = 2$ when $x = 0$.

SOLUTION The equation

$$\frac{dy}{dx} = 3y$$

is in the same form as

$$\frac{dQ}{dt} = kQ$$

By comparison, $k = 3$ and the general solution is

$$y = Ae^{3x}\quad\quad$$ with A a constant

Using the boundary condition $(x,y) = (0,2)$ we have on substituting these values into the general solution

$$2 = Ae^{3(0)}$$

$\Rightarrow\quad\quad\quad A = 2\quad\quad$ since $e^0 = 1$

Therefore the particular solution to

$$\frac{dy}{dx} = 3y\quad\quad$$ with $y = 2$ at $x = 0$

is given by
$$y = 2e^{3x}$$
or
$$y = 2\exp(3x)$$

Example 11-7-2 The acceleration dV/dt is related to the velocity of a body moving in a straight line by the differential equation

$$\frac{dV}{dt} = -3V$$

Solve this equation given that the velocity of the body is $10\,\text{m/s}$ at a time of 1 s.

SOLUTION The equation
$$\frac{dV}{dt} = -3V$$
is in the standard form
$$\frac{dQ}{dt} = kQ$$

with $k = -3$. Hence the general solution is
$$V = Ae^{-3t} \qquad \text{with } A \text{ a constant}$$

Using the boundary condition $V = 10\,\text{m/s}$ at $t = 1$ s, we can substitute into the general equation for A and we have the particular solution

$$V = 10e^3 e^{-3t}$$
$$V = 10e^{3(1-t)}$$

using the laws of indices.

11-8 MATHEMATICAL MODELLING AND DIFFERENTIAL EQUATIONS

We shall, in the next few sections, concern ourselves with mathematical modelling of physical situations with differential equations. Mathematical expressions connecting known, or defined, variables can be found by using the physical laws from science. These expressions invariably involve differential equations.

11-9 LINEAR EXPANSION

It is well known that, within certain limits, a rod expands linearly as its temperature rises. The expansion is proportional to its length. Consider the rod in Fig. 11-3 and let L be its length at some temperature $\theta°\text{C}$. In calculus terms, expansion is the rate of change of length with respect to the temperature θ.

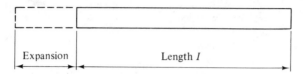

Figure 11-3

We can write

$$\frac{dL}{d\theta} = \alpha L$$

and we have a first-order differential equation of the second type, i.e.

$$\frac{dQ}{dt} = kQ$$

The boundary condition can be obtained by measurement and we require to know the length of the bar at some fixed temperature.

Example 11-9-1 A brass rod has a length 0.5 m at $0°C$. If the coefficient of linear expansion for brass is $18 \times 10^{-6}/°C$, find a mathematical model describing the expansion of the rod in terms of its length L and the temperature θ. Solve the resulting differential equation with the boundary condition to obtain a prediction equation for the length of the rod at a given temperature.

SOLUTION From

$$\frac{dL}{d\theta} = \alpha L$$

we have

$$\frac{dL}{d\theta} = (18)(10^{-6})L$$

A boundary condition is given as $L = 0.5$ m at $\theta = 0°C$. Therefore we have the mathematical model describing the expansion as

$$\frac{dL}{d\theta} = (18)(10^{-6})L \qquad \text{with } L = 0.5 \text{ m when } \theta = 0°C$$

Solving this equation using the standard form

$$\frac{dQ}{dt} = kQ$$

we have $k = (18)(10^{-6})$ and hence the general solution is

$$L = Ae^{(18)(10^{-6})\theta} \qquad \text{where } A \text{ is a constant}$$

Using the boundary condition when $\theta = 0°C$, $L = 0.5$ m, we can find the constant A. Substituting the values of the boundary condition into the general solution gives $A = 0.5$. Thus we have a particular solution

$$L = 0.5 \exp(18 \times 10^{-6}\theta)$$

This particular solution is a **prediction equation** for the rod's length in terms of its temperature.

11-10 MOVING BODIES

It is possible, using Newton's laws, to find mathematical models describing the motion of moving bodies. We shall consider a simple case in which the body of mass m is moving in a straight line along a horizontal plane. We shall assume that the body is subjected to resistance forces which in total can be considered to be proportional to the velocity. We shall also assume that once the body is in motion, then no tractive force is involved.

Consider Fig. 11-4 which defines the positive direction of motion. By Newton's second law

$$(\text{Mass})(\text{acceleration}) = - \text{ resistance force}$$

(the minus sign appearing since the resistance force opposes motion) and using that acceleration is the rate of change of velocity with respect to time, which in calculus terms is dV/dt, we have

$$m \frac{dV}{dt} = -kV$$

where kV is the resistance force proportional to the velocity.

The boundary condition is some known velocity at a given point in time. It is usual in this type of physical situation to take the velocity at time $t = 0$ for the boundary condition.

Example 11-10-1 A body of mass 2 kg is moving in a horizontal plane in a straight line. The motion is resisted by a force which is four times its velocity.

(*a*) If the initial velocity was 4m/s, find a mathematical model describing the motion.

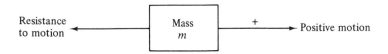

Resistance to motion ← Mass m + → Positive motion

Figure 11-4

(b) Solve the resulting differential equation with its boundary condition to find a prediction equation for the instantaneous velocity.

(c) Predict the velocity of the body at a time of 2.5 s.

SOLUTION A diagram should always be drawn and the positive direction of motion defined. This is illustrated in Fig. 11-5.

(a) From Newton's second law

$$(\text{Mass})(\text{acceleration}) = -\text{resistance}$$

$$\Rightarrow \qquad m\frac{dV}{dt} = -4V$$

Hence we have the mathematical model describing motion as

$$2\frac{dV}{dt} = -4V \qquad \text{with } V = 4\,\text{m/s at } t = 0\,\text{s}$$

(b) From Sec. 11-6, the general solution to an equation in the form

$$\frac{dQ}{dt} = kQ$$

is

$$Q = Ae^{kt}$$

Hence for

$$2\frac{dV}{dt} = -4V$$

we have the general solution

$$V = Ae^{-2t}$$

By using the condition $V = 4\,\text{m/s}$ at $t = 0\,\text{s}$ we can find the constant A. On substituting these values into the general solution, we have $A = 4$. Hence we have a particular solution

$$V = 4e^{-2t}$$

which is the *prediction* equation for velocity at any instant in time t.

(c) Using the prediction equation we have for $t = 2.5\,\text{s}$,

$$V = 4e^{-2(2.5)}$$

$$= 4e^{-5}$$

Hence velocity at $t = 2.5\,\text{s}$ is $0.0270\,\text{m/s}$.

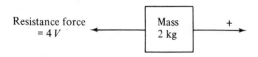

Resistance force = 4 V Mass 2 kg   +

Figure 11-5

Example 11-10-2 A body of mass 0.2 kg is projected into a fluid with an initial velocity of 3 m/s. Assuming that the body is moving along a horizontal straight path:

(*a*) Set up a mathematical model describing the motion. The fluid resistance to motion is 0.3 times the velocity.

(*b*) Find a prediction equation from the model for the instantaneous velocity.

(*c*) Transform the velocity prediction equation into a first-order differential equation involving distance travelled s and time t.

(*d*) Find a prediction equation for the distance travelled in metres at a time of t seconds. Assume that at $t = 0, s = 0$.

SOLUTION Figure 11-6 illustrates the physical situation.

(*a*) From Newton's second law

$$(\text{Mass})(\text{acceleration}) = -\text{resistance force}$$

$$\Rightarrow \qquad 0.2\frac{dV}{dt} = -0.3V$$

Hence we have the mathematical model

$$\frac{dV}{dt} = -1.5V \qquad \text{with } V = 3 \text{ m/s at } t = 0 \text{ s}$$

(*b*) Using the standard form

$$\frac{dQ}{dt} = kQ$$

we have $k = -1.5$. Hence we obtain the general solution

$$V = Ae^{-1.5t} \qquad \text{where } A \text{ is a constant}$$

Using the boundary condition we have $A = 3$. The particular solution and therefore the prediction equation for velocity is

$$V = 3e^{-1.5t}$$

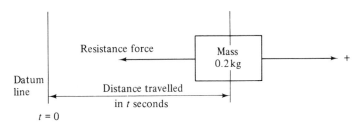

Figure 11-6 (*a*) $L-R$ circuit; (*b*) $C-R$ circuit.

or
$$V = 3 \exp(-1.5t)$$

(c) Since velocity is the rate of change of position with respect to time, we can substitute ds/dt in place of V in the equation

$$V = 3 \exp(-1.5t)$$

to give
$$\frac{ds}{dt} = 3 \exp(-1.5t)$$

(d) Using the techniques of Secs 11-4 and 11-5, we have

$$\int ds = \int 3e^{-1.5t}\, dt$$

$\Rightarrow \qquad \int ds = 3 \int e^{-1.5t} dt$

$\Rightarrow \qquad s = -2e^{-1.5t} + C \qquad$ where C is a constant

Using the boundary condition $(t,s) = (0,0)$, the constant $C = 2$. Hence we have a particular solution and hence a prediction equation for distance travelled at time t as

$$s = -2e^{-1.5t} + 2$$

Factorizing gives the distance travelled

$$s = 2(1 - e^{-1.5t})$$

11-11 ELECTRICAL CIRCUITS

We shall consider electrical circuits and build some mathematical models describing the relationships between time and other variables. Two simple circuits shown in Fig. 11-7 will be considered.

Consider the L–R circuit and allow the switch s to be thrown to position 2

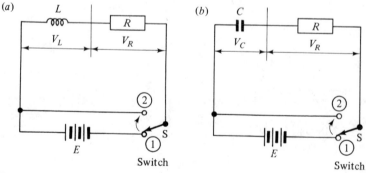

Figure 11-7

when the current flowing is X amperes. By Kirchhoff's law, that the algebraic sum of the voltage drops in a simple closed circuit is zero, we have

$$V_L + V_R = 0$$

By Sec. 5-11 we have

$$V_L = L\frac{di}{dt}$$

and

$$V_R = Ri$$

where L is the inductance in henries and R the resistance in ohms. Hence

$$V_L + V_R = 0$$

becomes

$$L\frac{di}{dt} + Ri = 0$$

and after dividing both sides by L we have the mathematical model which describes the current flow for this electrical circuit with the switch in position 2. The mathematical model is

$$\frac{di}{dt} + \frac{R}{L} = 0 \text{ with } i = X\text{ A at } t = 0\text{ s}$$

Consider the second circuit in Fig. 11-7 where a capacitor of C farads is in series with a resistor of R ohms. Let the switch be thrown to position 2 when the charge on the capacitor is Y coulombs. By Kirchhoff's law we have

$$V_R + V_C = 0$$

and from Ch. 5,

$$V_R = Ri$$

and

$$V_C = \frac{1}{C}q$$

where q is the instantaneous charge on the capacitor. Again by Ch. 5 we have

$$i = \frac{dq}{dt}$$

which implies that

$$V_R = R\frac{dq}{dt}$$

Hence

$$V_R + V_C = 0$$

becomes

$$R\frac{dq}{dt} + \frac{1}{C}q = 0$$

We have the mathematical model

$$\frac{dq}{dt} + \frac{1}{CR}q = 0 \quad \text{with } q = Y\text{C at } t = 0\text{ s}$$

This model describes the relationship between the variables, charge and time.

Example 11-11-1 A circuit has a resistor of 100 Ω in series with an inductor of 10 henries as shown in Fig. 11-8. The switch is thrown to position 2 when the current flowing is 0.2 A.

(a) Set up a mathematical model which describes the current flow within the circuit from the time $t = 0$.

(b) Solve the resulting differential equation to find a prediction equation for the current value at any instant in time.

(c) Calculate the value of (i) the current at $t = 0.1$ s, and (ii) the time at which the current is 0.15 A.

SOLUTION (a) Using Kirchhoff's law we have

$$V_L + V_R = 0$$

and hence

$$L\frac{di}{dt} + Ri = 0$$

On substituting the values for L and R, we have the mathematical model

$$10\frac{di}{dt} + 100i = 0 \qquad \text{with } i = 0.2 \text{ A at } t = 0 \text{ s}$$

(b) From Sec. 11-6, the general solution of the equation

$$\frac{dQ}{dt} = kQ$$

is

$$Q = Ae^{kt}$$

and hence, since our model is of this form, we have for

$$\frac{di}{dt} = -10i$$

the solution

$$i = Ae^{-10t}$$

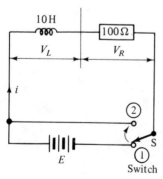

10 H

V_L

100 Ω

V_R

i

②

E

S

①

Switch

Figure 11-8

Using the initial condition that at $t = 0$ a current of 0.2 A is flowing, we have

$$0.2 = Ae^{-10(0)}$$

$\Rightarrow$ $\qquad\qquad A = 0.2$

Hence we have the particular solution

$$i = 0.2e^{-10t}$$

which is the prediction equation for current.

(c) (i) Using the prediction equation

$$i = 0.2e^{-10t}$$

and substituting the value $t = 0.1$ s we have

$$i = 0.2e^{-10(0.1)}$$

$$= 0.0736 \text{ A}$$

Therefore the current flowing at $t = 0.1$ s is 0.0736 A.

(ii) Again using

$$i = 0.2e^{-10t}$$

we find

$$\ln(i) = \ln(0.2) + \ln(e^{-10t})$$

$$= -1.6094 - 10t$$

by using the theory of logarithms. When $i = 0.15$ A we have

$$\ln(0.15) = -1.6094 - 10t$$

$$-0.2877 = -10t$$

or $\qquad\qquad t = 0.0288 \text{ s}$

Thus it takes 0.0288 s for the current to fall to 0.15 A.

Example 11-11-2 A circuit consists of a capacitor of $10 \,\mu\text{F}$ in series with a resistor of $1000 \,\Omega$ as shown in Fig. 11-9. The switch s is thrown to position 2 at $t = 0$ s and when the charge on the capacitor is 10×10^{-9} coulombs.

(a) Find a mathematical model which describes the change in the amount of charge on the capacitor with respect to time.

(b) Solve the resulting differential equation to find an equation for predicting the amount of charge at time t.

(c) By using the equation in part (b), find a prediction equation for the current flowing at any instant in time.

SOLUTION (a) By using Kirchhoff's law we have

$$V_R + V_C = 0$$

which implies

$$Ri + \frac{1}{C}q = 0$$

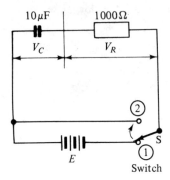

Figure 11-9

On substituting the values for R and C we have

$$\frac{dq}{dt} + 100q = 0$$

Hence the mathematical model is

$$\frac{dq}{dt} + 100q = 0 \qquad \text{with } q = 10^{-8} \text{ C at } t = 0 \text{ s}$$

(b) Since

$$\frac{dq}{dt} = -100q$$

we have a general solution, following Sec. 11-6, of

$$q = Ae^{-100t}$$

On substituting the initial condition at $t = 0$, $q = 10^{-8}$ C, we have the particular solution

$$q = 10^{-8} \exp(-100t)$$

which is the equation for charge at any instant in time.

(c) Since $i = dq/dt$ we differentiate both sides of the charge equation to obtain

$$i = \frac{dq}{dt} = -10^{-6} \exp(-100t)$$

Hence the prediction equation for current at any instant in time after the switch is thrown to position 2 is

$$i = -10^{-6} \exp(-100t)$$

Example 11-11-3 Show that for the capacitive circuit in Fig. 11-7 when the switch is in position 2 the current flowing is given by the mathematical model

$$i = -\frac{E}{R}\exp\left(-\frac{1}{CR}t\right)$$

assuming that the capacitor is fully charged.

SOLUTION By Kirchhoff's laws we have

$$V_R + V_C = 0$$

or

$$R\frac{dq}{dt} + \frac{q}{C} = 0$$

Hence, we have the mathematical model

$$\frac{dq}{dt} = -\frac{1}{CR}q \qquad q = CE \text{ at } t = 0 \text{ s}$$

where the charge at $t = 0$ is the maximum possible, CE. Solving the differential equation gives

$$q = K \cdot \exp\left(-\frac{1}{CR}t\right)$$

where K is an arbitrary constant and can be solved by using the initial condition that at $t = 0$ s, $q = CE$. Hence

$$q = K \cdot \exp(0) = CE \qquad \Rightarrow \qquad K = CE$$

and we have a prediction equation for charge

$$q = CE \cdot \exp\left(-\frac{1}{CR}t\right)$$

However

$$i = \frac{dq}{dt} = CE\left(-\frac{1}{CR}\right)\exp\left(-\frac{1}{CR}t\right)$$

$$\Rightarrow \qquad i = -\frac{E}{R}\exp\left(-\frac{1}{CR}t\right)$$

The reader will notice that since E and R are both positive values, we have a *negative* current. The direction of the current flow is opposite to that of the current flow when the capacitor is charging. This will be used later in Ch. 16.

PROBLEMS

11-1 A family of curves is defined by the relationship $y = 0.3x^2 + C$. Find the differential equation associated with this relationship.

For problems **11-2** to **11-4** plot six curves associated with the given relationship.

11-2 $y = x^5 + C.$

11-3 $y = 3x^2 - x + C.$

11-4 $s = 4t^3 - t + C.$

For problems **11-5** to **11-8** a family of curves is defined by the relationship $y = 2x^3 - x^2 + C$ where C is a constant. For the given point (x, y), find a *particular* curve which passes through it and belongs to the defined family.

11-5 $(x, y) = (1, 2).$

11-6 $(x, y) = (0, 8).$

11-7 $(x, y) = (-2, -6).$

11-8 $(x, y) = (-0.5, 9).$

For problems **11-9** to **11-13** find the family of curves associated with the given differential equation.

11-9 $\dfrac{dy}{dx} = 3x^2.$

11-10 $\dfrac{dy}{dx} = 4x.$

11-11 $\dfrac{dy}{dx} = 3x^3 - 2x^2 + x.$

11-12 $\dfrac{dy}{dx} = 4x^5 + 3x^4 - 2.$

*11-13 $\dfrac{dy}{dt} = t^{-4}.$

For problems **11-14** to **11-18** find the general solution for the given differential equation.

11-14 $\dfrac{ds}{dt} = t^4 - 6t^3.$

11-15 $\dfrac{ds}{dt} = -t^6 + 6t^3 - 5.$

11-16 $\dfrac{ds}{dt} = -5.8t^3 + 4t^2 - 1.$

11-17 $\dfrac{ds}{dt} = 7t^{-3}.$

11-18 $\dfrac{ds}{dt} = 3.2t^3 - 6t^2 + 7.$

For problems **11-19** to **11-23** solve the differential equation

$$\frac{dV}{dt} = 0.7t$$

given the boundary condition (t, V).

11-19 $(t, V) = (0, 0).$

11-20 $(t, V) = (0, 7).$

11-21 $(t, V) = (1, 3).$

11-22 $(t, V) = (-1, 2)$.

11-23 $(t, V) = (-2, -1)$.

11-24 Solve the differential equation

$$\frac{dV}{dt} = t^2 + 4t$$

given that at $t = 0$, $V = 4$.

11-25 Find a particular solution to the differential equation

$$\frac{ds}{dt} = 3t^2 + 4$$

for the boundary condition $(t, s) = (0, 5)$.

11-26 Solve the differential equation

$$\frac{dy}{dx} = 4 \sin 2x$$

if $y = 2$ at $x = 0$.

11-27 Solve the differential equation

$$\frac{dy}{dx} = 3 \exp(5x)$$

with the boundary condition $(x, y) = (1, 4)$.

11-28 Solve the differential equation

$$\frac{dy}{dx} = x^{-1}$$

if $y = 2$ at $x = 1$.

11-29 A conveyor belt system is used to transport goods during final assembly of a product. Technician engineers measured the velocity of the belt and found that the law

$$V = 3.5$$

best fitted the results. Using this relationship,

    (*a*) form a differential equation relating the distance the goods have travelled to the time taken to travel this distance, and

    (*b*) solve this differential equation to find a particular solution which predicts the distance travelled in time t. Assume the boundary condition $(s, t) = (0, 0)$.

For problems **11-30** to **11-35** find the general solution for the given differential equation.

11-30 $\frac{dy}{dx} = 6y$.

11-31 $\frac{dy}{dx} = -3y$.

11-32 $\frac{dy}{dx} = 9.8y$.

11-33 $4\frac{dy}{dx} = 12y$.

11-34 $\frac{ds}{dt} = -5.6s$.

11-35 $\frac{dV}{dt} = 4V$.

**11-36 The differential equation

$$3\frac{d^2 s}{dt^2} = -9\frac{ds}{dt}$$

is a second-order type which can be transformed into the first-order form

$$\frac{dQ}{dt} = kQ$$

Using this transformation technique, find the general solution to the second-order differential equation.

For problems **11-37** to **11-39** find the particular solution associated with the given differential equation.

11-37 $\frac{ds}{dt} = 8s$ with $(t, s) = (0, 1)$.

11-38 $\frac{ds}{dt} = -13s$ with $(t, s) = (0, 4)$.

11-39 $\frac{ds}{dt} = 7.5s$ with $(t, s) = (0, 2)$.

**11-40 Prove that the general solution to the first-order differential equation

$$\frac{dQ}{dt} = kQ$$

is

$$Q = A \exp(kt)$$

where A is an arbitrary constant.

**11-41 A body of mass 4 kg is moving in a straight line against a resistance force of 6 times its velocity. Assuming that the body travels horizontally and that there is no tractive force involved, construct a mathematical model describing the motion of the body whose initial velocity was 6 m/s.

Solve the resulting differential equation to find a particular solution which can be used to predict the velocity at time t seconds.

**11-42 A steel rod has a length 1.0 m at 0°C. If the coefficient of linear expansion is 0.000 011/°C, find a mathematical model which describes the expansion of the rod's length in terms of its temperature. Solve the differential equation with the related boundary condition to find a particular solution which will enable the length of the rod to be predicted for a given temperature. Predict the length of the rod when the temperature of the room is 35°C.

For problems **11-43** to **11-45** consider the $L-R$ circuit in Fig. 11-7. For the values of L and R given, find a mathematical model which describes the change in current with respect to time after the switch s has been thrown to position 2. Assume that the initial current is 0.1 A. Solve the resulting differential equation.

**11-43 $L = 10$ H, $R = 10\ \Omega$.

**11-44 $L = 5$ H, $R = 100\ \Omega$.

**11-45 $L = 20$ H, $R = 2000\ \Omega$.

For problems **11-46** to **11-48** consider the $C-R$ circuit in Fig. 11-7. For the values of C and R given, find a mathematical model relating the change in charge with respect to time assuming that the switch was thrown to position 2 when the charge $q = 10^{-6}$ coulombs.

Solve the resulting differential equation and hence find a prediction equation for the instantaneous charge on the capacitor.

***11-46** $C = 10\,\mu\text{F}, R = 10\,\Omega$.
***11-47** $C = 20\,\mu\text{F}, R = 1000\,\Omega$,
***11-48** $C = 15\,\mu\text{F}, R = 5000\,\Omega$.

Solutions

11-1 $\dfrac{dy}{dx} = 0.6x$.

11-2 to **11-4** See Sec. 11-2.
11-5 $y = 2x^3 - x^2 + 1$.
11-6 $y = 2x^3 - x^2 + 8$.
11-7 $y = 2x^3 - x^2 + 14$.
11-8 $y = 2x^3 - x^2 + 9.5$.
11-9 $y = x^3 + C$.
11-10 $y = 2x^2 + C$.
11-11 $y = 0.75x^4 - 0.6667x^3 + 0.5x^2 + C$.
11-12 $y = 0.6667x^6 + 0.6x^5 - 2x + C$.
11-13 $y = -0.3333t^{-3} + C$.
11-14 $s = 0.2t^5 - 1.5t^4 + C$.
11-15 $s = -0.142\,86t^7 + 1.5t^4 - 5t + C$.
11-16 $s = -1.45t^4 + 1.3333t^3 - t + C$.
11-17 $s = -3.5t^{-2} + C$.
11-18 $s = 0.8t^4 - 2t^3 + 7t + C$.
11-19 $V = 0.35t^2$.
11-20 $V = 0.35t^2 + 7$.
11-21 $V = 0.35t^2 + 2.65$.
11-22 $V = 0.35t^2 + 1.65$.
11-23 $V = 0.35t^2 - 2.4$.
11-24 $V = 0.3333t^3 + 2t^2 + 4$.
11-25 $s = t^3 + 4t + 5$.
11-26 $y = -2\cos(2x) + 4$.
11-27 $y = 0.6\exp(5x) - 85.0479$.
11-28 $y = \ln(x) + 2$.

11-29 (a) $\dfrac{ds}{dt} = 3.5$, (b) $s = 3.5t$.

11-30 $y = A\exp(6x)$.
11-31 $y = A\exp(-3x)$.
11-32 $y = A\exp(9.8x)$.
11-33 $y = A\exp(3x)$.
11-34 $s = A\exp(-5.6t)$.
11-35 $V = A\exp(4t)$.
11-36 Using the transformation $V = ds/dt$ we solve for V to obtain

$$V = A\exp(-3t)$$

Hence

$$s = -\frac{Ae^{-3t}}{3} + B$$

11-37 $s = \exp(8t)$.

11-38 $s = 4 \exp(-13t)$.

11-39 $s = 2 \exp(7.5t)$.

11-40 See Sec. 11-6.

11-41 Mathematical model is

$$\frac{dV}{dt} = -1.5V \qquad \text{with boundary condition } (t, V) = (0, 6)$$

Prediction equation for velocity is

$$V = 6 \exp(-1.5t)$$

11-42 Mathematical model is

$$\frac{dL}{d\theta} = \alpha L \qquad \text{with boundary condition } (\theta, L) = (0, 1)$$

Prediction equation for length L at temperature θ is

$$L = \exp(0.0000\,11\,\theta)$$

At $\theta = 35°C$, we have a predicted length of $1.000\,39$ m.

11-43 Mathematical model is

$$\frac{di}{dt} = -i \qquad \text{at } t = 0 \text{ s } i = 0.1 \text{ A}$$

Solution is

$$i = 0.1 \exp(-t)$$

11-44 Mathematical model is

$$\frac{di}{dt} = -20i \qquad \text{at } t = 0 \text{ s } i = 0.1 \text{ A}$$

Solution is

$$i = 0.1 \exp(-20t)$$

11-45 Mathematical model is

$$\frac{di}{dt} = -100i \qquad \text{at } t = 0 \text{ s } i = 0.1 \text{ A}$$

Solution is

$$i = 0.1 \exp(-100t)$$

11-46 Mathematical model is

$$\frac{dq}{dt} = -10^4 q \qquad \text{at } t = 0 \text{ s } q = 10^{-6} \text{ C}$$

Solution is

$$q = 10^{-6} \exp(-10^4 t)$$

11-47 Mathematical model is

$$\frac{dq}{dt} = -50q \qquad \text{at } t = 0 \text{ s } q = 10^{-6} \text{ C}$$

Solution is

$$q = 10^{-6} \exp(-50t)$$

11-48 Mathematical model is

$$\frac{dq}{dt} = -13\tfrac{1}{3}q \qquad \text{at } t = 0 \text{ s } q = 10^{-6} \text{ C}$$

Solution is

$$q = 10^{-6} \exp\left(-13\tfrac{1}{3}t\right)$$

TWELVE

PROBABILITY

Objectives After reading this chapter you should be able to:

1. Calculate probabilities for given events.
   (*a*) Define probability.
   (*b*) State that the total probability is unity.
   (*c*) Calculate simple probabilities.
   (*d*) Distinguish between classical and empirical definitions of probability.
2. Distinguish between independent and dependent events.
3. Apply the concepts of mutually exclusive and mutually non-exclusive events.
   (*a*) State the addition law of probabilities for mutually exclusive and mutually non-exclusive events.
   (*b*) State the multiplication law of probabilities.
   (*c*) Calculate successive probabilities.
   (*d*) Apply the rules of probability to simple engineering inspections or predictions.

12-1 INTRODUCTION

In the industrial world, it is very useful to be able to predict events. For example, if an automatic lathe is producing components, it would save resources if the machine could be stopped before it made too many faulty articles or defectives. One-hundred per cent inspection is extremely expensive, and hence an estimate of the possibility of the machine producing defective components in large numbers would be extremely useful. This leads on to the concept of probability, which we will define in a later section. In order to define probability, we have to be clear on some other concepts.

In any experiment, whether it be measuring the length of a component or throwing a six-sided die, we have to define all the possible **outcomes**. The outcomes of the experiment could be in the form of numerical data, discrete or continuous, or in the descriptive format, such as colours or sex. All possible outcomes from an experiment are referred to as the **sample space**.

Example 12-1-1 Write down all possible outcomes, that is the sample space, if we throw a six-sided die with the usual numbers on the faces.

SOLUTION All possible outcomes are placed between curly brackets (braces) indicating a set:

$$\text{Sample space} = \{1,2,3,4,5,6\}$$

Example 12-1-2 A box contains five balls, three red, one white and one black. If one ball is drawn and the colour noted, write down the sample space for this experiment.

SOLUTION

$$\text{Sample space} = \{\text{red ball, black ball, white ball}\}$$

The reader should note that the number of outcomes in the sample space does not equal the number of balls in the box.

Example 12-1-3 A machine is automatically producing clock spindles. The measured length of these spindles lies between 25.1 mm and 32.5 mm. Measurement of the length is to the nearest 0.1 mm. Write down the sample space for the measured values which are likely to occur during inspection.

SOLUTION The measured length will have values from 25.1 mm to 32.5 mm in increments of 0.1 mm. Thus the sample space is given by

$$\text{Sample space} = \{25.1, 25.2, 25.3, \ldots, 32.3, 32.4, 32.5\}$$

12.2 EVENTS

An **event** is a subset of the sample space. This implies that an event could consist of one or more of the outcomes of a particular experiment.

Example 12-2-1 A six-sided die with faces numbered 1, 2, 3, 4, 5, and 6 is thrown twice. Write down the sample space, and the event of obtaining two numbers which when added together equal 4.

Table 12-1 'Solution' (See page 256)

First throw	Second throw					
	1	2	3	4	5	6
1	(1,1)	(1,2)	(1,3)	(1,4)	(1,5)	(1,6)
2	(2,1)	(2,2)	(2,3)	(2,4)	(2,5)	(2,6)
3	(3,1)	(3,2)	(3,3)	(3,4)	(3,5)	(3,6)
4	(4,1)	(4,2)	(4,3)	(4,4)	(4,5)	(4,6)
5	(5,1)	(5,2)	(5,3)	(5,4)	(5,5)	(5,6)
6	(6,1)	(6,2)	(6,3)	(6,4)	(6,5)	(6,6)

SOLUTION In this example, the sample space is given in the form of a two-dimensional array as shown in Table 12-1.

The event of two numbers when added together equal 4 is

$$E = \{(1,3), (2,2), (3,1)\}$$

12-3 MUTUALLY EXCLUSIVE EVENTS

We can consider more than one defined event. If two or more events are **mutually exclusive** then they cannot occur together. Thus, the occurrence of one event automatically precludes the occurrence of the other event or events. An example of mutually exclusive events can be taken from card games. Consider a pack of 52 cards and let A be the event of drawing a queen and B be the event of drawing an ace. It is impossible to find a queen which is also an ace, so these two events are mutually exclusive. This is illustrated in Fig. 12-1.

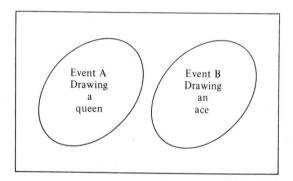

Figure 12-1 Mutually exclusive events.

12-4 MUTUALLY NON-EXCLUSIVE EVENTS

If two or more events can occur together, then they are **mutually non-exclusive**. Again, consider the pack of playing cards. Let A be the event of drawing a queen and B be the event of drawing a red card. These events are mutually non-exclusive since we can draw a card which is a *red queen*. There is an overlap between the two events which is illustrated in Fig. 12-2.

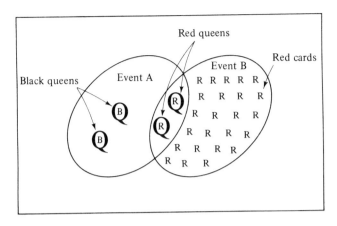

Figure 12-2 Mutually non-exclusive events.

Example 12-4-1 Consider the pack of 52 playing cards and state whether the events below are mutually exclusive or non-exclusive.

(a) Event A = {queen drawn},
   Event B = {king drawn}.
(b) Event A = {black card drawn},
   Event B = {ace drawn},
(c) Event A = {black card drawn},
   Event B = {red card drawn}.
(d) Event A = {red card drawn},
   Event B = {two of spades drawn},
   Event C = {ace of clubs drawn}.
(e) Event A = {red card drawn},
   Event B = {queen of hearts drawn}.

SOLUTION
(a) Exclusive.
(b) Non-exclusive.
(c) Exclusive.
(d) Exclusive.
(e) Non-exclusive.

Example 12-4-2 A factory contains a design office with six male and four female design engineers. Two of the men speak German, three of the women speak French, and the other design engineers do not speak a second language. If we choose one person, state whether the following events are mutually exclusive or mutually non-exclusive:

(a) Event A = {the person is a man},
   Event B = {the person is a woman}.

(b) Event A = {the person is a man},
   Event B = {the person speaks German}.
(c) Event A = {the person is a woman},
   Event B = {the person speaks German}.
(d) Event A = {the person speak French},
   Event B = {the person speaks German}.
(e) Event A = {the person speaks English},
   Event B = {the person speaks German}.

SOLUTION
(a) Exclusive.
(b) Non-exclusive.
(c) Exclusive.
(d) Exclusive.
(e) Non-exclusive.

12-5 PROBABILITY

Probability can be defined objectively in two ways, and as a consequence there are two different approaches to determine probabilistic values. On a question of notation, the probability of an event A occurring will be labelled $P(A)$. For example, the probability of the event,

$$A = \{\text{machine fails to start}\}$$

is written

$$P(\text{machine fails to start}) = P(A)$$

12-6 CLASSICAL PROBABILITY

The classical approach to probability relies on a knowledge of the total number of measurements made of one event which are possible in an experiment. All outcomes must be **equally likely** to occur and must be **mutually exclusive**. Under these conditions, if an event could occur a times out of a total possible number of measurements of b, then

$$P(\text{event occurring}) = \frac{a}{b}$$

Example 12-6-1 In a box there are 12 components, three of which are faulty. Find the probability that when picking a component at random it will be faulty.

SOLUTION The total number of components in box is 12. The number of faulty components is 3. Thus,

$$P(\text{picking a faulty component}) = 3/12$$
$$= 0.25$$

Example 12-6-2 A six-sided die numbered $1,1,2,2,2,3$ is thrown once. Assuming that each outcome is equally likely to occur, find (*a*) the probability of throwing a 1, and (*b*) the probability of throwing a 2.

SOLUTION Total number of possible results $= 6$.
(*a*) There are two results with the number 1, therefore we have

$$P(1) = 2/6$$
$$= \tfrac{1}{3}$$

(*b*) There are three possible results with the number 2, thus we have

$$P(2) = 3/6$$
$$= 0.5$$

12-7 EMPIRICAL PROBABILITY

Empirical probability is based on experimental results or survey data. This does not assume that the outcomes are equally likely to occur.

Example 12-7-1 On past record, the output from an automatic machine is expected to have 150 defective components in 10 000. Find the probability that the inspector finds in a day's output from that particular machine, (*a*) a defective component and (*b*) a 'good' component.

SOLUTION (*a*) Based on the past evidence

$$P(\text{defective component}) = \frac{150}{10\,000}$$

Hence
$$P(\text{defective component}) = 0.015$$

(*b*)
$$P(\text{`good' component}) = 1 - 0.015$$
$$= 0.985$$

or
$$P(\text{`good' component}) = \frac{9850}{10\,000}$$
$$= 0.985$$

as before

12-8 CERTAIN EVENTS

An event which is certain to happen has a probability of unity. On the other hand, an event which is impossible has a probability of zero.

Example 12-8-1 A firm has a workforce of 100 men. Find the probability that on visiting the firm a person would meet an employee who is (*a*) a man and (*b*) a woman.

SOLUTION
(*a*)

$$P(\text{meeting an employee who is a man}) = \frac{100}{100} = 1.0$$

This is a *certain* event.

(*b*) Since the firm does not employ women at this point in time, the event of meeting a woman employee is *impossible* and thus we have a probability of zero. That is

$$P(\text{meeting an employee who is a woman}) = 0$$

12-9 THE ADDITION LAW

If we have two events A and B, we can calculate the probability of the occurrence of A *or* B. This is given by the formula

$$P(A \text{ or } B) = P(A) + P(B) - P(A \text{ and } B)$$

By (A and B) we mean that the event A can occur at the same instant that B occurs. This will only happen if A and B are *non-exclusive* events.

Thus, for *exclusive* events $P(A \text{ and } B) = 0$ and the addition law reduces to

$$P(A \text{ or } B) = P(A) + P(B)$$

Example 12-9-1 A card is drawn from a pack of 52. Find the probability that this card is (*a*) red or black in colour, (*b*) red in colour or a queen, and (*c*) black in colour or from the suit of spades.

SOLUTION (*a*) Let A be the event of drawing a red card and let B be the event of drawing a black card. Since these events are mutually exclusive we can use

$$P(A \text{ or } B) = P(A) + P(B)$$

$$= \frac{26}{52} + \frac{26}{52}$$

$$= 1.0$$

This should be obvious to the reader since we are certain to obtain either a black or a red card.

(b) Let A be the event of drawing a red card and let B be the event of drawing a queen. These events are mutually non-exclusive since we have red queens; thus

$$P(A \text{ and } B) = P(\text{red queen}) = \frac{2}{52}$$

$$= 0.038\,46 \quad \text{(to 5 places of decimals)}$$

$$P(\text{red card}) = P(A)$$

$$= \frac{26}{52}$$

$$= 0.5$$

$$P(\text{queen}) = P(B)$$

$$= \frac{4}{52}$$

$$= 0.076\,92$$

Hence,

$$P(A \text{ or } B) = P(A) + P(B) - P(A \text{ and } B)$$

$$= 0.5 + 0.076\,92 - 0.038\,46$$

$$= 0.538\,46$$

Hence the probability of a red card or a queen (or both) being drawn is 0.538 46.

(c) Let A be the event of drawing a black card. Hence

$$P(A) = 0.5$$

Let B be the event of drawing a 'spade'. Hence

$$P(B) = \frac{13}{52}$$

Since it is possible to find a black spade, we have

$$P(A \text{ and } B) = P(\text{black spade})$$

$$= \frac{13}{52}$$

$$= 0.25$$

Thus, using the addition law,

$$P(A \text{ or } B) = P(A) + P(B) - P(A \text{ and } B)$$
$$= 0.5 + 0.25 - 0.25$$
$$= 0.5$$

Thus, the probability of drawing a black card or a spade is 0.5.

Example 12-9-2 A company's records show that from 8000 days, 400 were lost through strike action and 1200 days through illness.
(a) Write down the probability of the company losing a day through (i) strike action and (ii) illness.
(b) Assuming that days lost through strikes and illness are mutually exclusive events, find the expected number of days to be lost through strike or illness out of the next 5000 days.

SOLUTION (a) Let A be the event

$$A = \{\text{day lost through strike}\}$$

Hence

$$P(A) = \frac{400}{8000}$$
$$= 0.05$$

Let B be the event

$$B = \{\text{day lost through illness}\}$$

Hence

$$P(B) = \frac{1200}{8000}$$
$$= 0.15$$

(b) Since these events are mutually exclusive, we have the addition law,

$$P(A \text{ or } B) = P(A) + P(B)$$
$$= 0.05 + 0.15$$
$$= 0.20$$

Therefore, the probability of losing a day through a strike or illness is 0.2 and the expected number of days lost out of a possible 5000 is

$$(0.2)(5000) = 1000 \text{ days}$$

12-10 INDEPENDENT OR DEPENDENT EVENTS

Two events are said to be **independent** when one event does not affect the probability of occurrence of the other. For example, the outcomes of throwing a fair die once and the outcomes of throwing it a second time are considered to be independent events. The outcomes of the second throw are not affected by the outcomes of the first throw.

Two events are said to be **dependent** when one event *does* affect the probability of occurrence of the other. For example, consider drawing two cards from a pack of 52, without replacing the first one. The probability that the first card is a queen is 4/52 or 1/13. If the first card was a queen, then the probability of drawing another queen is now 3/51. The drawing of the first queen (first event) affected the probability of occurrence of the second queen.

12-11 CONDITIONAL PROBABILITY

The idea of dependent events leads on to the concept of conditional probability. Before proceeding, a word on notation. $P(A \mid B)$ means the probability of event A occurring *given* that B has already taken place.

If the events A and B are *independent*, then

$$P(A) = P(A \mid B)$$

Consider the events A and B shown in Fig. 12-3. If we know that B has already occurred, then we have the reduced form of the diagram. Hence.

$$P(A \mid B) = \frac{P(A \text{ and } B)}{P(B)}$$

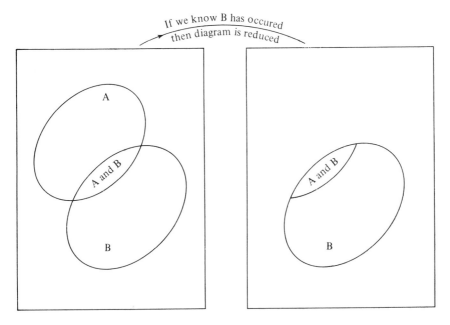

Figure 12-3

and we have the **general multiplication law**

$$P(B)P(A \mid B) = P(A \text{ and } B)$$

If A and B are *independent* events, then

$$P(B)P(A) = P(A \text{ and } B)$$

Example 12-11-1 Two coins are thrown simultaneously. Find the probability that both will land 'heads'.

SOLUTION Let A be the event of the first coin landing 'heads'. Let B be the event of the second coin landing 'heads'. Hence we have

$$P(A) = 0.5$$
$$P(B) = 0.5$$

Since we have independent events

$$P(A)P(B) = P(A \text{ and } B)$$
$$= (0.5)(0.5)$$
$$= 0.25$$

Thus the probability that two heads will appear is 0.25.

Example 12-11-2 A fair die is thrown twice. Find the probability that (*a*) the total of the two scores will be 5, and (*b*) the total of the two scores will be 5 given that the first score was 2.

SOLUTION (*a*) The sample space for two throws is given in a two-dimensional array as shown in Table 12-2. Let A be the event

$$A = \{\text{total score} = 5\} = \{(4,1), (3,2), (2,3), (1,4)\}$$

Table 12-2

First throw	Second throw					
	1	2	3	4	5	6
1	(1,1)	(1,2)	(1,3)	(1,4)	(1,5)	(1,6)
2	(2,1)	(2,2)	(2,3)	(2,4)	(2,5)	(2,6)
3	(3,1)	(3,2)	(3,3)	(3,4)	(3,5)	(3,6)
4	(4,1)	(4,2)	(4,3)	(4,4)	(4,5)	(4,6)
5	(5,1)	(5,2)	(5,3)	(5,4)	(5,5)	(5,6)
6	(6,1)	(6,2)	(6,3)	(6,4)	(6,5)	(6,6)

Then
$$P(A) = 4/36$$
$$= 0.1111$$

(b) Let B be the event

$$B = \{\text{first number} = 2\} = \{(2,3)\}$$

Thus we have

$$P(\text{total} = 5 \mid \text{first score} = 2) = P(A \mid B)$$

$$= \frac{P(A \text{ and } B)}{P(B)}$$

$$P(A \text{ and } B) = P(\text{total score} = 5 \text{ and, simultaneously, first score} = 2)$$

$$P(A \text{ and } B) = 1/36$$

$$P(B) = P(\text{first number} = 2)$$

$$= 6/36$$

Thus

$$P(A \mid B) = \frac{1/36}{6/36}$$

$$= \tfrac{1}{6}$$

The probability that the sum of the two scores will equal 5 given that the first number is 2 is 0.1667.

12-12 APPLICATIONS

Most applications in the industrial world rely heavily on the empirical definition of probability. It is usual to collect data and thus establish a probabilistic value for the particular application.

Example 12-12-1 A production engineer establishes that, for a certain type of numerical control, 530 defective components are produced in every 10 000. Find the expected number of components which are defective in a batch of 1000.

SOLUTION Based on the past evidence

$$P(\text{defective component}) = \frac{530}{10\,000}$$

$$= 0.053$$

Therefore, the expected number of defectives in a batch of 1000 is

$$(1000)(0.053) = 53 \text{ components}$$

Example 12-12-2 An inspection department's records show that for four automatic machines, all producing the same components, the percentage of defectives varied according to Table 12-3.

    If a component is chosen at random from the stores, find the probability that it is defective. What is the expected number of defectives in the annual output of 100 000 components?

Table 12-3

Machine	Output (%)	Defectives (%)
W	30	3
X	35	2
Y	25	4
Z	10	1

SOLUTION Let A be the event

$$A = \{\text{component is defective}\}$$

Let W be the event

$$W = \{\text{component produced on machine W}\}$$

Let X be the event

$$X = \{\text{component produced on machine X}\}$$

Let Y be the event

$$Y = \{\text{component produced on machine Y}\}$$

Let Z be the event

$$Z = \{\text{component produced on machine Z}\}$$

    The probability that the component is defective and is made on machine W is given by

$$P(W \text{ and } A) = P(W)P(A \mid W)$$
$$= 0.3(0.03)$$
$$= 0.009$$

Therefore, the probability that the component picked is defective and was made on machine W is 0.009.

    Similarly, the probability that the component is defective and made on machine X is given by

$$P(X \text{ and } A) = P(X)P(A \mid X)$$
$$= 0.35(0.02)$$
$$= 0.007$$

The probability that the component is defective and made on machine Y is given by

$$P(Y \text{ and } A) = P(Y)P(A \mid Y)$$
$$= 0.25(0.04)$$
$$= 0.01$$

The probability that the component is defective and made on machine Z is given by

$$P(Z \text{ and } A) = P(Z)P(A \mid Z)$$
$$= 0.1(0.01)$$
$$= 0.001$$

We now use the addition law to obtain the probability of picking a defective component from the stores. Hence,

$$P(\text{picking a defective}) = 0.001 + 0.009 + 0.007 + 0.01$$
$$= 0.027$$

Expected number of defectives in an annual output of 100 000 components is given by

$$(0.027)(100\,000) = 2700$$

PROBLEMS

12-1 Write down all possible outcomes to the experiment of throwing a six-sided die once, when the faces are numbered 1,1,2,2,3,3.

12-2 A box contains seven balls, three red, two black and two white. If one ball is drawn from the box, write down the sample space.

12-3 A box contains six balls, two red and the remainder white. Write down the sample space for the experiment of drawing two balls at a time.

12-4 A machine automatically produces components with diameters between 2.5 mm and 3.5 mm. If measurement of the diameter is to the nearest 0.01 mm write down the possible results of a single measurement.

12-5 A six-sided fair die, with the usual numbered faces, is thrown twice. Write down the sample space and the events:

(a) obtaining two numbers which when added together are (i) equal to 3, and (ii) less than 3, and

(b) obtaining two numbers which when multiplied together will be equal to 9.

12-6 A factory has 12 employees, four of whom have degrees, three of whom are qualified technician engineers but do not have degrees, and the remainder of whom are not qualified. State whether the following events are mutually exclusive or non-exclusive.

(a) Event A = {employee chosen with a degree}
   Event B = {employee chosen without a degree}
(b) Event A = {employee chosen who is a qualified technician engineer}
   Event B = {employee chosen who has a degree}
(c) Event A = {employee chosen who is not qualified}
   Event B = {employee chosen who is qualified}

12-7 Describe the difference between classical probability and empirical probability giving examples from engineering practice.

12-8 A coin is thrown once. What is the probability that it will fall 'heads'? State the definition of the type of probability used in calculation of the solution.

12-9 On past record, a machine produces 1000 defectives in 120 000. Write down (a) the probability of producing a defective component, and (b) the probability of producing a 'good' component.

12-10 What is the probability of obtaining a number under 10 when throwing a fair die once?

12-11 An inspection procedure in a factory has records produced once every year showing the number of defective components produced. If the number of defective resistors of a fixed value is 100 in every 10 000, find the expected number of defectives produced in the following year's output of 100 000.

12-12 A card is drawn from a pack of 52. Find the probability that the card is (a) red or black in colour, (b) red in colour or an ace, and (c) black in colour or a picture card.

12-13 A company lost in a period of 1000 days, 200 days through strike action and 250 days through illness. Assuming that days lost through strikes and through illness are mutually exclusive events find:

(a) the probability of a day being lost through strikes over the same period and

(b) the number of days expected to be lost through illness in a period of 2000 days.

12-14 Two coins are thrown simultaneously. Evaluate the probability that both will land 'tails'.

12-15 A fair six-sided die is thrown twice. Write down the sample space and find (a) the probability of obtaining scores totalling 6, and (b) the probability of the two scores adding together to give 6, assuming that the first throw produced a number 2.

12-16 A production engineer establishes that over a period of two months, an automatic lathe produces 300 defective wheel blanks out of a total output of 3000. Find the expected number of wheel blanks to be defective in an output of 10 000.

**12-17 A company's records show that producing a spindle on three automatic lathes has a varying effect on both the number of defectives and the output. This effect is shown in Table 12-14. If a component is chosen at random from the stores, find the probability that it is defective. What is the expected number of defectives in an annual output of 200 000 components?

Table 12-14

Machine	Output (%)	Defectives (%)
A	50	2
B	30	10
C	20	4

*12-18 During laboratory tests, an electronic system failed once in every one-hundred trials. This system is a vital part of an aircraft's landing-gear control mechanism, so two systems are installed in every aircraft for safety reasons. Find the probability that (a) one of these electronic systems fails during a laboratory test, and that (b) both systems will fail during operations.

*12-19 A machine produces 2 per cent defective components during one month. Find, when inspecting a sample of 2 from a batch of 1000, the probability that both will be defective.

Solutions

12-1 $\{1, 2, 3\}$.

12-2 $\{$Red ball, black ball, white ball$\}$.

12-3 $\{$Red and red, red and white, white and white$\}$.

12-4 $\{2.5, 2.6, 2.7, 2.8, \ldots, 3.3, 3.4, 3.5\}$.

12-5 For sample space, see Table 12-1. (*a*) (i) $\{(1,2), (2,1)\}$, (ii) $\{(1,1)\}$; (*b*) $\{3,3\}$.

12-6 (*a*) Exclusive, (*b*) exclusive, (*c*) exclusive.

12-7 See Secs 12-6 and 12-7.

12-8 0.5, classical.

12-9 0.008 33, 0.991 67.

12-10 1.0000.

12-11 1000.

12-12 (*a*) 1, (*b*) 0.5385, (*c*) 0.615 38.

12-13 (*a*) 0.2, (*b*) 500.

12-14 0.25.

12-15 See Table 12-1. (*a*) 5/36, (*b*) 1/6.

12-16 1000.

12-17 (*a*) 0.048, (*b*) 9600.

12-18 (*a*) 0.01, (*b*) 0.0001.

12-19 19/49950.

DISCRETE PROBABILITY DISTRIBUTIONS

Objectives After reading this chapter you should be able to:

1. Use the binomial distribution.
   (*a*) Relate the binomial distribution to the expansion of $(p + q)^n$.
   (*b*) Calculate probabilities using the binomial distribution.
   (*c*) Solve problems, formulated in engineering terms, using the binomial distribution.
   (*d*) Relate probability distributions to graphical representation.
2. Use the Poisson distribution.
   (*a*) Describe the conditions under which the binomial distribution approximates to the Poisson distribution.
   (*b*) Calculate probabilities using the Poisson distribution.
   (*c*) Relate the Poisson distribution to graphical representation.
   (*d*) Solve problems, formulated in engineering terms, using the Poisson distribution.

13-1 INTRODUCTION

It has been illustrated, Secs 12-1 and 12-2, that the set of outcomes from an experiment form a sample space and that events are defined in terms of these outcomes. It is possible to divide the sample space into mutually exclusive events. Having divided the sample space in this way, we can assign a number to each event. These numbers are the values of a **random variable**.

> **Example 13-1-1** A coin is tossed twice and the result noted.
> (*a*) Write down the sample space for this experiment in terms of the outcomes, 'heads' and 'tails'.
> (*b*) By considering the number of heads appearing in the two tosses, divide the sample space into *three* mutually exclusive events.
> (*c*) Assign a number to each of the events in part (*b*), and draw up a table of these random variable values.

SOLUTION (a) The sample space is given by

$$\{HH, HT, TH, TT\}$$

where H represents 'heads' and T represents 'tails'.
(b) By considering the number of heads in two tosses, we can divide the sample space into three mutually exclusive events. These are,

$$\text{Event A} = \{2 \text{ heads in 2 tosses}\} = \{HH\}$$

$$\text{Event B} = \{1 \text{ head in 2 tosses}\} = \{HT, TH\}$$

and $$\text{Event C} = \{2 \text{ tails in 2 tosses}\} = \{TT\}$$

(c) Numbers can be assigned to each of the events in part (b) by considering the number of heads in the two tosses. Table 13-1 illustrates these numbers and hence defines a random variable. In the last example, we defined a random variable according to mutually exclusive events. Since it takes on **discrete** values, it is called a **discrete random variable**. It is usual to denote the random variable by the upper case letters, for example X.

Table 13-1

	A	B	C
Event	$\{HH\}$	$\{HT, TH\}$	$\{TT\}$
Random variable	2	1	0

Example 13-1-2 A coin is tossed twice and the number of heads noted. Write down the probability of obtaining (a) two tails, (b) a head and a tail, and (c) two heads.

SOLUTION Let X be the random variable denoting the number of heads in two tosses. It is usual when considering random variables and probability values to use the symbol

$$P(X = x)$$

Using the classical definition of probability we have
(a) $$P(\text{two tails}) = P(\text{zero heads})$$
$$= P(X = 0)$$
$$= 0.25$$
(b) $$P(\text{a head and a tail}) = P(1 \text{ head})$$
$$= P(X = 1)$$
$$= 2/4$$
$$= 0.5$$

(c) $$P(\text{two heads}) = P(X = 2)$$
$$= 0.25$$

The results of Example 13-1-2 can be arranged in a table format, as shown in Table 13-2. Since

$$P(X = 0) + P(X = 1) + P(X = 2) = 0.25 + 0.5 + 0.25$$
$$= 1.00$$

we have

$$\sum_{x=0}^{2} P(X = x) = 1$$

Thus the **probability function**, $P(X = x)$, whose values add up to one, forms a **probability distribution**. Any probability function has two very important properties:

1. $$0 \leqslant P(X = x) \leqslant 1$$

2. $$\sum P(X = x) = 1$$

Table 13-2

Number of heads in two tosses, x	0	1	2
Probability function, $P(X = x)$	0.25	0.5	0.25

13-2 THE BINOMIAL DISTRIBUTION

There are many examples where an experiment has two, and only two, possible outcomes in one trial. Example 13-1-1 already illustrates one such experiment. We shall consider engineering examples in which the experiment has only two outcomes in any one trial.

Example 13-2-1 It is known from past production figures that 1 per cent of all components produced by a certain machine are defective and hence were rejected on inspection. Write down the probability that when checking one component from a very large batch we find that it is (a) defective and (b) it will pass the inspection procedure.

SOLUTION Let p be the probability of picking a defective component. Since there are only two possible outcomes, we have that the probability of picking a 'good' component is $1 - p$.
(a) Therefore, probability of picking a defective component is

$$p = 0.01$$

(b) The probability of picking a 'good' component is

$$q = 1 - p$$
$$= 1 - 0.01$$
$$= 0.99$$

Hence probability that the component will pass the inspection procedure is 0.99.

If X is the random variable denoting the number of defectives in one trial, we have from Example 13-2-1 that

$$P(X = 0) = 0.99 \qquad \text{and} \qquad P(X = 1) = 0.01$$

This single trial has a probability distribution given by Table 13-3.

Table 13-3

Number of defectives, x	0	1
Probability function, $P(X = x)$	0.99	0.01

Example 13-2-2 If 10 per cent of a very large output from a certain process are reject components, find a probability distribution for the number of rejects when a sample of two is drawn.

SOLUTION Let X be the random variable associated with the number of rejects in a sample of two components. The probability of picking a reject component in one trial is

$$p = 0.10$$

By one trial is meant picking one component.

As we have a very large batch, we shall assume that the probability of drawing the second reject is not affected by having removed one component. That is, we are assuming that the two drawings are independent trials. Therefore, the probability of picking a second reject is $p = 0.1$.

By Sec. 12-11, as we have two independent trials, the probability that both components are reject will be given by

$$P(1\text{st component reject}$$
$$\textit{and } 2\text{nd component reject}) = P(1\text{st component reject})$$
$$\cdot P(2\text{nd component reject})$$
$$= (0.1)(0.1)$$

or
$$p^2 = 0.01$$

In symbols

$$P(X = 2) = p^2$$
$$= 0.01$$

By similar arguments, the probability of picking two 'good' components in a sample of two is

$$P(X = 0) = (1 - p)^2$$
$$= q^2$$
$$= 0.9^2$$
$$= 0.81$$

The reader will notice that we have an equivalent situation, for 'two good components' we can read 'no rejects' in a sample of two.

If we now consider one reject and one good component we have two possibilities. We can draw the reject first, followed by the good component, or we can reverse these outcomes. Hence, we have the probability for a reject and a good component being chosen at the same time as

$$P(\text{reject followed by good component})$$
$$+ P(\text{good component followed by reject})$$

However,

$$P(\text{reject followed by good component}) = P(\text{reject}) \cdot P(\text{good})$$
$$= (0.1)(0.9)$$
$$= 0.09$$

and similarly,

$$P(\text{good component followed by reject}) = P(\text{good}) \cdot P(\text{reject})$$
$$= (0.9)(0.1)$$
$$= 0.09$$

Hence the probability of a reject and a good component in a sample of two is given by

$$P(X = 1) = 0.09 + 0.09$$
$$= 0.18$$

Table 13-4 illustrates the probability distribution which is an example of the **binomial probability distribution**.

Table 13-4

Number of rejects, x	0	1	2
Probability function, $P(X = x)$	0.81	0.18	0.01

The properties of the probability function can be checked. It is obvious from the table that $0 \leqslant P(X = x) \leqslant 1$. For the second property

$$P(X = 0) + P(X = 1) + P(X = 2) = 0.81 + 0.18 + 0.01$$

$$= 1.00$$

Hence

$$\sum_{x=0}^{2} P(X = x) = 1$$

as expected.

In any experiment where there are only two possible outcomes, we label one of these outcomes a 'success' and the other a 'failure'. In Example 13-2-2, the outcome of finding a reject component could be labelled a 'success' while the other outcome of finding a 'good' component would be a 'failure'. Of course, we could define the success or failure of this particular experiment by labelling a 'good' component a 'success' and finding a reject a 'failure'.

We now define p as the probability of a 'success' in one trial and from this it follows, as there are only two outcomes, that $(1 - p) = q$ will be the probability of 'failure'.

In this type of experiment where one trial has only two outcomes, we can under certain conditions use a probability function which is based on the binomial expansion. The function is given by

$$P(X = x) = \binom{n}{x} p^x \cdot q^{(n-x)}$$

where n is the number of trials, x is the number of successes, p the probability of a success, and q the probability of a failure. This function is *always positive* or *zero*. The probability function will lead to a distribution if we substitute the values of x into the equation. Hence

$$P(X = 0) = \binom{n}{0} p^0 \cdot q^{n-0}$$

$$P(X = 1) = \binom{n}{1} p^1 \cdot q^{n-1} \qquad \text{and so on}$$

Summing these probabilities gives

$$P(X = 0) + P(X = 1) + P(X = 2) + \ldots + P(X = n - 1) + P(X = n)$$

$$= \binom{n}{0} p^0 \cdot q^{n-0} + \binom{n}{1} p^1 \cdot q^{n-1} + \binom{n}{2} p^2 \cdot q^{n-2}$$

$$+ \ldots + \binom{n}{n-1} p^{n-1} q + \binom{n}{n} p^n \cdot q^0$$

which is the **binomial expansion** for $(q + p)^n$. Hence we have

$$(q + p)^n = P(X = 0) + P(X = 1) + P(X = 2) + \ldots + P(X = n-1) + P(X = n)$$

But $(q + p) = 1$. Thus we have

which implies that

$$(q + p)^n = 1^n = 1$$

$$\sum_{x=0}^{n} P(X = x) = 1$$

The function

$$P(X = x) = \binom{n}{x} p^x \cdot q^{n-x}$$

has values of probability which form the **binomial distribution.**

Before giving further examples, it should be stressed that this binomial model is based on the following assumptions:

(a) any one trial has only two outcomes,

(b) the probability p is the same for all trials,

(c) the number of trials is finite and must be established before the experiment is carried out, and

(d) the trials are independent.

When constructing the binomial model, the reader should take into account the assumptions made and check that these have *not* been violated.

Example 13-2-3 An automatic lathe produces, on past evidence, 2 per cent defectives or reject components. Find, when drawing a sample of four components from a *very* large batch, the probability that (a) exactly two components are defective, and (b) less than two components are defective.

SOLUTION Since we have a very large batch, we can assume that the trials are independent. Let a 'success' be the drawing of a defective and a 'failure' be the drawing of a good component. Since p is the probability of a 'success', this implies that

$$p = \frac{2}{100}$$

$$= 0.02$$

Since $p = 0.02$, we have from $(q + p) = 1$ that

$$q = 1 - 0.02$$
$$= 0.98$$

Hence we can construct a binomial probability function $P(X = x)$ where

$$P(X = x) = \binom{4}{x} (0.02)^x (0.98)^{4-x}$$

which was obtained from

$$P(X = x) = \binom{n}{x} p^x \cdot q^{n-x}$$

(a) Using the binomial probability function, we substitute $x = 2$ to obtain

$$P(X = 2) = \binom{4}{2}(0.02)^2(0.98)^{4-2}$$

$$= 6(0.02)^2(0.98)^2$$

$$= 0.0023$$

Hence, the probability of finding two defectives in a sample of four is given, by the binomial model, as 0.0023.

(b)

$$P(X < 2) = P(X = 0 \text{ or } X = 1)$$

$$= P(X = 0) + P(X = 1)$$

Using the binomial probability function, we have

$$P(X = 1) = \binom{4}{1}(0.02)^1(0.98)^{4-1}$$

$$= 0.0753$$

and

$$P(X = 0) = \binom{4}{0}(0.02)^0(0.98)^{4-0}$$

$$= 0.9224$$

Hence

$$P(X < 2) = P(X = 0) + P(X = 1)$$

$$= 0.9224 + 0.0753$$

$$= 0.9977$$

Hence we have that the probability of finding a sample of four components with less than two defectives is 0.9977.

Example 13-2-4 A factory manufacturing electronic components produced 3 per cent defective integrated circuits (IC) of a certain type.
(a) Write down a mathematical model which describes the chance of finding, in a sample of 10 integrated circuits, x circuits which will be defective.
(b) Using the model developed in (a) find the probability that exactly (i) 1, (ii) 2, (iii) 3, and (iv) 0 circuits will be defective in a sample of 10.
(c) Calculate the probability that if a customer buys 10 integrated circuits of this type, *four or more* will be defective.

SOLUTION (a) We are considering a finite number of trials $n = 10$, and if we make the assumption that the sample will be drawn from a *very large* batch of integrated circuits, then assuming that the trials are independent, we can use the binomial probability function. In this case, one trial is the choosing of an IC and testing it.

Let p be the probability that in one trial we find a defective IC. Thus $p = 0.03$ which implies

$$q = 1 - p$$

$$= 1 - 0.03$$

$$= 0.97$$

Hence we can construct the model

$$P(X = x) = \binom{10}{x}(0.03)^x(0.97)^{10-x}$$

(b) (i)
$$P(X = 1) = \binom{10}{1}(0.03)^1(0.97)^{10-1}$$

$$= 0.2281$$

(ii)
$$P(X = 2) = \binom{10}{2}(0.03)^2(0.97)^{10-2}$$

$$= 0.0317$$

(iii)
$$P(X = 3) = \binom{10}{3}(0.03)^3(0.97)^{10-3}$$

$$= 0.0026$$

(iv)
$$P(X = 0) = \binom{10}{0}(0.03)^0(0.97)^{10-0}$$

$$= 0.7374$$

(c) $P(X \geqslant 4) = P(X = 4 \text{ or } X = 5 \text{ or } X = 6 \text{ or } X = 7 \text{ or } X = 8 \text{ or }$
$$X = 9 \text{ or } X = 10)$$

$$= P(X = 4) + P(X = 5) + \ldots + P(X = 9) + P(X = 10)$$

Since
$$\sum_{x=0}^{10} P(X = x) = 1$$

we have

$$P(X = 0) + P(X = 1) + P(X = 2) + \ldots + P(X = 9) + P(X = 10) = 1$$

Hence

$$1 - P(X = 0) - P(X = 1) - P(X = 2) - P(X = 3) = P(X = 4) + \ldots + P(X = 10)$$
$$= P(X \geqslant 4)$$

Therefore
$$P(X \geqslant 4) = 1 - 0.7374 - 0.2281 - 0.0317 - 0.0026$$
$$= 0.0002$$

The probability that a customer, on buying 10 ICs of this type, will find four or more defective is 0.0002.

13-3 PROBABILITY DISTRIBUTIONS AND THE MEAN

There is a connection between a probability distribution and the arithmetic mean. We shall illustrate this by examples.

Example 13-3-1 For the data shown in Table 13-5, construct a probability distribution.

Table 13-5

x	0	1	2	3	4	5
f	200	200	600	300	200	100

SOLUTION The total number of measurements is 1600. Hence, using the empirical definition, we have

$$P(X = 0) = \frac{200}{1600} = 0.125$$

$$P(X = 1) = \frac{200}{1600} = 0.125$$

$$P(X = 2) = \frac{600}{1600} = 0.375$$

$$P(X = 3) = \frac{300}{1600} = 0.1875$$

$$P(X = 4) = \frac{200}{1600} = 0.125$$

$$P(X = 5) = \frac{100}{1600} = 0.0625$$

$$\overline{}$$
$$1.0000$$

In example 13-3-1 we constructed a probability distribution from experimental data. Here we divided each frequency by the total frequency of the results. Consider the formula for the arithmetic mean

$$\text{Mean} = \frac{\sum_{i=1}^{n} f_i x_i}{\Sigma f}$$

where Σf is the total frequency. Therefore we have

$$\text{Mean} = \frac{1}{\Sigma f}(f_1 x_1 + f_2 x_2 + \ldots + f_n x_n)$$

$$= \frac{f_1 x_1}{\Sigma f} + \frac{f_2 x_2}{\Sigma f} + \ldots + \frac{f_n x_n}{\Sigma f}$$

$$= x_1 P(X = x_1) + x_2 P(X = x_2) + \ldots + x_n P(X = x_n)$$

$$= \sum_{i=1}^{n} x_i P(X = x_i) \qquad \left[\text{where } P(X = x_i) = \frac{f_i}{\Sigma f} \right]$$

This is also known as the **expectation** of the random variable X. Hence

$$\text{Mean} = \sum_{i=1}^{n} x_i P(X = x_i) = E(X)$$

where $E(X)$ is the expectation of X.

Example 13-3-2 For the data in Table 13-5 and using the probability distribution constructed in Example 13-3-1, find the arithmetic mean.

SOLUTION As

$$\text{Mean} = \sum_{i=1}^{n} x_i P(X = x_i)$$

$$= 0 \cdot P(X = 0) + 1 \cdot P(X = 1) + 2 \cdot P(X = 2) + \ldots + 5 \cdot P(X = 5)$$

$$= (0)(0.125) + (1)(0.125) + (2)(0.375) + (3)(0.1875)$$

$$+ (4)(0.125) + (5)(0.0625)$$

$$= 0 + 0.125 + 0.75 + 0.5625 + 0.5 + 0.3125$$

$$= 2.25$$

It can can be shown that for a binomial distribution we have a mean given by

$$\text{Mean} = E(X) = np$$

where n is the number of trials and p the probability of success.

Example 13-3-3 The data shown in Table 13-6 were collected during an inspection process which sampled four components from a very large batch and the number of rejects counted.

(*a*) Assuming that the mean number of rejects/batch is equal to the binomial mean np, find a distribution by using the probability function

$$P(X = x) = \binom{n}{x} p^x q^{n-x}$$

(*b*) Predict the number of samples with two or more rejects if 1000 batches are to be inspected by the same method.

Table 13-6

Number of rejects, x	0	1	2	3	4
Number of batches, f	50	100	200	100	50

SOLUTION

(*a*) $\quad$ Mean $= \dfrac{(0)(50) + (1)(100) + (2)(200) + (3)(100) + (4)(50)}{50 + 100 + 200 + 100 + 50}$

$\qquad\qquad = 2.0$

Hence since binomial mean $= np$ where n is number in sample, we let

$$np = 2.0$$

or $\qquad\qquad\qquad\qquad 4p = 2.0$

which implies that $\qquad\qquad p = 0.5$

The binomial probability function is given by

$$P(X = x) = \binom{n}{x} p^x q^{n-x}$$

which gives the model

$$P(X = x) = \binom{4}{x} (0.5)^x (0.5)^{4-x}$$

$$= \binom{4}{x} (0.5)^4$$

on adding the indices. Hence we have the probability distribution given in Table 13-7. It can be seen that

$$\Sigma P(X = x) = 1$$

Table 13-7

x	$P(X = x)$
0	0.0625
1	0.2500
2	0.3750
3	0.2500
4	0.0625
	1.0000

(b)
$$P(X \geqslant 2) = P(X = 2 \text{ or } X = 3 \text{ or } X = 4)$$
$$= P(X = 2) + P(X = 3) + P(X = 4)$$
$$= 0.375 + 0.25 + 0.0625$$
$$= 0.6875$$

We assume that we take one sample of four components/batch. Hence in 1000 batches we would have 1000 samples and therefore number of samples with two or more rejects is given by

$$(1000)[P(X \geqslant 2)] = 687.5$$
$$= 688$$

It should always be remembered that the binomial probability function will give a *theoretical* distribution, and careful checks should be made, graphical or otherwise, before adopting it as the mathematical model for a particular situation.

13-4 THE POISSON DISTRIBUTION

Another theoretical probability distribution is based on the **Poisson probability function**. This is in the form

$$P(X = x) = \frac{\lambda^x e^{-\lambda}}{x!}$$

where λ is the mean of the theoretical distribution. As in previous cases, we can show that the total probability is unity:

$$P(X = x) = \frac{\lambda^0 e^{-\lambda}}{0!} + \frac{\lambda^1 e^{-\lambda}}{1!} + \frac{\lambda^2 e^{-\lambda}}{2!} + \ldots$$

$$= e^{-\lambda}\left(1 + \lambda + \frac{\lambda^2}{2!} + \frac{\lambda^3}{3!} + \ldots\right)$$

$$= e^{-\lambda} e^{\lambda}$$

(by using the definition of the exponential function). Thus

$$P(X=x) = e^{-\lambda+\lambda}$$
$$= e^0$$
$$= 1$$

The Poisson model is useful where the discrete random variable can take on *any* positive integer or zero. For example, if we consider the random variable as the number of flaws in a steel slab, then we can see that this number could be zero or any other positive number.

Example 13-4-1 A steel-making process produces steel in 150 m rolls. The average number of flaws/50 m length is one. Find the probability that in the 150 m roll there will be more than four flaws.

SOLUTION Let X be the random variable associated with the number of flaws in the steel roll. For the 150 m roll we have an average number of three flaws.

Let $\lambda = 3$ and the Poisson probability function is given by

$$P(X=x) = \frac{\lambda^x e^{-\lambda}}{x!}$$

Hence

$$P(X=x) = \frac{3^x e^{-3}}{x!}$$

will be the probability function based on the Poisson model. We have that

$$P(X>4) = P(X \geqslant 5)$$
$$= P(X = 5 \text{ or } X = 6 \text{ or } X = 7 \text{ or } \dots)$$
$$= P(X = 5) + P(X = 6) + P(X = 7) + \dots$$

Since the total probability must equal unity, we have

$$P(X=0)+P(X=1)+P(X=2)+P(X=3)+P(X=4)+P(X=5)+\dots = 1$$

Hence

$$1 - P(X = 0) - P(X = 1) - P(X = 2) - P(X = 3) - P(X = 4)$$
$$= P(X = 5) + P(X = 6) + \dots$$
$$= P(X > 4)$$

Using the Poisson probability function we have

$$P(X = 0) = \frac{3^0 e^{-3}}{0!} = e^{-3} = 0.049\,79$$

$$P(X = 1) = \frac{3^1 e^{-3}}{1!} = 3 \cdot e^{-3} = 0.149\,36$$

$$P(X = 2) = \frac{3^2 e^{-3}}{2!} = (4.5)e^{-3} = 0.224\,04$$

$$P(X = 3) = \frac{3^3 e^{-3}}{3!} = (4.5)e^{-3} = 0.224\,04$$

$$P(X = 4) = \frac{3^4 e^{-3}}{4!} = (3.375)e^{-3} = 0.168\,03$$

Thus

$$P(X > 4) = 1 - 0.049\,79 - 0.149\,36 - 0.224\,04 - 0.224\,04 - 0.168\,03$$

$$= 0.184\,74$$

Thus, using the Poisson model, the probability that there will be more than four flaws in a 150 m roll is 0.184 74.

Example 13-4-2 It is found on average that the number of faults in a particular microcomputer after assembly is 0.2. What proportion of microcomputer assemblies have (a) no faults, (b) one fault, (c) less than two faults, and (d) more than two faults, in future production runs.

SOLUTION In theory, there can exist an infinite number of faults in any one of the assemblies. We therefore can consider using the Poisson probability function in order to predict the proportion of assemblies required. We have

$$P(X = x) = \frac{\lambda^x e^{-\lambda}}{x!}$$

which implies that the Poisson model is given by

$$P(X = x) = \frac{0.2^x e^{-0.2}}{x!}$$

(a)
$$P(X = 0) = \frac{0.2^0 e^{-0.2}}{0!} = 0.818\,73$$

Hence, the proportion of microcomputers with no faults is 81.873 per cent, nearly 82 per cent. It should be stressed that this is a prediction based on past evidence and the Poisson model

(b)
$$P(X = 1) = \frac{0.2^1 e^{-0.2}}{1!} = 0.163\,75$$

Therefore, the predicted number of assemblies with one fault will be 16.375 per cent of the future production total.

(c) For $P(X < 2)$ we have

$$P(X < 2) = P(X = 0 \text{ or } X = 1)$$
$$= P(X = 0) + P(X = 1)$$
$$= 0.818\,73 + 0.163\,75$$
$$= 0.982\,48$$

Hence, predicted proportion of assemblies with *less* than two faults is 98.25 per cent in future production runs.

(d) $$P(X > 2) = 1 - P(X = 0) - P(X = 1) - P(X = 2)$$

and $$P(X = 2) = \frac{0.2^2 e^{-0.2}}{2!} = 0.016\,38$$

Hence
$$P(X > 2) = 1 - 0.818\,73 - 0.163\,75 - 0.016\,38$$
$$= 0.001\,14$$

Hence, the predicted proportion of future assemblies with *more* than two faults is 0.114 per cent.

13-5 A USEFUL FORMULA

From the Poisson probability function, we have

$$P(X = 0) = \frac{\lambda^0 e^{-\lambda}}{0!} = e^{-\lambda}$$

$$P(X = 1) = \frac{\lambda^1 e^{-\lambda}}{1!} = \lambda e^{-\lambda} = \lambda \cdot P(X = 0)$$

$$P(X = 2) = \frac{\lambda^2 e^{-\lambda}}{2!} = \frac{\lambda^2}{2} e^{-\lambda} = \frac{\lambda}{2} \cdot P(X = 1)$$

$$P(X = 3) = \frac{\lambda^3 e^{-\lambda}}{3!} = \frac{\lambda}{3}\left(\frac{\lambda^2}{2} e^{-\lambda}\right) = \frac{\lambda}{3} \cdot P(X = 2)$$

Noting the pattern, we have

$$P(X = n + 1) = \frac{\lambda}{n + 1} \cdot P(X = n) \qquad (\text{for } n = 0,1,2,3,4,\dots)$$

Example 13-5-1 A company receives on average eight complaints, concerning faults in their products, during every month. Calculate the probability that there will be more than four complaints in any one month.

SOLUTION As the number of complaints could be infinite, we use the Poisson model. Let the random variable X be the number of complaints. We have

$$P(X=x) = \frac{\lambda^x e^{-\lambda}}{x!}$$

which becomes on substituting $\lambda = 8$,

$$P(X=x) = \frac{8^x e^{-8}}{x!}$$

$$P(X>4) = P(X \geqslant 5)$$

$$= P(X = 5 \text{ or } X = 6 \text{ or } \dots)$$

$$= 1 - P(X=0) - P(X=1) - P(X=2) - P(X=3) - P(X=4)$$

Using the Poisson probability function and the formula developed in this section, we have

$$P(X=0) = \frac{8^0 e^{-8}}{8!} = 0.000\,335$$

$$P(X=1) = 8 \cdot P(X=0) = 0.002\,6837$$

$$P(X=2) = \frac{8}{2} \cdot P(X=1) = 0.010\,735$$

$$P(X=3) = \frac{8}{3} \cdot P(X=2) = 0.028\,626$$

$$P(X=4) = \frac{8}{4} \cdot P(X=3) = 0.057\,252$$

Hence

$$P(X>4) = 1 - 0.099\,632$$

$$= 0.900\,37$$

Hence the probability of a month having more than four complaints is 0.9.

13-6 POISSON APPROXIMATION TO THE BINOMIAL DISTRIBUTION

It can be seen from Secs 13-4 and 13-5 that the Poisson probability function is easier to use than the binomial equivalent. We shall consider under what conditions the binomial probability values can be approximated by using the Poisson model.

Consider the binomial probability function for n trials. We have

$$P(X=x) = \binom{n}{x} (p)^x (q)^{n-x}$$

and from the Poisson model we have a mean λ. Let $\lambda = np$, the binomial distribution mean. Hence $p = \lambda/n$ which can be substituted into the binomial probability function to give

$$P(X = x) = \binom{n}{x}\left(\frac{\lambda}{n}\right)^x (q)^{n-x}$$

But

$$q = (1 - p)$$
$$= \left(1 - \frac{\lambda}{n}\right)$$

and hence we have

$$P(X = x) = \binom{n}{x}\left(\frac{\lambda}{n}\right)^x \left(1 - \frac{\lambda}{n}\right)^{(n-x)}$$

However by Example 3-3-1 we have

$$\binom{n}{x} = \frac{(n)(n-1)(n-2)(n-3)\ldots(n-x+1)}{x!}$$

Therefore the binomial function becomes

$$P(X = x) = \frac{(n)(n-1)(n-2)\ldots(n-x+1)}{x!} \cdot \frac{\lambda^x}{n^x} \cdot \left(1 - \frac{\lambda}{n}\right)^{(n-x)}$$

Dividing each factor in the numerator by one of the factors of n in the denominator we have

$$P(X = x) = \frac{(1)(1 - 1/n)(1 - 2/n)\ldots(1 - x/n + 1/n)}{x!} \cdot (\lambda)^x \cdot \left(1 - \frac{\lambda}{n}\right)^{(n-x)}$$

We know from Chapter 3 that

$$\lim_{n \to \infty} \left(\frac{k}{n}\right) = 0$$

for any fixed number k. Also from Chapter 3, we have

$$\lim_{n \to \infty} \left(1 + \frac{u}{n}\right)^n = \exp(u) = e^u$$

Our binomial function in its new form has the term

$$\left(1 - \frac{\lambda}{n}\right)^{(n-x)} = \left(1 - \frac{\lambda}{n}\right)^n \cdot \left(1 - \frac{\lambda}{n}\right)^{-x}$$

which tends to $\exp(-\lambda) = e^{-\lambda}$ as $n \to \infty$. Therefore letting $n \to \infty$ we have

$$\lim_{n \to \infty} \frac{(1)(1 - 1/n)\ldots(1 - x/n + 1/n)}{x!}(\lambda)^x \left(1 - \frac{\lambda}{n}\right)^n \left(1 - \frac{\lambda}{n}\right)^{-x} = \frac{1}{x!}(\lambda)^x e^{-\lambda}$$

$$= \frac{\lambda^x e^{-\lambda}}{x!}$$

which is the Poisson probability function. However $\lambda = np$ and as λ is a fixed number as $n \to \infty$, we have $p \to 0$. Therefore it follows that the Poisson probability function will approximate to the binomial probability function, or vice versa, when p is small and n is large. In practice, it is common to take $n \geqslant 50$ and $np \leqslant 5$ as a good guide.

Example 13-6-1 A machine produces, on past evidence, 1 per cent defectives. If a sample of 50 is taken, find by using the Poisson approximation to the binomial distribution, the probability of finding (a) no and (b) one defective.

SOLUTION As $n \geqslant 50$ and $np = 0.5 \leqslant 5$ we can use the Poisson probability function in place of the binomial probability function, with

$$\lambda = np = 50(0.01) = 0.5$$

Hence

$$P(X = x) = \frac{0.5^x e^{-0.5}}{x!}$$

is the Poisson probability function for this case.

(a)
$$P(X = 0) = e^{-0.5} = 0.606\,53$$

(b)
$$P(X = 1) = \lambda \cdot P(X = 0) = 0.303\,265$$

If we used the binomial probability function, we would obtain,

$$P(X = 0) = 0.605\,01$$

and

$$P(X = 1) = 0.305\,56$$

These values are close to the Poisson approximations.

13-7 GRAPHICAL REPRESENTATION OF PROBABILITY DISTRIBUTIONS

A bar chart or histogram is normally constructed from the frequencies of the events. As the probability of a particular event is proportional to the frequency of that event, we can plot the probability values instead of the frequency values.

The bar charts and histograms constructed by using probability values are known as **probability distribution graphs**. It is well known that we can use the bar chart for **discrete** data and the histogram representation when it is **continuous**. There are times, as we shall see in Chapter 14, where discrete data are used to construct the class intervals for a continuous variable. In this case, graphical representation would be in the form of a histogram.

Example 13-7-1 An old piece of machinery has a starting mechanism which on average failed to work twice in five trials. By using the binomial probability function, draw up a table of probability values for the number of failures of the starting mechanism in the five trials. Using this table, construct a bar chart for the probability distribution.

SOLUTION From mean $= np$ where n is the number of trials we have

$$2 = 5p$$

hence

$$p = 0.4$$

The probability of the mechanism failing to work is $p = 0.4$, which implies that $q = 1 - p = 0.6$. Hence we have the binomial probability function

$$P(X = x) = \binom{5}{x}(0.4)^x (0.6)^{5-x}$$

Using this function, we can calculate the values of the probability distribution. These are shown in Table 13-8. The usual check to see that

Table 13-8

x	$P(X = x)$
0	0.077 76
1	0.259 20
2	0.345 60
3	0.230 40
4	0.076 80
5	0.010 24
	1.000 00

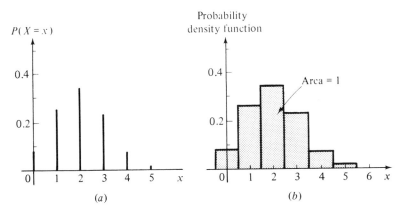

Figure 13-1 (*a*) Discrete data — bar chart; (*b*) continuous data — histogram.

$$\sum_{x=0}^{5} P(X=x) = 1$$

has been carried out.

The bar chart in Fig. 13-1 was constructed from Table 13-8. Alongside this bar chart is a histogram constructed under the assumption that we considered the data as if they were continuous. For example, $x = 1$ will be considered to be the interval from $x = 0.5$ to $x = 1.5$.

PROBLEMS

13-1 A coin is tossed three times and the result noted.

(a) Write down the sample space for this experiment.

(b) By considering the number of heads appearing in the three tosses, divide the sample space into mutually exclusive events.

13-2 A coin is tossed twice and the number of tails noted. By using the classical definition of probability, draw up a table showing the probability distribution for the number of tails appearing in two tosses.

13-3 State the two important properties of a probability function.

13-4 Given the binomial probability function

$$P(X = x) = \binom{4}{x} (0.2)^x (0.8)^{4-x}$$

calculate the probability that (a) $X = 0$, (b) $X = 1$, (c) $X = 2$, and (d) $X = 3$ to 4 decimal places.

13-5 Given the binomial probability function

$$P(X = x) = \binom{5}{x} (0.2)^x (0.8)^{5-x}$$

calculate the probability distribution values and plot a suitable diagram to illustrate these results.

13-6 An automatic machine produces over a year 6 per cent reject components. If a sample of six is drawn from a *very large* batch, find the probability that the number of rejects will be (a) 3, (b) 2, and (c) 1 when inspected.

*13-7 A batch of components is manufactured on a machine which, on past record has produced 1 per cent defective components, or defectives. If this batch is *very large* and a sample of 10 is drawn, find the probability that the number of defectives found on inspection will be (a) 1, (b) 2, and (c) 0.

What is the probability that there will be less than two defectives in this sample of 10?

*13-8 A sample of 50 components is drawn from the stores containing a million of the same type. From past records it is known that 5 per cent of these components will be defective. Find the probability that, in this sample, the number of defective components will be (a) 1, (b) 2, (c) 3, and (d) 4, using the binomial model.

13-9 Given the Poisson probability function

$$P(X = x) = \frac{0.1^x e^{-0.1}}{x!}$$

calculate the probability that (a) $X = 0$, (b) $X = 1$, and (c) $X = 2$ to 4 place of decimals.

*13-10 On average, a firm receives two complaints a month regarding its products. Calculate the probability that it will receive in any one month (a) no complaints, (b) one complaint, and (c) two complaints.

*13-11 A steel sheet has on average 4.9 flaws/m^2. Find the probability that, on inspection, a steel sheet will have in one square metre, (a) no flaws, (b) one flaw, (c) two flaws, and (d) three flaws.

*13-12 A cable when inspected has on average 1 fault/100 metre length. Find when inspecting a 50 m length of this type of cable the probability of observing (a) no faults, (b) one fault, (c) two faults, and (d) three faults.

**13-13 A pipeline on being inspected has on average 1 flaw/500 m length. Find the probability on inspecting a 100 m length that there will be (a) no flaws, (b) one flaw, and (c) more than one flaw.

**13-14 A company finds that on average 2.5 faults are found in a particular electronic subassembly. If 1000 of these assemblies are inspected, find the expected number with three or more faults.

*13-15 Repeat problem **13-8** using the Poisson approximation to the binomial distribution. State the conditions under which this type of approximation holds and state whether these conditions have been satisfied in this case.

13-16 If 20 per cent of the output from an assembly line is faulty, find the average number of assemblies which will be faulty from a sample of eight.

13-17 The average number of components rejected in a sample of 50 is 0.1. Find the probability that if one component is inspected, it will be rejected.

**13-18 It is known from past records that 0.2 per cent of a certain type of integrated circuit are defective. If a sample of 60 ICs are drawn at random, find by using (a) the binomial distribution and (b) the Poisson approximation to the binomial distribution, the probability that all 60 will pass the inspection test.

***13-19 The data shown in Table 13-9 were collected by sampling a very large batch of components. By assuming that the mean number of rejects is equal to the binomial mean $= np$, fit a probability distribution and hence predict from 1000 samples of four components the number with (a) no rejects, (b) one reject, and (c) two rejects.

Table 13-9

Number of rejects, x	0	1	2	3	4
Number of samples, f	18	70	103	68	17

***13-20 The data shown in Table 13-10 were collected during inspection of electronic control devices. Fit a suitable probability distribution by assuming that the mean number of faults $= \lambda$. Hence predict the number of control devices with one or more faults, from a batch of 1000.

Table 13-10

Number of faults, x	0	1	2	3	4	5	$\geqslant 6$
Number of samples, f	20	32	26	14	5	3	0

Solutions

13-1 (a) $\{(H,H,H), (H,H,T), (H,T,H), (T,H,H), (T,T,H), (T,H,T), (H,T,T), (T,T,T)\}$;
(b) $\{(H,H,H)\}, \{(H,H,T), (H,T,H), (T,H,H)\}, \{(T,T,H), (H,T,T), (T,H,T)\}, \{(T,T,T)\}$.

13-2

Number of tails, x	0	1	2
$P(X = x)$	0.25	0.5	0.25

13-3 The probability function values must *all* be *positive* or *zero*. The *sum* of the probability function values must *equal one*.

13-4 (a) 0.4096, (b) 0.4096, (c) 0.1536, (d) 0.0256.

13-5 $P(X = 0) = 0.3277$, $P(X = 1) = 0.4096$, $P(X = 2) = 0.2048$, $P(X = 3) = 0.0512$, $P(X = 4) = 0.0064, P(X = 5) = 0.0003$.

13-6 (a) $P(X = 3) = 0.0036$, (b) $P(X = 2) = 0.0422$, (c) $P(X = 1) = 0.2642$.

13-7 (a) $P(X = 1) = 0.0914$, (b) $P(X = 2) = 0.0042$, (c) $P(X = 0) = 0.9044$; $P(X < 2) = 0.9958$.

13-8 (a) $P(X = 1) = 0.2025$, (b) $P(X = 2) = 0.2611$, (c) $P(X = 3) = 0.2199$, (d) $P(X = 4) = 0.1360$.

13-9 (a) $P(X = 0) = 0.9048$, (b) $P(X = 1) = 0.0905$, (c) $P(X = 2) = 0.0045$.

13-10 (a) $P(X = 0) = 0.1353$, (b) $P(X = 1) = 0.2707$, (c) $P(X = 2) = 0.2707$.

13-11 (a) $P(X = 0) = 0.0074$, (b) $P(X = 1) = 0.0365$, (c) $P(X = 2) = 0.0894$, (d) $P(X = 3) = 0.1460$.

13-12 (a) $P(X = 0) = 0.6065$, (b) $P(X = 1) = 0.3033$, (c) $P(X = 2) = 0.0758$, (d) $P(X = 3) = 0.0126$.

13-13 (a) $P(X = 0) = 0.8187$, (b) $P(X = 1) = 0.1637$, (c) $P(X > 1) = 0.0176$.

13-14 $P(X \geqslant 3) = 0.4562, \Rightarrow 456$.

13-15 (a) $P(X = 1) = 0.2052$, (b) $P(X = 2) = 0.2565$, (c) $P(X = 3) = 0.2138$, (d) $P(X = 4) = 0.1336$. $n \geqslant 50$ and $np =$ mean $\leqslant 5$; conditions are satisfied.

13-16 1.6.

13-17 0.002.

13-18 (a) $P(X = 0) = 0.8868$, (b) $P(X = 0) = 0.8869$.

13-19 (a) $P(X = 0) = 0.0643 \Rightarrow 64$ samples from 1000 with no rejects/sample; (b) $P(X = 1) = 0.2536 \Rightarrow 254$ samples from 1000 with one reject/sample; (c) $P(X = 2) = 0.3750 \Rightarrow 375$ samples from 1000 with two rejects/sample.

13-20 $\lambda = 1.61$, $P(X \geqslant 1) = 0.8001 \Rightarrow$ number of control devices with one or more faults from 1000 is expected to be 800.

CONTINUOUS PROBABILITY
DISTRIBUTIONS

Objectives After reading this chapter you should be able to:

1. Recognize the difference between measurement values and the continuous variable values.
   (*a*) Construct class intervals based on known accuracies of measurement values.
   (*b*) Use class intervals to set up continuous probability distributions from measurements.
2. Use the normal distribution.
   (*a*) Standardize continuous variable values by using the Z transformation.
   (*b*) Evaluate the area under a normal distribution curve by means of tables of Z values.
   (*c*) Relate the areas under the normal distribution curve to probabilities.
   (*d*) Evaluate the probability of obtaining a particular measurement value by using a normal distribution.
   (*e*) Solve problems using the normal distribution.
   (*f*) Determine whether a series of values are normally distributed by means of probability graph paper.
   (*g*) Determine graphically the mean and standard deviation of a normally distributed set of values.

14-1 MEASUREMENT VALUES

The relationship between the measurement value of a continuous variable and the continuous scale is extremely important in engineering and science applications. Variables such as temperature, resistance, current, velocity, and time are all continuous. Measurement of these continuous variables usually yields values which are discrete. We shall define a **measurement value** as one obtained from an experiment or inspection procedure. Consider the measurement of temperature using a digital meter with a readout as shown in Fig. 14-1. This meter reads to the nearest $0.1°C$ and the measurement value of $231.2°C$ gives an indication

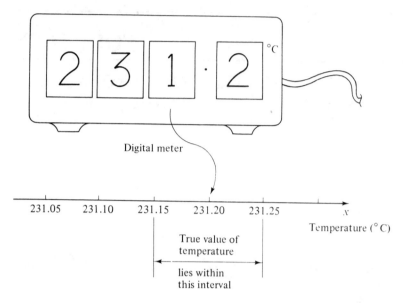

Figure 14-1

of the exact or true value of the variable. We construct a class interval within which the exact value of the temperature will lie. This particular class interval has boundaries 231.15 and 231.25 as shown in Fig. 14-1. Hence *all* temperatures between 231.15°C and 231.25°C will have a measurement value of 231.2°C using the specified digital meter. This example illustrates that measurement values must be translated into a **class interval** which contains the exact or true value of the variable. The **class endpoints** depend on the accuracy of the measuring instrument and the inspection procedure involved.

Example 14-1-1 For the following measurement values, construct a class interval on the continuous scale which includes the exact value of the continuous variable. It may be assumed that the measurements are accurate to the nearest whole unit: (*a*) 4 A, (*b*) 30 mm, and (*c*) 2 V.

SOLUTION (*a*) A 4 A measurement value to the nearest 1 A implies that the exact value of the current flowing lies within the class interval 3.5 to 4.5 A.
(*b*) A 30 mm measurement value to the nearest 1 mm implies that the true value of this length measurement lies within the class interval of 29.5 to 30.5 mm.
(*c*) A 2 V measurement value to the nearest 1 V implies that the exact value of the voltage lies within the class interval 1.5 to 2.5 V.

Example 14-1-2 Measurement of the resistance of a batch of coils using a

Table 14-1

Resistance (Measurement value)(Ω)	Number of coils (frequency)
29	200
30	500
31	720
32	1210
33	710
34	520
35	180

digital meter which reads to the nearest whole unit produced the set of results in Table 14-1.

(a) Draw up a table showing (i) the measured values, (ii) the range within which the exact value of resistance lies, and (iii) the probability distribution for the measurement values.

(b) Draw diagrams representing the probability distributions for the measurement values, M, and the continuous variable, 'resistance'.

(c) Using the probability distribution constructed in part (a), evaluate the *expected* number of coils whose exact value of resistance lies within the range 30.5 to 32.5 Ω, from a total production target of 100 000.

SOLUTION (a) Consider the measurement value of 29 Ω. This implies that the exact value of resistance lies within the class interval or range 28.5 to 29.5 Ω. The measurement value of 29 Ω occurred 200 times out a total of 4040 coils. Therefore, using the empirical definition, we can construct a probability value for obtaining this particular measurement. Thus,

$$P(\text{measured value} = 29\,\Omega) = P(28.5 \leqslant \text{exact value} < 29.5)$$

$$= \frac{200}{4040}$$

$$= 0.049\,505$$

Continuing in this manner for each measurement value, we can produce Table 14-2.

(b) Figure 14-2 illustrates the diagrams constructed from the values calculated in part (a).

(c) From Table 14-2, we have

$$P(30.5 \leqslant \text{resistance} < 31.5) = 0.178\,218$$

and $$P(31.5 \leqslant \text{resistance} < 32.5) = 0.299\,505$$

Table 14-2

Measured value, M, of the resistance in ohms	Range within which the exact value, X, of the resistance lies Class interval a to b^-	$P(\text{measured value} = M)$ $= P(a \leqslant X < b)$ Probability distribution
29	28.5 to 29.5$^-$	0.049 505
30	29.5 to 30.5$^-$	0.123 762
31	30.5 to 31.5$^-$	0.178 218
32	31.5 to 32.5$^-$	0.299 505
33	32.5 to 33.5$^-$	0.175 743
34	33.5 to 34.5$^-$	0.128 713
35	34.5 to 35.5$^-$	0.044 554
		Total probability = 1.000 000

Therefore using the addition law we have

$$P(30.5 \leqslant \text{resistance} < 32.5) = 0.178\,218 + 0.299\,505$$

$$= 0.477\,723$$

Hence estimated, or expected, number of coils with resistance between 30.5 and 32.5 ohm from a production target of 100 000, is given by

$$(100\,000)(0.477\,723) = 47\,772.3 \text{ coils}$$

It is usual practice to round off to the nearest whole number and thus the expected number of coils within the range required is 47 772.

14-2 THEORETICAL DISTRIBUTIONS

In Example 14-1-2, we constructed a probability distribution from experimental results. The total area under the histogram represents the total probability of one. In general, the area under the graph of a probability distribution of a continuous random variable always equals one. It is therefore possible to construct theoretical distributions for continuous random variables providing we allow the area under the graph and above the x axis to equal one. Figure 14-3 illustrates two such theoretical distributions from the infinite number that are possible.

The function $f(x)$ is called the **probability density function**. The area between two lines $x = a$ and $x = b$, under the curve and above the x axis, represents the probability of finding X, the random variable value, between a and b. That is

$$\text{Area} = P(a \leqslant X \leqslant b)$$

We have seen in the chapter on applications of integration theory that this type of area can be found by

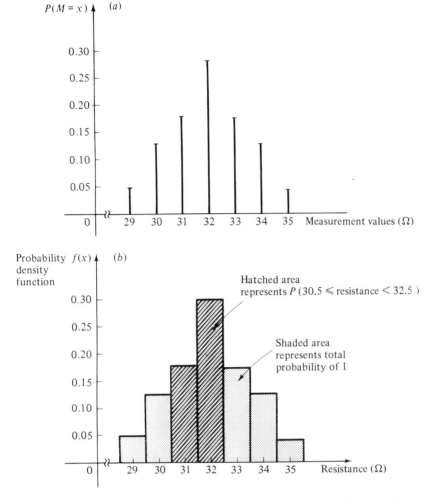

Figure 14-2 (*a*) Probability distribution for measurement values, *M*. (*b*) Probability distribution for the continuous random variable *X* representing the 'true' values of the variable, resistance.

$$A = \int_a^b y\,dx$$

Therefore

$$P(a \leqslant X \leqslant b) = \int_a^b f(x)\,dx$$

It is important that we stress the theoretical nature of these distributions and, during any modelling process, application of the same should be carried out with extreme caution. A check should be made, either empirically or theoretically,

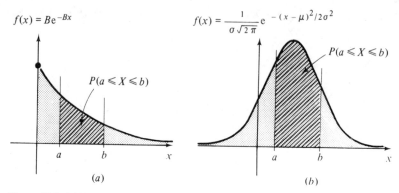

Figure 14-3 (a) An exponential distribution; (b) a normal distribution.

that the measurements under consideration do indeed follow the probability distribution chosen.

14-3 THE NORMAL DISTRIBUTION

One distribution which is used extensively in engineering inspection is the **normal distribution**. This has a density function of

$$f(x) = \frac{1}{\sigma\sqrt{2\pi}} \exp[-(x-\mu)^2/2\sigma^2]$$

where μ is the mean of the population and σ is the standard deviation. Figure 14-3 illustrates the curve and, once again, the area between a and b represents the

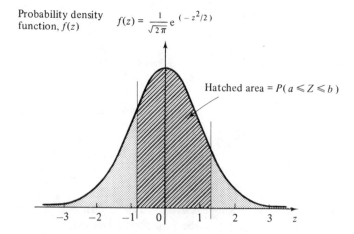

Figure 14-4 The standardized normal distribution.

probability of finding the value X between a and b. That is, area $= P(a \leqslant X \leqslant b)$. Therefore the area under this function between the lines $x = a$ and $x = b$ is given by

$$A = P(a \leqslant X \leqslant b) = \int_a^b \frac{1}{\sigma\sqrt{2\pi}} \exp[-(x-\mu)^2/2\sigma^2]\, dx$$

This integral *cannot* be evaluated by reverse differentiation and we resort to numerical methods such as the mid-ordinate, trapezoidal or Simpson's rule. This in itself is very time-consuming, so it is usual practice to use areas precalculated by a computer and brought together in a table form. Table A-3 in the appendix gives these areas for a normal distribution with a mean $\mu = 0$, and a standard deviation $\sigma = 1$.

In order to use this standard table, we have to *transform* any normal distribution into one with a mean $\mu = 0$, and a standard deviation $\sigma = 1$. Let

$$z = \frac{x-\mu}{\sigma} = \frac{x}{\sigma} - \frac{\mu}{\sigma} \qquad (\mu/\sigma \text{ is a constant})$$

$\Rightarrow$

$$\frac{dz}{dx} = \frac{1}{\sigma}$$

or

$$dx = \sigma\, dx$$

Since

$$z = \frac{x-\mu}{\sigma}$$

$$z^2 = \frac{(x-\mu)^2}{\sigma^2}$$

which, along with $dx = \sigma\, dz$, can be substituted into the integral for the *general* normal distribution.

$$P(a \leqslant X \leqslant b) = \int_a^b \frac{1}{\sigma\sqrt{2\pi}} \exp[-(x-\mu)^2/2\sigma^2]\, dx$$

$$= \int_{z_a}^{z_b} \frac{1}{\sqrt{2\pi}} \exp(-z^2/2)\, dz$$

$$= \int_{z_a}^{z_b} \frac{1}{\sqrt{2\pi}} e^{(-z^2/2)}\, dz$$

$$= P(z_a \leqslant Z \leqslant z_b)$$

It should be noticed that the limits of the integral have been changed by using

$$z = \frac{x-\mu}{\sigma}$$

That is, when $x = b$

$$z_b = \frac{b - \mu}{\sigma}$$

and when $x = a$,

$$z_a = \frac{a - \mu}{\sigma}$$

It follows that if we require the area under the normal curve between two points a and b, we can use Table A-3 after transforming these points, or limits, to z values. The process of transforming the endpoints, or limits of the integral, is known as **standardizing** the variable values.

Example 14-3-1 A continuous random variable X is normally distributed with a mean $\mu = 20$ and a standard deviation of $\sigma = 4$. Standardize the following values of this random variable: (a) $X = 24.0$, (b) $X = 22.5$, (c) $X = 28.0$, (d) $X = 18.3$, and (e) $X = 12.0$.

SOLUTION Standardizing values of a continuous random variable means transforming them into Z values by using

$$Z = \frac{X - \mu}{\sigma}$$

(a)
$$Z_{24} = \frac{24.0 - 20}{4}$$
$$= 1$$

(b)
$$Z_{22.5} = \frac{22.5 - 20}{4}$$
$$= 0.625$$

(c)
$$Z_{28} = \frac{28.0 - 20}{4}$$
$$= 2$$

(d)
$$Z_{18.3} = \frac{18.3 - 20}{4}$$
$$= -0.425$$

(e)
$$Z_{12} = \frac{12.0 - 20}{4}$$
$$= -2$$

Example 14-3-2 Find the area under the standard normal curve for the ranges (a) $0 \leqslant Z \leqslant 1$, (b) $-1 \leqslant Z \leqslant 1$, and (c) $Z \geqslant 2$.

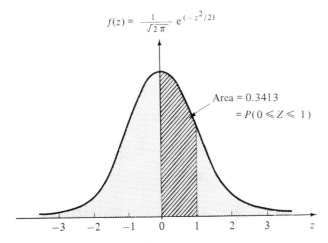

$$f(z) = \frac{1}{\sqrt{2\pi}}\, e^{(-z^2/2)}$$

Area = 0.3413
= $P(0 \leqslant Z \leqslant 1)$

Figure 14-5

SOLUTION The areas for all parts of this solution are to be found in Table A-3 in the appendix. This table of areas was calculated by using a computer programmed with Simpson's rule.

(*a*) Area for $0 \leqslant Z \leqslant 1$ is shown in Fig. 14-5. From Table A-3 we have area for $0 \leqslant Z \leqslant 1$ is 0.3413.

(*b*) The area for $-1 \leqslant Z \leqslant 1$ consists of two parts. Table A-3 in the appendix gives the area for $0 \leqslant Z \leqslant 1$ and since the normal curve is symmetrical, this is identical with the area for $-1 \leqslant Z \leqslant 0$. Figure 14-6 illustrates these two equal areas and from Table A-3 we have area for $0 \leqslant Z \leqslant 1$ is 0.3413. This implies area for $-1 \leqslant Z \leqslant 1$ is given by $2(0.3413) = 0.6826$.

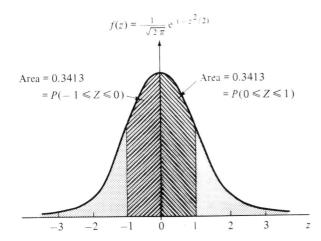

$$f(z) = \frac{1}{\sqrt{2\pi}}\, e^{(-z^2/2)}$$

Area = 0.3413
= $P(-1 \leqslant Z \leqslant 0)$

Area = 0.3413
= $P(0 \leqslant Z \leqslant 1)$

Figure 14-6

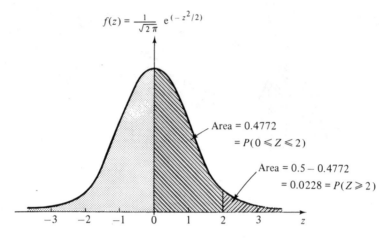

$$f(z) = \frac{1}{\sqrt{2\pi}} \, e^{(-z^2/2)}$$

Area = 0.4772
= $P(0 \leqslant Z \leqslant 2)$

Area = 0.5 − 0.4772
= 0.0228 = $P(Z \geqslant 2)$

Figure 14-7

(c) Figure 14-7 illustrates the area for $Z \geqslant 2$. Since Table A-3 gives the area for $0 \leqslant Z \leqslant 2$, we have to subtract this value from 0.5, half the total area. Therefore, area for $0 \leqslant Z \leqslant 2$ is 0.4772 and area for $Z \geqslant 2$ is $0.5 - 0.4772$, i.e. 0.0228.

Example 14-3-3 Find the value of a when the range $Z \geqslant a$ is equivalent to an area under the normal curve of 0.025.

SOLUTION From Table A-3 in the appendix we have the area for $0 \leqslant Z \leqslant a$. This area is equal to $0.5 - 0.025 = 0.475$. Therefore value of a is 1.960 for $Z \geqslant a$ to have an area of 0.025.

14-4 APPLICATIONS

Example 14-4-1 The resistance of $\frac{1}{4}$ W carbon film resistors is normally distributed with a mean of 560 Ω and a standard deviation of 9 Ω. Find the proportion of resistors which on inspection will be within the design limits of 533 to 587 Ω. It may be assumed that measurement of resistance is by a digital meter reading to the nearest 1 Ω.

SOLUTION Design limits take into account the inspection instruments and procedure. Thus it may be assumed that a resistor having a measurement value of 533 Ω or 587 Ω, will be within the design limits.
 As we are concerned with measurement values, we have to construct the interval within which the exact value of resistance lies. For the measurement value of 533 Ω, we have the range 532.5 to 533.5 Ω. Similarly, for the

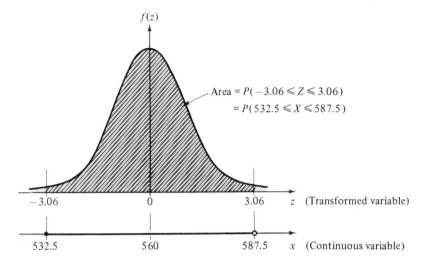

Figure 14-8

other design limit, also a measurement value, we have a range of 586.5 to 587.5 Ω. Hence for measurement values from 533 to 587 Ω in steps of 1 Ω, we have the class interval, 532.5 to 587.5 Ω on the continuous scale. This is illustrated in Fig. 14-8 along with the normal distribution curve.

Transforming the endpoints of the constructed interval, we have

$$z_{587.5} = \frac{587.5 - 560}{9}$$

$$= 3.0555$$

$$= 3.06$$

$$z_{532.5} = \frac{532.5 - 560}{9}$$

$$= -3.0555$$

$$= -3.06$$

From Table A-3 in the appendix, we have the area from $0 \leqslant Z \leqslant 3.06$ as 0.4989. Since the curve is symmetrical, the area for $-3.06 \leqslant Z \leqslant 0$ is also 0.4989. Hence

$$P(-3.06 \leqslant Z \leqslant 3.06) = 0.4989 + 0.4989$$

$$= 0.9978.$$

This implies, when X represents the continuous random variable, that

$$P(532.5 \leqslant X \leqslant 587.5) = P(\text{measured value lies between 532 and 587}\,\Omega)$$

$$= 0.9978$$

Hence proportion of resistors within the design limits on inspection is 99.78%.

Example 14-4-2 A machine produces shafts with a mean diameter of $\mu = 10.1\,\text{mm}$ and a standard deviation of $\sigma = 0.1\,\text{mm}$. Assuming that the diameters of the shafts are normally distributed, what is the probability that when these are measured the size will be (a) over 10.3 mm, (b) under 10.3 mm, and (c) equal to 10.3 mm. It may be assumed that the inspection procedure produces results to the nearest 0.1 mm.

SOLUTION (a) For a measurement value of over 10.3 mm, we have the event $\{10.4, 10.5, 10.6, 10.7, \dots\}$. Thus the endpoint of 10.4 implies that we construct a class interval, within which the exact values of the diameters lie, of 10.35 mm upwards. This is illustrated in Fig. 14-9 and can be written as $(10.35, \infty)$. Using

$$z = \frac{x - \mu}{\sigma}$$

we have

$$z = \frac{10.35 - 10.1}{0.1}$$

$$= 2.5$$

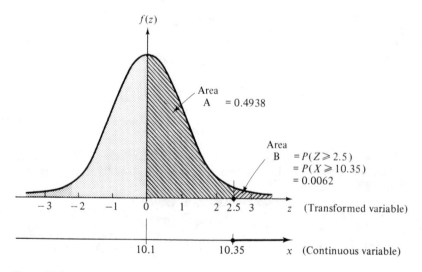

Figure 14-9

Therefore
$$P(\text{measured value is over } 10.3) = P(X \geqslant 10.35)$$
$$= P(Z \geqslant 2.5)$$

Again using Table A-3 in the appendix we have

$$(\text{Area for } 0 \leqslant Z \leqslant 2.5) = 0.4938 \qquad (\text{area A in Fig. 14-9})$$

$$(\text{Area for } Z \geqslant 2.5) = 0.5 - 0.4938$$

$$= 0.0062 \qquad (\text{area B in Fig. 14-9})$$

Hence $P(Z \geqslant 2.5) = 0.0062$, which implies that

$$P(\text{measured diameter value being over } 10.3 \text{ mm}) = 0.0062$$

(*b*) For a measurement value to be under 10.3 mm, we have the event $\{\ldots, 10.0, 10.1, 10.2\}$. Hence on constructing the interval within which the exact value of the variable lies, we have 10.25 downwards. This is illustrated in Fig. 14-10 and may be denoted by the interval $(-\infty, 10.25)$. Transforming 10.25 to standard values we have

$$z = \frac{10.25 - 10.1}{0.1}$$

$$= 1.5$$

Therefore
$$P(\text{measured value is under } 10.3 \text{ mm}) = P(X \leqslant 10.3)$$
$$= P(Z \leqslant 1.5)$$

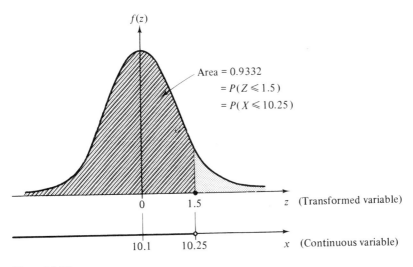

Figure 14-10

Again using Table A-3 in the appendix, we have for $0 \leqslant Z \leqslant 1.5$, the area is 0.4332. Hence for $Z \leqslant 1.5$, we have the area $0.5 + 0.4332 = 0.9332$. Therefore $P(Z \leqslant 1.5) = 0.9332$, which implies that

$$P(\text{measured diameter value being under } 10.3 \text{ mm}) = 0.9332$$

(c) For the measured value to be equal to 10.3 mm, we construct the interval 10.25 to 10.35. Both these values have already been standardized:

Hence
$$z_{10.35} = 2.5 \quad \text{and} \quad z_{10.25} = 1.5$$

$$P(\text{measured value} = 10.3 \text{ mm}) = P(10.25 \leqslant X \leqslant 10.35)$$

$$= P(1.5 \leqslant Z \leqslant 2.5)$$

Figure 14-11 illustrates the area required. From Table A-3 we have

$$\text{for } 0 \leqslant Z \leqslant 1.5 \quad \text{area} = 0.4332$$

and
$$\text{for } 0 \leqslant Z \leqslant 2.5 \quad \text{area} = 0.4938$$

Subtracting these two areas gives the area for $1.5 \leqslant Z \leqslant 2.5$. Hence

$$P(1.5 \leqslant Z \leqslant 2.5) = 0.4938 - 0.4332$$

$$= 0.0606$$

Therefore
$$P(\text{measured value} = 10.3 \text{ mm}) = P(10.25 \leqslant X \leqslant 10.35)$$

$$= 0.0606$$

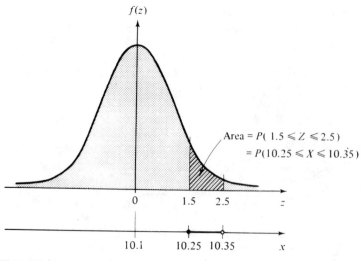

$f(z)$

Area $= P(1.5 \leqslant Z \leqslant 2.5)$
$= P(10.25 \leqslant X \leqslant 10.35)$

0   1.5   2.5 z

10.1   10.25   10.35 x

Figure 14-11

The reader should observe that all components will fit into one of the above categories. Thus we are certain to obtain during inspection either a component whose diameter is over 10.3 mm, under 10.3 mm or equal to 10.3 mm. This implies that if we sum the probabilities for each of these cases we should arrive at the total probability of unity.

P(measured diameter is over 10.3 mm) + P(measured value is under 10.3 mm)

$$+ P\text{(measured value} = 10.3\,\text{mm)} = 0.0062 + 0.9332 + 0.0606$$
$$= 1.0000$$

as expected.

14-5 PROBABILITY GRAPH PAPER

The variables within the section on applications were either *known* or *assumed* to be **normally distributed**. We shall now proceed to introduce a method which will enable this assumption to be checked.

Fitting a normal distribution to values of a continuous variable is a modelling process which involves two stages. Stage one is the collection of experimental results in the form of measurement values and translating these to the class intervals which contain the exact values of the continuous variable. This has been demonstrated in Example 14-1-2. The second stage is the plotting of the upper boundary of the constructed class interval against the percentage cumulative frequency on special probability paper. This will be illustrated in Example 14-5-1. The degree to which these plotted points lie on a straight line determines the closeness of fit to the normal distribution. We shall determine the degree of closeness of these points to a straight line by 'eye', though in practice numerical methods are available.

The special probability paper has a vertical scale constructed from the area under the normal distribution graph. This is illustrated in Fig. 14-12. In this figure, the vertical scale, of the special probability paper, is in the horizontal position to indicate the relationship between it and the areas under the curve.

> **Example 14-5-1** It is required to predict the proportions of resistors within design limits from a given manufacturing process. An inspection procedure has been adopted whereby measurement of resistance is made to the nearest ohm. The process of manufacture was monitored by this inspection method and the results are tabulated in Table 14-3.
> (*a*) Construct a table showing (i) measured values, (ii) class intervals and frequency, (iii) cumulative frequency, and (iv) percentage cumulative frequency.
> (*b*) Plot on probability paper the percentage cumulative frequency against the upper class boundary.
> (*c*) Using the graph, estimate whether the resistance values could follow the normal distribution.

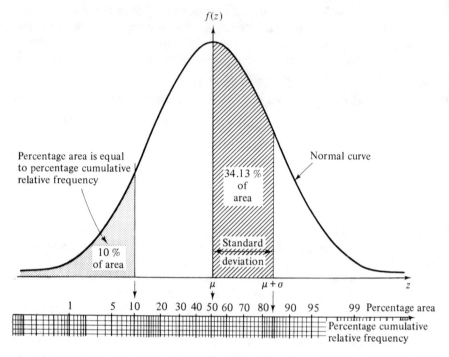

Figure 14-12 Relationship between 'normal' probability paper and the area under the normal curve.

Table 14-3

Resistance, measurement value (Ω)	Number of resistors, Frequency	Resistance, measurement value (Ω)	Number of resistors, Frequency
95	18	101	175
96	29	102	120
97	66	103	65
98	121	104	28
99	176	105	17
100	197		

SOLUTION (*a*) The result is Table 14.4.

(*b*) Figure 14-13 illustrates the plotted graph with the 'best' straight line drawn through the points.

(*c*) Since it appears that the points are very close to a straight line, the resistance values can be considered to be normally distributed.

Fitting a normal distribution requires the mean μ and the standard deviation to be specified. We can calculate these values from the measurements. However,

Table 14-4

Resistance, measured value (Ω)	Class interval	Frequency	Cumulative frequency	Percentage cumulative frequency
95	94.5–95.5	18	18	1.8
96	95.5–96.5	29	47	4.6
97	96.5–97.5	66	113	11.2
98	97.5–98.5	121	234	23.1
99	98.5–99.5	176	410	40.5
100	99.5–100.5	197	607	60.0
101	100.5–101.5	175	782	77.3
102	101.5–102.5	120	902	89.1
103	102.5–103.5	65	967	95.6
104	103.5–104.5	28	995	98.3
105	104.5–105.5	17	1012	100.0

another way is to use the probability graph paper, and the fact that the normal distribution is symmetrical about the mean. Thus the mean of a normal distribution lies at the 50th percentile on the percentage cumulative frequency graph. From Table A-3 in the appendix, we have for $Z = 1$, one standard deviation from the mean, an area of 0.3413 which implies that 34.13 per cent of components lie between the mean and one standard deviation. Therefore, on the cumulative frequency graph for the normal distribution, the standard deviation can be estimated by considering the 84th percentile and subtracting from the mean, the 50th percentile. This process of estimating the mean and standard deviation of the required normal distribution is illustrated in the next example.

Example 14-5-2 For the measurements in Example 14-5-1, fit a normal distribution giving the mean and standard deviation.

SOLUTION From the graph in Fig. 14-13, the 50th percentile is 100 and the 84th percentile is 102.1. Hence mean of normal distribution is $\mu = 100 \, \Omega$ and standard deviation is

$$\sigma = (102.1 - 100)$$

or

$$\sigma = 2.1 \, \Omega$$

Example 14-5-3 Using the fitted normal distribution with $\mu = 100 \, \Omega$ and standard deviation $\sigma = 2.1$, estimate the proportion of resistors whose resistance, when inspected, will be over 99 Ω.

SOLUTION From

$$z = \frac{x - \mu}{\sigma}$$

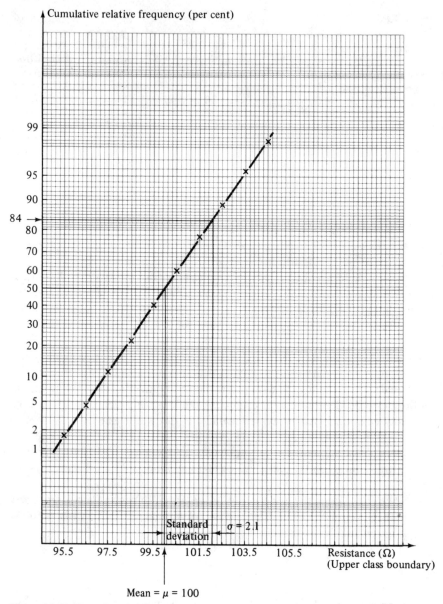

Figure 14-13 Normal probability paper.

assuming that inspection is made to the nearest 1 Ω, we have

$$z = \frac{99.5 - 100}{2.1}$$

$$= -0.2381$$

From Table A-3, the area for $0 \leqslant Z \leqslant 0.24$ is 0.0948 which implies for $-0.24 \leqslant Z \leqslant 0$ that the area is also 0.0948. Hence

$$P(Z \geqslant -0.24) = P(X \geqslant 99.5)$$
$$= P(\text{measurement value} > 99)$$
$$= 0.0948 + 0.5 = 0.5948$$

Hence the proportion of resistors whose resistance, when inspected to the nearest 1 Ω, will be over 99 Ω, is 59.48 per cent.

PROBLEMS

14-1 Explain the difference between a measurement value and the exact value of a variable.

14-2 Construct a class interval which includes the value of the continuous random variable, resistance, if we measured a component and the result was 12.6 Ω to the nearest 0.1 Ω.

14-3 An inspection procedure revealed measurement values of 25 mm, 26 mm, and 27 mm. State the class endpoints for the interval which includes these values on the continuous scale.

14-4 For the following measurement values, 23 Ω, 30 m, 4 A, and 2°, construct intervals which include the exact value of the continuous variable. It may be assumed that the measurement procedure produces results accurate to the nearest whole unit.

14-5 A continuous random variable X is normally distributed with a mean $\mu = 120$ and a standard deviation of 20. Standardize the following values of the random variable: (a) $X = 122$, (b) $X = 126$, (c) $X = 118$, (d) $X = 160$, and (e) $X = 80$.

14-6 What is the value of the random continuous variable whose standardized value $Z = 10$, assuming that it is normally distributed with a mean $\mu = 24$ and a standard deviation $\sigma = 2$?

14-7 A continuous random variable X is normally distributed with a mean $\mu = 10$ and a standard deviation $\sigma = 2$. Standardize the following values of the random variable: (a) 12, (b) -2, (c) 0, and (d) 11.5.

14-8 The length of a clock spindle is normally distributed with a mean $\mu = 12.1$ mm and a standard deviation $\sigma = 0.05$ mm. During inspection, the length is measured and found to be 12.1 mm to the nearest 0.1 mm. Construct a class interval within which the exact length of this spindle lies. Standardize the endpoints of the constructed class interval and hence write down the range within which the standardized random variable Z lies.

For problems **14-9** to **14-18** find the area under the standardized normal curve for the range of values shown.

14-9 $0 \leqslant Z < 1.8$.

14-10 $-1.3 < Z \leqslant 0$.

*14-11 $2.5 > Z$.

*14-12 $2.5 \leqslant Z$.

*14-13 $Z \geqslant 1.4$.

*14-14 $3 \leqslant Z$.

14-15 $-1.2 \leqslant Z \leqslant 1.2$.

*14-16 $-2 < Z < 2.1$.

**14-17 $1.2 \leqslant Z < 2$.

**14-18 $-1 < Z \leqslant -0.5$.

For problems **14-19** to **14-22** find the value of a when the range $Z \leqslant a$ is equivalent to an area under the standard normal curve of A.

14-19 $A = 0.05$.

14-20 $A = 0.025$.

14-21 $A = 0.01$.

14-22 $A = 0.005$.

For problems **14-23** to **14-26** find the proportion of resistors whose resistance is equivalent to the range $Z \leqslant a$.

*14-23 $a = 2$.

*14-24 $a = -1.5$.

14-25 $a = 0$.

*14-26 $a = 1.22$.

For problems **14-27** to **14-30**, a component has a length which is normally distributed with a mean $= \mu$ and a standard deviation $= \sigma$. Find in each case the percentage of components whose lengths have measured values within the range 400.0 to 400.2 mm. Assume measurement is to the nearest 0.1 mm.

14-27 $\mu = 400$ mm, $\sigma = 0.1$ mm.

14-28 $\mu = 400.05$ mm, $\sigma = 0.1$ mm.

14-29 $\mu = 399.95$ mm, $\sigma = 0.1$ mm.

14-30 $\mu = 399.95$ mm, $\sigma = 0.2$ mm.

***14-31 It was decided to keep the amount of rejected components, when measuring the component's diameter to the nearest 0.01 mm, down to 5 per cent of the total production. Assuming that the design limits are 20.10 to 20.30 mm inclusive and that the diameters are normally distributed with a mean $\mu = 20.20$ mm, find the maximum value of the standard deviation.

**14-32 A machine produces cases with a diameter which is normally distributed with a mean $\mu = 300$ mm and a standard deviation $\sigma = 2.5$ mm. If the inspection procedure allows a diameter to be measured to the nearest 0.1 mm, find how many cases, within the design limits of 296 mm to 304 mm inclusive, will pass the inspection test.

*14-33 The resistance of $\frac{1}{4}$ W resistors is normally distributed with a mean of 400 Ω and a standard deviation of 10 Ω. Find the percentage of resistors whose measurement values will be (*a*) within the range 390 and 405 Ω inclusive, and (*b*) equal to 420 Ω. It may be assumed that the resistance is measured to the nearest ohm.

*14-34 It is required to build a probability model for prediction of the proportions of components whose diameters lie within design limits. Measurement of these diameters to the nearest 0.01 mm leads to the data in Table 14-5. Construct a table showing (*a*) the measure-

Table 14-5

Diameter, measurement value (mm)	Number of components
19.97	6
19.98	61
19.99	242
20.00	383
20.01	241
20.02	60
20.03	6

ment values, (b) the class intervals related to the measurement values and the frequency values, (c) the cumulative frequency, and (d) the percentage cumulative frequency.

14-35 Using the information in the table constructed in question **14-34** plot on probability paper the percentage cumulative frequency against the upper class boundaries. Draw the best straight line through the plotted points and hence assess whether the diameters of this particular component are normally distributed.

14-36 From the graph in question 14-35, find the mean and standard deviation of the distribution.

**14-37 Fit a normal distribution to the measurement data shown in Table 14-6 and hence predict the number of resistors whose exact value of resistance lies between 16.1 and 18.2 Ω.

Table 14-6

Resistance, measurement value (Ω)	Number of resistors (f)
15	22
16	136
17	341
18	341
19	136
20	22

**14-38 Fit a normal distribution to the data in Table 14-7 and hence predict the number of resistors whose measurement values lie between 100 and 104 Ω, inclusive.

Table 14-7

Resistance, measurement value (Ω)	Number of resistors
99	66
100	121
101	175
102	197
103	175
104	121
105	66

Solutions

14-2 12.55–12.65⁻.
14-3 24.5 mm, 27.5 mm.
14-4 22.5–23.5⁻, 29.5–30.5⁻, 3.5–4.5⁻, 1.5–2.5⁻.
14-5 (a) 0.1, (b) 0.3, (c) −0.1, (d) 2, (e) −2.
14-6 $X = 44$.

14-7 (*a*) 1, (*b*) −6, (*c*) −5, (*d*) 0.75.

14-8 12.05−12.15⁻, −1 ≤ *Z* ≤ 1.

14-9 0.4641.

14-10 0.4032.

14-11 0.9938.

14-12 0.0062.

14-13 0.0808.

14-14 0.0013.

14-15 0.7698.

14-16 0.9593.

14-17 0.0923.

14-18 0.1498.

14-19 1.65.

14-20 1.96.

14-21 2.33.

14-22 2.58.

14-23 97.72%.

14-24 6.68%.

14-25 50%.

14-26 88.88%.

14-27 68.53%.

14-28 81.85%.

14-29 49.87%.

14-30 43.32%.

14-31 0.0536.

14-32 89.48%.

14-33 (*a*) 56.19%, (*b*) 0.54%.

14-36 $\mu = 20\,\text{mm}$, $\sigma = 0.01\,\text{mm}$.

14-37 $\mu = 17.5\,\Omega$, $\sigma = 1\,\Omega$.

14-38 $\mu = 102\,\Omega$, $\sigma = 2\,\Omega$, 78.88%.

COMPLEX NUMBERS

Objectives After reading this chapter you should be able to:
1. Extend the number system to the complex numbers.
   (*a*) Define a complex number.
   (*b*) Plot complex numbers on the Argand diagram.
   (*c*) Determine the sum and difference of complex numbers.
   (*d*) Determine the product of complex numbers.
   (*e*) Define the conjugate of a complex number.
   (*f*) Determine the quotient of two complex numbers.
2. Understand the polar form of a complex number.
   (*a*) Define the polar form.
   (*b*) Convert the complex number $x + jy$ into polar form.
   (*c*) Multiply and divide complex numbers using polar form.
   (*d*) Apply complex numbers to engineering problems.

15-1 INTRODUCTION

Consider trying to solve the equation

$$x^2 - x + 2.5 = 0$$

By using the usual quadratic formula, we have

$$x = \frac{1 \pm \sqrt{(-1)^2 - 4(1)(2.5)}}{2(1)}$$

$$= \frac{1 \pm \sqrt{-9}}{2}$$

As we cannot find a *real* number equal to $\sqrt{-9}$, we have to turn to the **complex number system**. This system takes into account square roots of *negative* numbers.
   With the equation $x^2 - x + 2.5 = 0$ we have the solutions

$$x = \frac{1 \pm \sqrt{-9}}{2} = \frac{1}{2} \pm \frac{1}{2}\sqrt{-9}$$

Consider the *imaginary* part of this solution, that is the part containing $\sqrt{-9}$: we have

$$\tfrac{1}{2}\sqrt{-9} = \tfrac{1}{2}\sqrt{-1(9)}$$
$$= \tfrac{1}{2}(\sqrt{-1})(\sqrt{9})$$
$$= \tfrac{1}{2}(3)(\sqrt{-1})$$
$$= 1.5(\sqrt{-1})$$

As there is no number which is equal to the $\sqrt{-1}$, we use an algebraic symbol j. Thus $j = \sqrt{-1}$, though in some books the symbol $i = \sqrt{-1}$ is used. We shall use the j notation to avoid any possible confusion with the symbol i used for instantaneous current.

Hence the solutions to the equation $x^2 - x + 2.5 = 0$ are **complex numbers** of the form

$$x = 0.5 \pm 1.5j$$

In general then a **complex number** is of the form $a + jb$ where $j = \sqrt{-1}$ and a and b are *numbers*. The **real** part of the complex number is the number a, while the **imaginary** part is the number b.

15-2 ADDITION AND SUBTRACTION OF COMPLEX NUMBERS

Addition of complex numbers can be defined by

$$(a + jb) + (c + jd) = (a + c) + (jb + jd)$$
$$= (a + c) + j(b + d)$$

Example 15-2-1 Evaluate $z_1 + z_2$ where $z_1 = 2 + 3j$ and $z_2 = -4 + 6j$.

SOLUTION
$$z_1 + z_2 = (2 + 3j) + (-4 + 6j)$$
$$= [2 + (-4)] + (3j + 6j)$$
$$= -2 + 9j$$

Example 15-2-2 Evaluate $z_1 - z_2$ where $z_1 = 3 - j$ and $z_2 = -3 + 2j$.

SOLUTION
$$z_1 - z_2 = (3 - j) - (-3 + 2j)$$
$$= 3 - j + 3 - 2j$$
$$= (3 + 3) + (-j - 2j)$$
$$= 6 - 3j$$

15-3 THE ARGAND DIAGRAM

Complex numbers can be represented on a diagram called the **Argand** diagram. This is illustrated in Fig. 15-1. The numbers represented are $(3 + 2j)$, $(-4 + 6j)$, and $(-2 - 4j)$. The reader will notice that the effect of $j = \sqrt{-1}$ is to turn numbers from the horizontal axis through $90°$.

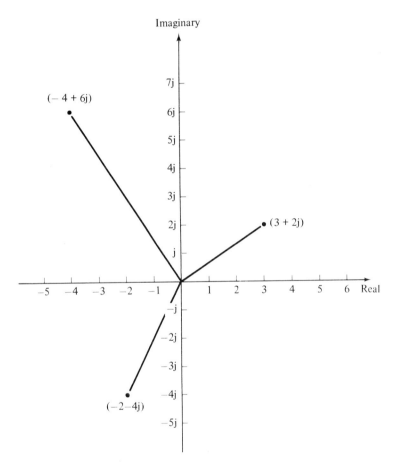

Figure 15-1 Argand diagram.

15-4 APPLICATIONS I

A two-dimensional vector can be represented by a complex number. Consider

$$\text{Velocity} = a + jb$$

where b is the vertical component of the vector velocity and a is the horizontal component. By adding complex numbers when they represent vectors, we are also adding vectors and hence finding the **resultant**.

Example 15-4-1 Two coplanar forces act at the same point on a body. These forces are $F_1 = 3 + 2j$ and $F_2 = -5 + 4j$. Find the resultant force and its magnitude.

SOLUTION

$$\text{Resultant force} = F_1 + F_2 \qquad \text{(vectorial addition)}$$

$$= (3 + 2j) + (-5 + 4j)$$

$$= (3 - 5) + (2j + 4j)$$

$$= -2 + 6j$$

Using the Argand diagram, we can represent these vectors in the normal way by a vector diagram. This is illustrated in Fig. 15-2.

By Pythagoras' theorem, the magnitude of the resultant force is

$$\sqrt{(2)^2 + (6)^2} = 6.32 \, \text{N}.$$

15-5 POLAR FORM OF COMPLEX NUMBERS

Consider Fig. 15-3 which shows the complex number $(a + jb)$ on an Argand diagram. The distance from the origin is r. From basic trigonometry (see Chapter 2) we have

$$r \cdot \cos(\theta) = a \qquad \text{and} \qquad r \cdot \sin(\theta) = b$$

Hence

$$a + jb = r \cdot \cos(\theta) + j \cdot r \cdot \sin(\theta)$$

$$= r[\cos(\theta) + j \sin(\theta)]$$

This is the **polar form** of the complex number $a + jb$. It is sometimes written as $r \, \underline{/\theta}$ as in vector notation.

15-6 MULTIPLICATION OF COMPLEX NUMBERS

Consider the two complex numbers

$$z_1 = a + bj \qquad \text{and} \qquad z_2 = c + dj$$

then we have

$$z_1 \cdot z_2 = (a + bj)(c + dj)$$

$$= ac + adj + cbj + bd(j)^2$$

$$= (ac - bd) + j(ad + cb) \qquad \text{since } j^2 = -1$$

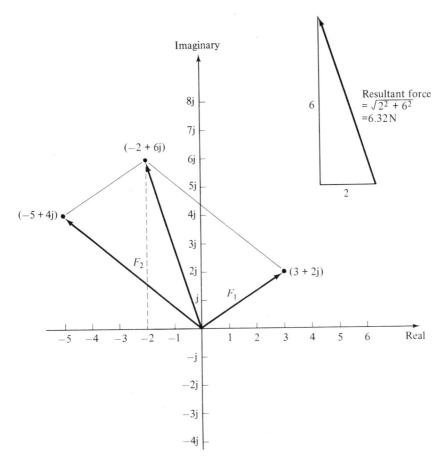

Figure 15-2

In polar form, we have

$$z_4 \cdot z_3 = (r_4 \,\underline{/\theta_4})(r_3 \,\underline{/\theta_3})$$

$$= r_4 \cdot r_3 \,\underline{/\theta_4 + \theta_3}$$

Example 15-6-1 Find the value of $z_1 \cdot z_2$ if $z_1 = 3 + 10j$ and $z_2 = -2 + 4j$.

SOLUTION
$$z_1 \cdot z_2 = (3 + 10j)(-2 + 4j)$$
$$= (3)(-2) + (3)(4j) + (10j)(-2) + (10j)(4j)$$
$$= -6 + 12j - 20j + 40j^2$$
$$= -6 - 8j - 40 \qquad \text{since } j^2 = -1$$
$$= -46 - 8j$$

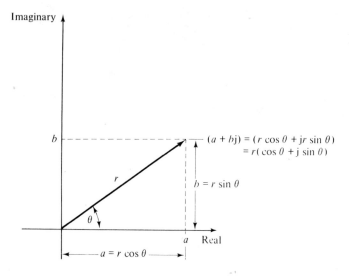

Figure 15-3 Polar form.

Example 15-6-2 If $z_1 = 3 \underline{/30°}$ and $z_2 = 2 \underline{/60°}$, find $z_1 \cdot z_2$.

SOLUTION

$$z_1 \cdot z_2 = (3 \underline{/30°})(2 \underline{/60°})$$

$$= (3)(2) \underline{/30° + 60°}$$

$$= 6 \underline{/90°}$$

Example 15-6-3 Given $z_1 = 2 \underline{/30°}$ and $z_2 = 3 \underline{/60°}$, find the value of (a) $z_1 + z_2$ and (b) $z_1 \cdot z_2$.

SOLUTION (a) Converting the polar forms of z_1 and z_2 into the form $a + jb$, we have by Sec. 15-5,

$$r \cdot \cos(\theta) = a \quad \text{and} \quad r \cdot \sin(\theta) = b$$

For z_1,

$$r \cdot \cos(\theta) = 2 \cdot \cos(30°)$$

$$= 1.7320$$

and

$$r \cdot \sin(\theta) = 2 \cdot \sin(30°)$$

$$= 1.0000$$

Hence

$$z_1 = 2 \underline{/30°}$$

$$= 1.732 + j$$

Similarly for z_2,

$$r \cdot \cos(\theta) = 3 \cdot \cos(60°)$$

$$= 1.5$$

and

$$r \cdot \sin(\theta) = 3 \cdot \sin(60°)$$

$$= 2.5981$$

Hence

$$z_2 = 3 \underline{/60°}$$

$$= 1.5 + 2.5981j$$

Hence

$$z_1 + z_2 = (1.732 + j) + (1.5 + 2.5981j)$$

$$= 3.232 + 3.5981j$$

If we wish to convert back to polar form then

$$z_1 + z_2 = 4.8365 \underline{/48.07°}$$

(b)

$$z_1 \cdot z_2 = (2 \underline{/30°})(3 \underline{/60°})$$

$$= (2)(3) \underline{/30° + 60°}$$

$$= 6 \underline{/90°}$$

In the form $a + bj$ we have

$$6 \underline{/90°} = 0 + 6j$$

15-7 DIVISION OF COMPLEX NUMBERS

Complex numbers can be divided by multiplying the numerator and the denominator by the complex conjugate of the denominator. The **complex conjugate** of a number $a + bj$ is defined as the number $a - bj$.

Example 15-7-1 Show that if the complex number $a + bj$ is multiplied by its complex conjugate, then the result is a number without an imaginary part.

SOLUTION

$$(a + bj)(a - bj) = a^2 - abj + abj - (bj)^2$$

$$= a^2 - b^2 j^2$$

$$= a^2 + b^2 \qquad \text{since } j^2 = -1$$

Thus we have a real number $a^2 + b^2$.

Example 15-7-2 Evaluate the product of the number $(2 - 5j)$ with its complex conjugate.

SOLUTION As $(2 - 5j)$ has $(2 + 5j)$ as its complex conjugate, we have

$$(2 - 5j)(2 + 5j) = 2^2 + 5^2$$
$$= 4 + 25$$
$$= 29$$

Example 15-7-3 Evaluate

$$\frac{(2 - 3j)}{(-4 + 2j)}.$$

SOLUTION Multiplying numerator and denominator by $(-4 - 2j)$ gives

$$\frac{(2 - 3j)(-4 - 2j)}{(-4 + 2j)(-4 - 2j)} = \frac{-14 + 8j}{20}$$
$$= -0.7 + 0.4j$$

Example 15-7-3 Evaluate

$$\frac{(1 + j)(2 - 3j)}{(1 - j)}$$

SOLUTION

$$\frac{(1 + j)(2 - 3j)}{(1 - j)} = \frac{(5 - j)}{(1 - j)}$$
$$= \frac{(5 - j)(1 + j)}{(1 - j)(1 + j)}$$
$$= \frac{6 + 4j}{2}$$
$$= 3 + 2j$$

15-8 APPLICATIONS II

In electrical engineering, we have in inductive circuits that the voltage drop across the resistance is in phase with the current. The voltage drop across the inductance is out of phase with the current in that it leads the current by $90°$ or $\pi/2$ radians. Consider Fig. 15-4 and we see that the voltage drops for inductive and capacitive circuits have been shown in complex form.

$$\text{Voltage across inductance} = V_L = jIX_L$$
$$\text{Voltage across resistance} = V_R = IR$$

(a)

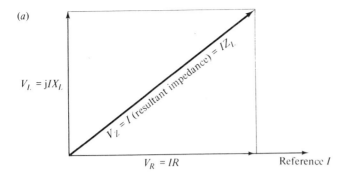

(b)

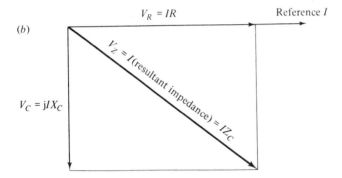

Figure 15-4 Voltage diagrams – (a) inductive and (b) capacitive circuits.

Therefore

$$\text{Voltage across impedance} = V_Z = V_R + V_L$$

$$= IR + jIX_L$$

However

$$V_Z = IZ_L = IR + jIX_L$$

$$= I(R + jX_L)$$

On dividing both sides by I we have

$$Z_L = (R + jX_L)$$

This is the complex form for the impedance Z_L of an inductive circuit.

Example 15-8-1 Two impedances are represented by the complex numbers $(3 + 8j)$ and $(2 + 3j)$. Find the resultant impedance in its complex form and hence calculate its magnitude. Evaluate the phase angle between the voltage across the resultant impedance and the current flowing through it.

SOLUTION By Sec. 15-2 we have

$$\text{Resultant impedance} = (3 + 8j) + (2 + 3j)$$

$$= 5 + 11j$$

As the imaginary part of the resultant impedance is positive, i.e. 11, we know that the reactance is inductive so that $X_L = 11\,\Omega$. Translating this complex number into polar form we have

$$r \cdot \cos(\theta) = 5 \quad \text{and} \quad r \cdot \sin(\theta) = 11$$

This implies that

$$r^2 = 5^2 + 11^2$$

$$= 146$$

or

$$r = 12.083$$

In electrical terms we have

$$|Z_L|^2 = R^2 + X_L^2$$

Hence in this case

$$r = |Z_L|$$

The magnitude of the resultant impedance is $r = |Z_L| = 12.083\,\Omega$.
Since $r \cdot \cos(\theta) = 5$ and $r \cdot \sin(\theta) = 11$ we have

$$\tan(\theta) = \frac{11}{5}$$

$$= 2.2$$

or

$$\theta = 65.56°$$

Hence, phase angle between voltage across resultant impedance and current flowing through it is $65.56°$. Therefore

$$Z_L = 5 + 11j = 12.083\,\underline{/65.56°}$$

With a capacitive circuit we have the voltage drop V_C across the capacitance as $-jIX_C$ as shown in Fig. 15-4. The voltage across the resistance is IR and therefore the voltage across the impedance is

$$V_Z = I\dot{Z}_C$$

$$= V_R + V_C$$

$\Rightarrow$

$$IZ_C = IR - jIX_C$$

On dividing both sides by I we have

$$Z_C = R - jX_C$$

This is the complex form for the impedance Z_C of a capacitive circuit.

Example 15-8-2 Three impedances are represented by the complex numbers (3 + j), (4 + 2j), and (2 − 12j). Find the resultant impedance and calculate its magnitude. State whether the circuit is capacitive or inductive.

SOLUTION By adding the complex forms together, we obtain the resultant impedance. Hence

$$\text{Resultant impedance} = (3 + j) + (4 + 2j) + (2 - 12j)$$
$$= (3 + 4 + 2) + (j + 2j - 12j)$$
$$= 9 - 9j$$

Magnitude of resultant is

$$\sqrt{9^2 + (-9)^2} = \sqrt{162}$$
$$= 12.7279 \, \Omega$$

As the imaginary part of this impedence is negative we have a capacitive circuit.

Example 15-8-3 A capacitor of $50 \, \mu\text{F}$ is in series with a $20 \, \Omega$ resistor and these components are in parallel with a coil having inductance 0.15 H and resistance of $10 \, \Omega$. Calculate in complex form the overall impedance of the circuit. State the magnitude of this impedance. Assume a supply voltage frequency of 50 Hz.

SOLUTION

$$X_C = \frac{1}{2\pi f C}$$
$$= \frac{1}{2\pi(50)(50 \times 10^{-6})}$$
$$= 63.6620 \, \Omega$$

Hence for the capacitor and resistor in series we have

$$Z_C = R - jX_C$$
$$= 20 - 63.662j$$

For the inductor of 0.15 H we have

$$X_L = 2\pi f L$$
$$= 2\pi(50)(0.15)$$
$$= 47.1239 \, \Omega$$

Hence for the inductor and resistor in series, the coil, we have

$$Z_L = R + jX_L$$

$$= 10 + 47.1239j$$

As the capacitor and 20 Ω resistor are in parallel with the inductor and 10 Ω resistor, we have

$$\frac{1}{Z} = \frac{1}{Z_C} + \frac{1}{Z_L}$$

where Z is the total impedance of the circuit. Hence

$$Z = \frac{Z_C Z_L}{Z_C + Z_L}$$

$$Z_C + Z_L = (20 - 63.662j) + (10 + 47.1239j)$$

$$= 30 - 16.5381j$$

$$Z_C \cdot Z_L = (20 - 63.662j)(10 + 47.1239j)$$

$$= 3200 + 305.858j$$

Hence

$$Z = \frac{Z_C Z_L}{Z_C + Z_L}$$

$$= \frac{3200 + 305.858j}{30 - 16.5381j}$$

Multiplying numerator and denominator by the complex conjugate of the denominator, we have

$$\frac{(3200 + 305.858j)(30 + 16.3581j)}{(30 - 16.5381j)(30 + 16.5381j)} = \frac{90996.7 + 61521.7j}{1173.51 + 0j}$$

⇒

$$Z = 77.54 + 52.42j$$

Hence overall impedance of this circuit is 77.54 + 52.42j which has a magnitude of

$$\sqrt{(77.54)^2 + (52.42)^2} = 93.6 \, \Omega$$

PROBLEMS

15-1 Solve the equation $x^2 - 3x + 5 = 0$.

15-2 If $a + jb = 3 - 6j$, state the values of a and b.

15-3 If $z_1 = (3 + 4j)$ and $z_2 = (-3 - 5j)$ find the value of $z_1 + z_2$.

15-4 If $z_1 = j$ and $z_2 = 3j$ find the value of $z_1 \cdot z_2$.

15-5 If $z_1 = 1 - j$ and $z_2 = 2 + 6j$ find the value of $z_1 - 2z_2$.

15-6 If $z_1 = 3 - 7j$ and $z_2 = -6 + 4j$ find the value of (a) $z_1 + j \cdot z_2$ and (b) $j \cdot z_1 - z_2$.

**15-7 Three coplanar forces act at a single point. If these forces are $F_1 = 1 + 8j$, $F_2 = 3 - 3j$, and $F_3 = -2 + j$, find in complex form the resultant. Calculate the magnitude of the resultant and state its direction with respect to the real axis in the Argand diagram.

***15-8** Two coplanar forces act on a body, mass 3 kg, moving it in a straight line. Assuming the body meets no resistance and the two forces are $F_1 = (3 + 2j)$ and $F_2 = (6 - 5j)$, find the acceleration in complex number form. Evaluate the magnitude of this acceleration and its direction with respect to the real axis in the Argand diagram.

15-9 Transform to *polar* form the complex numbers (*a*) 3j, (*b*) 2, (*c*) 4 −j, and (*d*) −1 + 2j.

15-10 Transform to the form $a + jb$, the numbers (*a*) 3 $\underline{/30°}$, (*b*) 2 $\underline{/45°}$, and (*c*) 6 $\underline{/34°}$.

15-11 If $z_1 = (3 - 2j)$ and $z_2 = (1 - j)$ find $z_1 \cdot z_2$.

15-12 If $z_1 = 2\underline{/30°}$ and $z_2 = 3\underline{/40°}$ calculate $z_1 \cdot z_2$.

15-13 Evaluate $(2 - 8j)(4 - 4j)$.

15-14 Evaluate $(-2 + 5j)(3 + j)$.

15-15 If $z = 2 -j$, find $1/z$.

15-16 If $z = 3 + j$, calculate $1/z$.

15-17 Evaluate $2/z$ where $z = 3 + 5j$.

15-18 Evaluate $\dfrac{(7 - j)}{(3 + 2j)}$

15-19 Evaluate $\dfrac{(-1 + 2j)}{(3 - 5j)}$

***15-20** Calculate the real and imaginary parts of $\dfrac{(3 - j)}{(2 + 2j)}$

***15-21** Evaluate $\dfrac{(2.3 - 6.87j)}{(12.4 + 7.81j)}$

****15-22** Evaluate the product of $(2 + 6j)$ with the complex conjugate of $(2 - 6j)^2$.

****15-23** Two impedances are represented by the complex numbers $(2 + 6j)$ and $(6.2 + j)$. Find the complex number representing the resultant impedance and calculate its magnitude.

****15-24** Within one circuit there are only two impedances $z_1 = (3 - j)$ and $z_2 = (5 + 7j)$. By finding the resultant impedance, state whether the circuit is inductive or capacitive. Hence calculate the magnitude of the resultant impedance.

*****15-25** Two impedances are $z_1 = (2 + 8j)$ and $z_2 = (5 + 4j)$. Find the phase angle between the current flowing through the resultant impedance and the voltage across it.

****15-26** Three impedances are represented by the complex numbers $(2 - j)$, $(4 + j)$, and $(1 + 2j)$. Find the resultant impedance and state its magnitude. State whether the circuit is inductive or capacitive in nature.

*****15-27** A coil with inductance of 0.1 H and resistance 30 Ω is in parallel with a capacitor of 70 μF. If the supply voltage frequency is 50 Hz find, in complex form, the overall impedance of the circuit.

Solutions

15-1 $1.5 \pm \dfrac{\sqrt{11}}{2}j$.

15-2 $a = 3, b = -6$.

15-3 −j.

15-4 −3.

15-5 $-3 - 13j$.

15-6 $-1 - 13j, 13 - j$.

15-7 $2 + 6j, 6.32, 71.56°$.

15-8 $3 - j, 3.16, -18.43°$.

15-9 $3 \underline{/90°}, 2 \underline{/0°}, 4.12 \underline{/-14°}, 2.23 \underline{/116.56°}$.

15-10 $2.598 + 1.5j, 1.4142 + 1.4142j, 4.974 + 3.355j$.

15-11 $1 - 5j$.

15-12 $6 \underline{/70°}$.

15-13 $-24 - 40j$.

15-14 $-11 + 13j$.

15-15 $0.4 + 0.2j$.

15-16 $0.3 - 0.1j$.

15-17 $0.1765 - 0.2941j$.

15-18 $1.4615 - 1.3077j$.

15-19 $-0.3824 + 0.0294j$.

15-20 0.5 = real part, -1 = imaginary part.

15-21 $-0.117 - 0.4803j$.

15-22 $-208 - 144j$.

15-23 $8.2 + 7j, 10.78 \, \Omega$.

15-24 $8 + 6j$, inductive, $10 \, \Omega$.

15-25 $59.74°$.

15-26 $7 + 2j, 7.28 \, \Omega$, inductive.

15-27 $9.1 + 22.1j$.

SIXTEEN

REVISION–FURTHER MATHEMATICAL MODELLING

Objectives After reading this chapter you should be able to:

1. Understand the process of mathematical modelling.
   (*a*) Build mathematical models concerned with simple engineering systems.
   (*b*) Build mathematical models from experimental data.
   (*c*) Build mathematical models by using differential equations of first order.
2. Predict outcomes from mathematical models.

16-1 INTRODUCTION

This chapter has two purposes in that it brings together, for revision, some of the important concepts discussed in the course and at the same time applies the mathematics to specified engineering systems. We have chosen three studies, two from electrical and one from mechanical engineering. Each section is concerned with one particular application and uses revision examples to show how mathematical modelling can be used to obtain further information. It should be stressed that each section should be read with the engineering application in mind and the reader may like to extend the interpretations of the mathematical models and the prediction equations given in those sections.

16-2 AN ELECTRICAL SYSTEM

Figure 16-1 illustrates a capacitor and resistor in series across a 100 V d.c. supply. When the capacitor is fully charged, the switch is thrown to position 2. It is required to find mathematical models to predict the current flowing and the potential difference across each component. We shall use a series of examples to lead the reader through the process of finding mathematical models.

> **Example 16-2-1** The switch in Fig. 16-1 is thrown to position 2 after the capacitor has been fully charged. By using Kirchhoff's laws find (*a*) a mathematical model describing the rate of change of charge in terms of

329

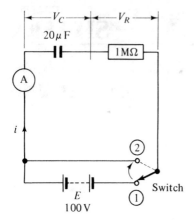

Figure 16-1 $C-R$ circuit.

the charge on the capacitor at a time t seconds, and (b) a prediction equation for the current flowing in the circuit at a time t seconds.

SOLUTION We use, in this example, the theory of Chapters 3, 5, and 11. (a) By Kirchhoff's laws, we have

$$V_R + V_C = 0$$

when the switch is in position 2. By Chapter 5, we have

$$V_R = iR$$

where i is the current flowing, and

$$V_C = \frac{q}{C}$$

Since, by Chapter 5,

$$i = \frac{dq}{dt}$$

we have

$$V_R + V_C = iR + \frac{q}{C}$$

$$= R\frac{dq}{dt} + \frac{q}{C}$$

This implies that

$$R\frac{dq}{dt} + \frac{q}{C} = 0$$

or

$$10^6\left(\frac{dq}{dt}\right) + \frac{10^6}{20}q = 0$$

We have at time $t = 0$ s, a current flowing of E/R, by Chapter 3, and since the capacitor is fully charged, the charge is CE. Hence initial current flowing is $100/10^6 = 100\,\mu$A with an initial charge of $CE = 0.002$ coulombs. We have a mathematical model describing the relationship between the rate of change of charge and the variable charge. That is,

$$\frac{dq}{dt} + 0.05q = 0 \qquad \text{at } t = 0\,\text{s}, q = 0.002\,\text{C}$$

(b) By using the theory of Chapter 11, we have for

$$\frac{dQ}{dt} = kQ$$

a solution

$$Q = Ke^{kt}$$

Therefore, solving our differential equation we have

$$\frac{dq}{dt} = -0.05q$$

which implies

$$q = K \cdot \exp(-0.05t)$$

or $\qquad q = K \cdot e^{-0.05t}$ $\qquad$ where K is an arbitrary constant

To find the constant K we use the boundary condition at $t = 0$ s. At $t = 0$, $q = 0.002$. Hence for

$$q = K \cdot e^{-0.05t}$$

with $(t, q) = (0, 0.002)$ we have

$$q = 0.002 = K \cdot e^{(0)}$$

or $\qquad K = 0.002$

Hence we have prediction equations for charge

$$q = 0.002\,e^{-0.05t}$$

and on differentiation, by Chapter 5, current,

$$i = -0.0001\,e^{-0.05t}$$

Example 16-2-2 The electrical circuit shown in Fig. 16-1 was set up in a laboratory and the current measured at fixed intervals of time. The results shown in Table 16-1 indicate the current flowing when the switch is in position 2.

(a) Build a mathematical model describing the relationship between current and time.

(b) Use the model to predict the current flow at a time of 37 s after the switch is thrown to position 2.

Table 16-1

Time(s)	Current (μA)
5	77.8
10	60.6
15	47.2
20	36.8
25	28.6
30	22.3
35	17.4
40	13.5
45	10.5
50	8.2
55	6.4
60	5.0

SOLUTION From Example 16-2-1 we suspect that the mathematical model will be of the form

$$i = a \cdot e^{bt}$$

where a and b are constants. The reader will observe that we shall be concerned with the magnitude of the current and we shall leave its direction until the numerical values of a and b are established.

By Chapter 4 we have

$$\ln(i) = \ln(a) + bt$$

which implies that we could use log–linear paper and plot the variables i and t. Figure 16-2 shows the graph of i against t on log–linear paper and a straight line fitted by eye. From this graph we obtain the values of a and b.

From the graph we can see directly that $a = 100\,\mu A$. For the value of b we choose a time value, say 32.5 s, and note the corresponding value of $i = 19.5\,\mu A$. Hence since

$$\ln(i) = \ln(a) + bt$$

we have

$$\ln(i) - \ln(a) = bt$$

or

$$\ln\left(\frac{i}{a}\right) = bt$$

or

$$\ln\left(\frac{19.5}{100}\right) = 32.5b$$

$\Rightarrow$ $\qquad\qquad b = -0.05 \qquad$ to 2 decimal places

Hence we have the mathematical model

$$i = 0.0001\, e^{-0.05t}$$

which describes the relationship between the magnitude of the current and

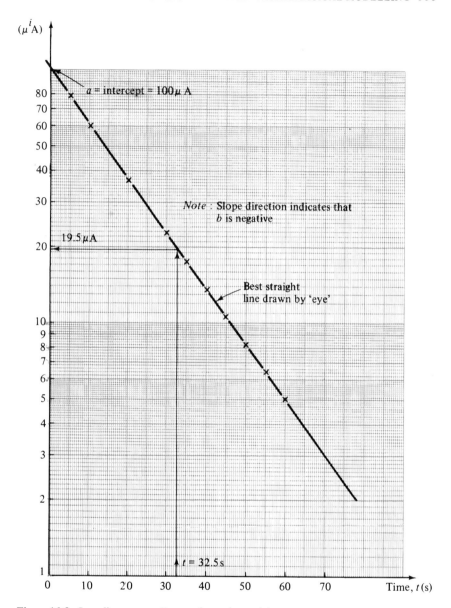

Figure 16-2 Log–linear paper (two cycles on log scale).

time after the switch has been thrown to position 2. It should be noted that if we add a negative sign to indicate that the current flows in the opposite direction to the charging current, the model becomes

$$i = -0.0001 \, e^{-0.05t}$$

This mathematical model found by empirical means is the same as the prediction equation developed by differential equation methods.

(b) At $t = 37$ s we have a current of

$$i = -0.0001 \, e^{-0.05(37)}$$

$$= -15.7 \, \mu A$$

The *predicted* current at $t = 37$ s has a magnitude of $15.7 \, \mu A$ to 1 decimal place.

Example 16-2-3 illustrates the fitting of a normal distribution to measurements.

Example 16-2-3 The current flowing in the circuit shown in Fig. 16-1 was measured at $t = 37$ s with the switch in position 2. The results are shown in Table 16-2. By using graphical methods, fit a normal distribution to the measurements.

Table 16-2

Current (μA)	Number of measurements (f)
15.66	6
15.67	24
15.68	64
15.69	113
15.70	129
15.71	94
15.72	46
15.73	14
15.74	3

SOLUTION Fitting a normal distribution by graphical methods was illustrated in Chapter 14. We construct Table 16-3 containing the class intervals associated with the measurement values and the percentage cumulative frequency. Figure 16-3 illustrates the upper class boundary plotted against the percentage cumulative frequency. By the methods of Chapter 14 we find the mean and standard deviation for the normal distribution, that is

$$\mu = 15.698 \, \mu A$$

and

$$\sigma = 0.015 \, \mu A$$

Table 16-3

Current	Class interval	Frequency	Cumulative frequency (%)
15.66	15.655–16.665⁻	6	1.2
15.67	15.665–15.675⁻	24	6.0
15.68	15.675–15.685⁻	64	19.1
15.69	15.685–15.695⁻	113	42.0
15.70	15.695–15.705⁻	129	68.2
15.71	15.705–15.715⁻	94	87.2
15.72	15.715–15.725⁻	46	96.6
15.73	15.725–15.735⁻	14	99.4
15.74	15.735–15.745⁻	3	100.0

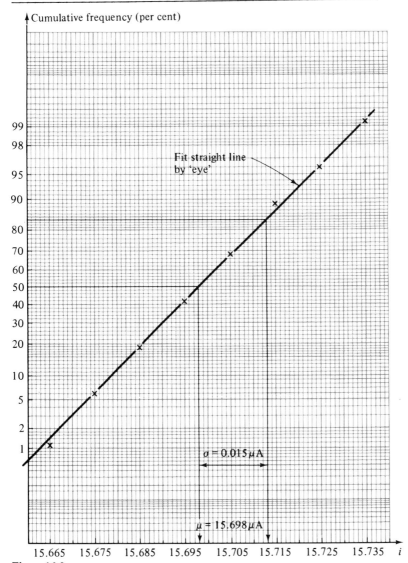

Figure 16-3

Example 16-2-4 Consider the circuit shown in Fig. 16-1 and let the switch be thrown to position 2 when the capacitor has reached its maximum charge of $CE = 0.002$ C. Find equations which could predict the p.d. across each component at a given time.

SOLUTION Consider Example 16-2-1 in which we obtained a prediction equation for the charge q on the capacitor at any time t. That is,

$$q = 0.002 \, e^{-0.05t}$$

Since p.d. across capacitor is given by

$$V_C = \frac{q}{C}$$

we have

$$V_c = \frac{0.002 \, e^{-0.05t}}{20 \times 10^{-6}}$$

$$= (100)(e^{-0.05t}) \text{ volts}$$

Since p.d. across the resistor is

$$V_R = iR$$

$$= R \frac{dq}{dt}$$

$$= (10^6)(-0.0001 \, e^{-0.05t})$$

$$= (-100)(e^{-0.05t}) \text{ volts}$$

16-3 A PROTOTYPE INVESTIGATION

In this section we shall be concerned with a new design for a boat hull. The prototype is on trial on calm water with a controlled amount of fuel entering the motor. The velocity of the boat was measured in metres/second whilst it was travelling in a straight line from rest.

Example 16-3-1 The results of the first trial are shown in Table 16-4. By curve-fitting techniques, show that

$$V = 0.02 \, t^{1.2}$$

is a mathematical model describing the relationship between the variable

Table 16-4

Time (s)	Velocity (m/s)
30	1.18
60	2.72
90	4.43
120	6.25
150	8.17
180	10.17
210	12.24
240	14.36
270	16.54
300	18.77

velocity and time. From this relationship, establish the relationship between distance travelled and time.

SOLUTION We shall leave the curve-fitting part to the reader as an exercise following the principles of Chapter 4.

Since velocity is the rate of change of position with respect to time, we have

$$V = \frac{ds}{dt}$$

by Chapter 5. Since

$$V = 0.02\, t^{1.2}$$

$$\frac{ds}{dt} = 0.02\, t^{1.2}$$

and we have a first-order differential equation with a boundary condition. The boundary condition is given by $(s, t) = (0,0)$. We hence have a slope equation and we can use the principles of Chapter 7 and integrate by reverse differentiation:

$$\frac{ds}{dt} = 0.02\, t^{1.2}$$

implies

$$s = \int 0.02\, t^{1.2}\, dt$$

$$= \frac{0.02\, t^{2.2}}{2.2} + C$$

To find C, the arbitrary constant, we use the boundary condition to give $C = 0$ (see Chapter 11). Hence we have the equation

$$s = 0.0091\, t^{2.2}$$

which describes the relationship between distance travelled and time.

Example 16-3-2 Using the equation $V = 0.02\, t^{1.2}$ find mathematical models which describe the relationship between (a) acceleration and time, and (b) kinetic energy and time.

SOLUTION (a) Since

$$\text{Acceleration} = \frac{dV}{dt}$$

we have, by Chapter 5,

$$\frac{dV}{dt} = 0.024\, t^{0.2}$$

(b)

$$\text{Kinetic energy} = \tfrac{1}{2}(\text{mass})(\text{velocity})^2$$

$$= \tfrac{1}{2}m(0.02\, t^{1.2})^2$$

$$= 0.0002m(t^{2.4})$$

where m is the mass of the boat.

16-4 THE $L-C-R$ CIRCUIT

We shall consider a second electrical system with an inductor, resistor, and capacitor in series as shown in Fig. 16-4. When the capacitor has reached the maximum charge of $CE = 0.002$ coulombs, the switch is thrown to position 2. It is required to build mathematical models to describe the relationship between charge and time, and hence obtain prediction equations for the current flowing and the related topics.

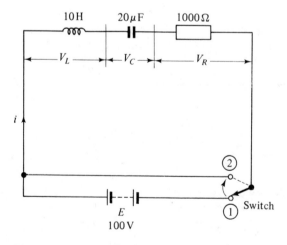

Figure 16-4 $L-C-R$ circuit.

Example 16-4-1 By using Kirchhoff's laws, find a differential equation relating charge and time variables when the switch is thrown to position 2 after the capacitor has reached its maximum charge of 0.002 C.

SOLUTION From Chapter 5, we have

$$V_L = L\frac{d^2q}{dt^2} = 10\frac{d^2q}{dt^2}$$

$$V_R = R\frac{dq}{dt} = 10^3\frac{dq}{dt}$$

and

$$V_C = \frac{1}{C}q = \frac{10^6}{20}q$$

By Kirchhoff's laws we have, with the switch in position 2,

$$V_L + V_R + V_C = 0$$

Hence

$$10\frac{d^2q}{dt^2} + 10^3\frac{dq}{dt} + \frac{10^6}{20}q = 0$$

or

$$\frac{d^2q}{dt^2} + 100\frac{dq}{dt} + 5000q = 0$$

We have the mathematical model which includes two boundary conditions at $t = 0$ s:

$$\frac{d^2q}{dt^2} + 100\frac{dq}{dt} + 5000q = 0$$

at $t = 0$ s, $q = 0.002$ C

and $i = \dfrac{dq}{dt} = 0$ A

The mathematical model built in Example 16-4-1 involved a differential equation which is of second order. In this book, we have discussed first-order equations and so we shall not be able to solve the second-order equation at this stage. We shall give the solution which will be verified by the principles of Chapter 5.

Example 16-4-2 Verify that if

$$q = 0.002e^{-50t}[\sin(50t) + \cos(50t)]$$

then

$$\frac{d^2q}{dt^2} + 100\frac{dq}{dt} + 5000q = 0$$

SOLUTION Let the function be represented by $q = u \cdot v$ where

$$u = 0.002\,e^{-50t}$$

and

$$v = \sin(50t) + \cos(50t)$$

By Chapter 5, we have the product rule. Since

$$q = u \cdot v$$

$$\frac{dq}{dt} = u \cdot \frac{dv}{dt} + v \cdot \frac{du}{dt}$$

Hence we have to find the first derivatives of u and v. Since

$$u = 0.002 \, e^{-50t}$$

$$\frac{du}{dt} = -0.1 \, e^{-50t}$$

and

$$v = \sin(50t) + \cos(50t)$$

$$\frac{dv}{dt} = 50 \cos(50t) - 50 \sin(50t)$$

Using the product rule we have

$$\frac{dq}{dt} = 0.002 \, e^{-50t} \cdot [50 \cos(50t) - 50 \sin(50t)]$$

$$- [\sin(50t) + \cos(50t)](0.1e^{-50t})$$

$$= -0.2 \, e^{-50t} \sin(50t) \qquad \text{(the current flowing at time } t\text{)}$$

For the second differential, we again use the product rule. Let

$$u = -0.2e^{-50t} \qquad \Rightarrow \qquad \frac{du}{dt} = 10e^{-50t}$$

and $\qquad v = \sin(50t) \qquad \Rightarrow \qquad \frac{dv}{dt} \; 50 \cos(50t)$

Hence we have for

$$\frac{dq}{dt} = -0.02e^{-50t} \sin(50t)$$

$$= u \cdot v$$

and $\qquad \dfrac{d^2q}{dt^2} = u \dfrac{dv}{dt} + v \dfrac{du}{dt}$

$$= -0.2e^{-50t} \, 50 \cos(50t) + 10e^{-50t} \sin(50t)$$

$$= -10e^{-50t} \cos(50t) + 10e^{-50t} \sin(50t)$$

Since

$$5000q = 10e^{-50t} \sin(50t) + 10e^{-50t} \cos(50t)$$

and $\qquad 100 \dfrac{dq}{dt} = -20e^{-50t} \sin(50t)$

and
$$\frac{d^2q}{dt^2} = -10e^{-50t}\cos(50t) + 10e^{-50t}\sin(50t)$$

we add to obtain
$$\frac{d^2q}{dt^2} + 100\,\frac{dq}{dt} + 5000q = 0$$

We have shown that
$$q = 0.002e^{-50t}\,[\sin(50t) + \cos(50t)]$$

is a solution of the differential equation
$$\frac{d^2q}{dt^2} + 100\,\frac{dq}{dt} + 5000q = 0$$

Example 16-4-3 (*a*) If
$$q = 0.002e^{-50t}\,[\sin(50t) + \cos(50t)]$$

transform q into the form
$$Ke^{-50t}\,[\sin(50t + \alpha)]$$

Hence state the amplitude of this function.
(*b*) Calculate the frequency, periodic time, and amplitude at (i) $t = 0\,\text{s}$, and (ii) $t = 0.02\,\text{s}$.

SOLUTION (*a*) We concentrate on the $\sin(50t) + \cos(50t)$ part and using the principles of Chapter 2 we have
$$R \cdot \sin(50t + \alpha) = \cos(50t) + \sin(50t)$$
$$= R\sin(\alpha)\cos(50t) + R\cos(\alpha)\sin(50t)$$

Hence
$$R\sin(\alpha) = 1 \qquad \text{and} \qquad R\cos(\alpha) = 1$$

$\Rightarrow$
$$R^2 = 1^2 + 1^2$$

or
$$R = \sqrt{2}$$
$$= 1.414\,213$$

Since $\sin(\alpha)$ and $\cos(\alpha)$ are *both* positive, the angle α belongs to the *first* quadrant and
$$\tan(\alpha) = 1$$

$\Rightarrow$
$$\alpha = \pi/4$$

Therefore
$$\sin(50t) + \cos(50t) = 1.414\,213\,\sin(50t + \pi/4)$$

On multiplying both sides by $0.002e^{-50t}$ we have
$$0.002e^{-50t}\,[\sin(50t) + \cos(50t)] = 0.00283e^{-50t}\,[\sin(50t + \pi/4)]$$

For the amplitude of this function, we notice that it varies with time, that is,

$$\text{Amplitude} = 0.00283e^{-50t}$$

This implies that the charge on the capacitor decays.

(b) (i)
$$\text{Frequency} = \frac{\omega}{2\pi}$$

$$= \frac{50}{2\pi}$$

$$= 7.96 \text{ Hz}$$

$$\text{Periodic time} = T = \frac{1}{f}$$

$$= \frac{1}{7.96}$$

$$= 0.126 \text{ s}$$

$$\text{Amplitude} = 0.00283 \, e^0 \qquad (\text{at } t = 0 \text{ s})$$

$$= 0.002 \, 83 \text{ C}$$

(ii) Frequency and periodic time are identical at $t = 0.02$ s to the values at $t = 0$ s in part (i).

$$\text{Amplitude} = 0.002 \, 83 \, e^{-50(0.02)}$$

$$= 0.001 \, 04 \text{ C}$$

Example 16-4-4 If

$$q = 0.002e^{-50t} [\sin(50t) + \cos(50t)]$$

find the current flowing in the circuit shown in Fig. 16-4 at $t = 0.003$ s.

SOLUTION Example 16-4-2 illustrated that

$$\frac{dq}{dt} = -0.2e^{-50t} [\sin(50t)]$$

Hence at $t = 0.003$ s we have

$$i = \frac{dq}{dt} = -0.2e^{-50(0.003)} \sin(0.15)$$

$$= -0.0257 \text{ A}$$

The current flowing has a magnitude of 0.0257 A at $t = 0.003$ s.

The negative sign indicates current direction and in the circuit under consideration, with the switch in position 2, we can see that the capacitor is discharging.

REVISION

SHORT-ANSWER QUESTIONS

16-1 Define the angle between a line and a plane.

16-2 Define the angle between two intersecting planes.

16-3 A line is lying at $30°$ to a plane. Find the length of the projection in that plane.

16-4 A force vector is at an angle of $48°$ to a horizontal plane. Calculate, by the method of projection, the horizontal and vertical components if the magnitude of the force is 20 N.

16-5 A rectangular box has sides 3 m, 2 m, and 1.5 m. Evaluate the length of the longest diagonal.

16-6 Given $\sin(30°) = 0.5$ and $\cos(45°) = 1/2$ find the value of $\operatorname{cosec}(105°)$.

16-7 Show that $\sin(A + B) + \sin(A - B) = 2 \sin(A) \cdot \cos(B)$.

16-8 Define the term 'constant angular velocity'.

16-9 Calculate the periodic time for the function represented by $y = \sin(5.2t)$.

16-10 Define the term 'periodic time'.

16-11 Define the term 'frequency'.

16-12 Calculate the frequency of the function represented by $y = \sin(2.3t)$.

16-13 If $y = \sin(4t - 2)$, state the amplitude, frequency, and periodic time of this particular sine wave.

16-14 The current flowing in a circuit is given by $i = 3 \sin(2.1\,\dot{t} + 1)$. Calculate the amplitude, periodic time, and frequency of this sine wave.

16-15 Transform $4 \cos(10t) + 3 \sin(10t)$ into the form $R \cdot \sin(10t + \alpha)$ by using the phasor method.

16-16 Expand by using the binomial theorem the expression $(1 + x)^5$.

16-17 Expand in a power series the expression $(2 + x)^4$.

16-18 Expand in a power series the expression $(1 + x)^{-2}$.

16-19 Expand in a power series the expression $(1 - x)^{0.2}$.

16-20 Evaluate the binomial coefficient $\binom{14}{2}$ without using tables or a calculator.

16-21 Evaluate the limits

$$(a) \lim_{\delta x \to 0} (4x + 2\delta x) \qquad (b) \lim_{h \to \infty} x^2 + \frac{x}{h} \ .$$

16-22 Write down the power series for $\exp(x)$ and hence find a power series for $\exp(-2x)$.

16-23 By using the power series for $\exp(x)$, find the value of $e^{0.1}$.

16-24 Sketch the graph of the function $\exp(x)$.

16-25 Define the Napierian logarithmic function.

16-26 Solve the equation $e^{3.1t} = 4$.

16-27 Solve the equation $\ln(45t) = -0.4$.

16-28 Solve the equation $\exp(x^2) = 10$.

16-29 If $T = T_0 [\exp(0.3\theta)]$, find the value of T when $\theta = 90°$.

16-30 Transform the equation $s = 10a(t^b)$ into straight-line form.

16-31 Transform the equation $s = a(e^{3bt})$ into straight-line form.

16-32 Transform the equation $s = a(b^{3t})$ into straight-line form.

16-33 Differentiate (a) $y = 3 \sin(2x)$ and (b) $y = 4 \cos(3x)$ with respect to x.

16-34 If $y = 4 \tan(2x)$ find dy/dx.

16-35 If $y = 2 \exp(3x)$ find dy/dx.

16-36 Differentiate with respect to t the function $f(t) = 4[\ln(2t + 1)]$.

16-37 Differentiate with respect to t the function $f(t) = \exp(t^2)$.

16-38 If $y = \cos(2t)$ find dy/dt and d^2y/dt^2.

16-39 The velocity of a body moving in a straight line is given by $v = 2t(e^t)$. Find an equation describing the acceleration.

16-40 By using the product rule, find the first differential $f'(x)$ of $f(x) = 2x[\cos(x)]$.

16-41 Find the value of dy/dx at the point $x = 1$ of $y = 3x(x + 1)^{100}$.

16-42 Evaluate the value of the slope of the curve $y = \cos(x)$ at the point $x = 1.2$.

16-43 Find the value of $f'(0)$ if $f(x) = \sin(2x)$.

16-44 If $y = \tan(x) + \exp(2x)$, find dy/dx.

16-45 If $y = \theta^2 + 1$ and $x = \sin(\theta)$, find dy/dx.

16-46 Define the turning point of a curve $y = f(x)$.

16-47 If $y = x^2 - 2x + 1$, find the cartesian coordinates of the turning point.

16-48 Find the function $f(x)$ if $f(x) = \int [x^2 + \cos(x)]\, dx$.

16-49 Evaluate $\int_0^1 \sin(x)\, dx$.

16-50 Evaluate $\int_0^{0.5} \sec^2(x)\, dx$.

16-51 Evaluate the area between the curve $y = \sin(x)$ and the x axis assuming $0 \leqslant x \leqslant \pi$.

16-52 Calculate the area under the curve $y = e^x$, above the x axis and between the ordinates $x = 0$ and $x = 1$.

16-53 Evaluate the area between the curve $y = \cos(x)$ and the x axis assuming $0 \leqslant x \leqslant \pi/2$.

16-54 Calculate the first moment of area about the y axis for the area bounded by the curve $y = x^2/2$, the x axis and the ordinates $x = 0$ and $x = 1$.

16-55 Find the cartesian coordinates of the centroid of a sector of radius 2 m and angle $30°$.

16-56 Evaluate the second moment of area of a rectangular plate with sides 3 m and 4.2 m about the 3 m edge.

16-57 Calculate the second moment of area of a circle, radius 1.4 m, about its polar axis.

16-58 Evaluate the second moment of area of a circle 3 m radius about its diameter.

16-59 Evaluate the second moment of area of a semicircle of radius 3 m about its base, or diameter.

16-60 Solve the differential equation

$$\frac{dy}{dx} = 3x^2 \qquad \text{with } (x, y) = (0, 1).$$

16-61 Solve the differential equation

$$\frac{dy}{dx} = \cos(x) \qquad \text{with } (x, y) = (0, 2).$$

16-62 Solve the differential equation

$$\frac{dq}{dt} = 2q \qquad \text{with } (t, q) = (0, 3).$$

16-63 A six-sided die is numbered 1, 1, 1, 2, 2, 3. Find the probability that in one throw the outcome will be (*a*) a number 3, and (*b*) a number 1.

16-64 A firm has 200 employees of which 30 are female. Evaluate the probability that when visiting the firm we would meet an employee who is a man.

16-65 An automatic machine produces over one year 3 per cent reject components. If a sample of three is drawn at random, what is the probability that (a) all three will be rejects, (b) two will be rejects, and (c) at least two will be rejects.

16-66 Construct a class interval which contains the exact value of the random variable when its measurement value is 32 mm to the nearest 1 mm.

16-67 A continuous random variable X is normally distributed with a mean $\mu = 10$ mm and a standard deviation $\sigma = 2$ mm. Find the probability that this variable will lie between 10 mm and 12.5 mm.

16-68 If $z_1 = 1 + j$ and $z_2 = 2 - j$, evaluate (a) $z_1 + z_2$ and (b) $z_1 \cdot z_2$.

16-69 Evaluate $\dfrac{2 - 3j}{1 + 2j}$

16-70 Transform to polar form $4 + 2j$.

LONG-ANSWER QUESTIONS

16-71 Sketch the graph of the function $f(t) = 3 \sin(2t)$ for $0 \leqslant t \leqslant 4$.

16-72 Sketch the graph of the function $f(t) = 2 \sin(23t + 4)$ for $0 \leqslant t \leqslant 6$.

16-73 An electrical circuit has two currents flowing towards the same point. If these currents are $i_1 = \sin(2t)$ and $i_2 = 4 \cos(2t)$, find the resultant current equation and evaluate its frequency, periodic time, and amplitude.

16-74 A coil has a resistance of $1 \, \Omega$ and an inductance of 10 H. If the potential difference across this component is 10 V, show that the growth of the current in the coil is given by

$$i = 10[1 - \exp(-0.1t)]$$

State the assumptions made. Using the model for the growth of current calculate (a) the current flowing at $t = 10$ s and (b) the time at which the current reaches half of its maximum value.

16-75 Fit the curve $s = a \cdot t^b$ to the data shown in Table 16-5.

Table 16-5

t	1	2	3	4	5
s	2	4.9	8.3	12.1	16.2

16-76 A body moving in a straight line has its velocity measured every 5 s. The results are shown in Table 16-6. Find a mathematical model of the form $v = a \cdot \exp(bt)$ which describes the relationship between velocity and time.

Table 16-6

t (s)	5	10	15	20	25
v (m/s)	4.8	4.5	4.3	4.1	3.9

16-77 The velocity of a body whose mass is 2 kg is given by the equation $v = 4te^t$. Find equations which describe (a) the KE possessed by the body and (b) its acceleration at a time t.

16-78 A body is moving through a liquid with its distance from some fixed point given by the equation

$$s = -t^4 + \sin(t)$$

If the body has a mass of 3 kg, find equations which describe (a) the velocity, (b) the KE, (c) the acceleration, and (d) the retardation force.

16-79 (a) A coil has resistance of $10\,\Omega$ and inductance of 2 H. If the current flowing through the coil is given by $i = 3 \sin(2t)$, find the p.d. across the component.

(b) The current flowing in an electrical circuit is given by $i = e^{-0.1t}[\cos(3t)]$. If the circuit consists of an inductor of 12 H and a resistor of $100\,\Omega$ in series, find the p.d. across each component.

16-80 (a) Find the coordinates of all stationary points on the curve $y = -x^3 + x^2 - 2$ within the defined interval $x = -2$ to $x = 2$. State the nature of each stationary point.

(b) Evaluate the overall maximum and overall minimum values for the function in part (a) over the defined interval.

16-81 Evaluate the area between the curves $y = x$ and $y = x^2/3$.

16-82 (a) Calculate the area under the curve $y = 3x^2$, above the x axis and between the ordinates $x = 0$ and $x = 1$.

(b) If this area is revolved about the x axis, find the volume generated in one revolution.

16-83 (a) Find the area between the curve $y = -x^2 - 1$, the x axis and the ordinates $x = 0$ and $x = 1$.

(b) If the area in part (a) is revolved about the x axis, find the volume generated in one revolution.

16-84 (a) Find the first moment of the area bounded by the curve $y = -x^2$, the x axis, and the lines $x = 0$ and $x = 1$, about the x and y axes.

(b) By using the results from part (a), find the centroid of the stated area.

16-85 A body of mass 10 kg is moving in a straight line through a thick liquid. The motion is resisted by a force which is 20 times its velocity.

(a) If the initial velocity is 3 m/s, find a mathematical model describing the motion.

(b) Solve the resulting differential equation with its boundary condition to find a prediction equation for the instantaneous velocity.

(c) Predict the velocity at a time of 0.2 s.

16-86 It is known from past records that 15 per cent of a certain type of integrated circuit are defective. If a sample of 100 ICs is drawn from the stores at random to be inspected, find by using (a) the binomial distribution and (b) the Poisson approximation to the binomial distribution the probability that the number of defectives will be less than three.

16-87 The resistance of $\frac{1}{4}$ W carbon film resistors is normally distributed with a mean $\mu = 1000\,\Omega$ and a standard deviation $\sigma = 19\,\Omega$. Find the proportion of resistors which on inspection will be within the design limits $950\,\Omega$ to $1050\,\Omega$ inclusive. It may be assumed that the inspection procedure measures resistance to the nearest ohm. If the standard deviation of the population changed to $\sigma = 40\,\Omega$, what proportion of resistors have measurement values over $1050\,\Omega$.

Solutions

16-1 See Chapter 2.

16-2 See Chapter 2.

16-3 $0.8660(x)$ where x is the length of the line.

16-4 13.3826 N, 14.8629 N.

16-5 3.9051 m.

16-6 $\dfrac{1}{2\sqrt{2}}\,(\sqrt{3} + 1)$.

16-7 See Chapter 2.

16-8 See Chapter 2.

16-9 1.21 s.

16-10 See Chapter 2.

16-11 See Chapter 2.

16-12 0.3660 Hz.

16-13 1, 0.6366 Hz, 1.5708 s.

16-14 3 A, 2.9920 s, 0.3342 Hz.

16-15 $5 \sin(10t + 0.9273)$.

16-16 $1 + 5x + 10x^2 + 10x^3 + 5x^4 + x^5$.

16-17 $16 + 32x + 24x^2 + 8x^3 + x^4$.

16-18 $1 - 2x + 3x^2 - 4x^3 + \ldots$. Valid for $-1 < x < 1$.

16-19 $1 - 0.2x + 0.12x^2 - 0.044x^3 + \ldots$. Valid for $-1 < x < 1$.

16-20 91.

16-21 (a) $4x$, (b) x^2.

16-22 $\exp(-2x) = 1 - 2x + 2x^2 - \frac{4}{3}x^3 + \ldots$. Valid for all x.

16-23 1.1052.

16-24 See Chapter 3.

16-25 See Chapter 3.

16-26 0.4472.

16-27 0.0149.

16-28 ± 1.5174.

16-29 $1.6020T_0$.

16-30 $\ln(s) = b \cdot \ln(t) + \ln(10a)$.

16-31 $\ln(s) = 3b \cdot t + \ln(a)$.

16-32 $\ln(s) = 3[\ln(b)]\,t + \ln(a)$.

16-33 (a) $6 \cos(2x)$, (b) $-12 \sin(3x)$.

16-34 $8 \sec^2(2x)$.

16-35 $6e^{3x}$.

16-36 $8/(2t + 1)$.

16-37 $2t \cdot \exp(t^2)$.

16-38 $-2 \sin(2t)$, $-4 \cos(2t)$.

16-39 $\dfrac{dv}{dt} = e^t(2 + 2t)$.

16-40 $2 \cos(x) - 2x \sin(x)$.

16-41 $1.9395(10^{32})$.

16-42 -0.9320.

16-43 2.

16-44 $\sec^2(x) + 2 \exp(2x)$.

16-45 $2\theta \cdot \sec(\theta)$.

16-46 See Chapter 6.

16-47 $(1, 0)$.

16-48 $x^3/3 + \sin(x) + C$ where C is an arbitrary constant.

16-49 0.4597.

16-50 0.5463.

16-51 2.

16-52 1.7183.

16-53 1.

16-54 1/8.

16-55 $(1.2732, 0)$.

16-56 $74.088 \, \text{m}^4$

16-57 $6.0344 \, \text{m}^4$.

16-58 $63.6172 \, \text{m}^4$.

16-59 $31.8086 \, \text{m}^4$.

16-60 $y = x^3 + 1$.

16-61 $y = \sin(x) + 2$.

16-62 $q = 3 \exp(2t)$.

16-63 1/6, 1/2.

16-64 0.85.

16-65 (a) 0.000 027, (b) 0.002 619, (c) 0.002 646.

16-66 $31.5 - 32.5^-$.

16-67 0.3944.

16-68 (a) 3, (b) $3 + j$.

16-69 $-0.8 - 1.4j$.

16-70 $4.4721\underline{/26.56°}$.

16-71 See Chapter 2.

16-72 See Chapter 2.

16-73 $i = 4.1231 \sin(2t + 1.3258)$, 0.3183 Hz, 3.1416 s, 4.1231 A.

16-74 (a) 6.32 A, (b) 6.9315 s.

16-75 $s = 2t^{1.3}$.

16-76 $5\text{e}^{-0.01t}$.

16-77 $\text{KE} = 16t^2 \text{e}^{2t}$, $\dfrac{\text{d}v}{\text{d}t} = 4\text{e}^t(1 + t)$.

16-78 $v = -4t^3 + \cos(t)$, $\text{KE} = 1.5[-4t^3 + \cos(t)]^2$, $\dfrac{\text{d}v}{\text{d}t} = -12t^2 - \sin(t)$,

force $= 3[-12t^2 - \sin(t)]$.

16-79 (a) $V_R = 30 \sin(2t)$, $V_L = 12 \cos(2t)$.

(b) $V_R = 100\text{e}^{-0.1t}[\cos(3t)]$, $V_L = \text{e}^{-0.1t}[-1.2 \cos(3t) - 36 \sin(3t)]$.

16-80 $(0, -2)$ minimum, $(0.6667, -1.8518)$ maximum; overall minimum $= -6$, overall maximum $= 10$.

16-81 1.5.

16-82 1, 5.6549.

16-83 1.3333, 5.8643.

16-84 $A_y = 0.25, A_x = 0.1$; centroid has coordinates $(x, y) = (0.75, -0.3)$.

18-85 $(a) \dfrac{dv}{dt} + 2v = 0$ at $t = 0$ s, $v = 3$ m/s.

(b) $v = 3e^{-2t}$.
(c) v at $t = 0.2$ s is 2.011 m/s.
16-86 (a) 1.511 59(10^{-5}), (b) 3.9308(10^{-5}).
16-87 99.2%, 10.4%.

APPENDIX

Table A-1   Generalized binomial coefficients $\binom{n}{r}$

n \ r	0	1	2	3	4	5	6	7	8	9	10	11	12
1	1	1											
2	1	2	1										
3	1	3	3	1									
4	1	4	6	4	1								
5	1	5	10	10	5	1							
6	1	6	15	20	15	6	1						
7	1	7	21	35	35	21	7	1					
8	1	8	28	56	70	35	28	8	1				
9	1	9	36	84	126	126	84	36	9	1			
10	1	10	45	120	210	252	210	120	45	10	1		
11	1	11	55	165	330	462	462	330	165	55	11	1	
12	1	12	66	220	495	792	924	792	495	220	66	12	1
13	1	13	78	286	715	1287	1716	1716	1287	715	286	78	13
14	1	14	91	364	1001	2002	3003	3432	3003	2002	1001	364	91
15	1	15	105	455	1365	3003	5005	6435	6435	5005	3003	1365	455

Table A-2   Mathematical notation

Symbol	Explanation	Chapter
$f(x)$	f is a function of x	1
y	y is the value of the function	1
⟶	rounds off to . . .	1
$\bar{x}$	arithmetic mean of a sample	1
s	standard deviation of a sample	1
$\Rightarrow$	implies	1
a, b, c	sides of a triangle	2
A, B, C	angles of a triangle	2
T	periodic time	2
f	frequency	2
ω	angular velocity	2
t	time variable	2
$r\underline{/\theta}$	vector or phasor, magnitude r	2
i	instantaneous current	2
$n!$	n factorial	3

Table A-2 *(continued)*

Symbol	Explanation	Chapter
$\binom{n}{r}$	generalized binomial coefficients	3
$\lim_{\delta x \to 0}$	limit as the quantity δx tends to 0	3
e^x, $\exp(x)$	exponential function	3
$\log_a(x)$	logarithmic function, base a	3
$\ln(x)$	logarithmic function, base e	3
$\lg(x)$	logarithmic function, base 10	3
L	inductance	3
V	voltage drop	3
E	supply voltage	3
C	capacitance	3
R	resistance	3
$\sum_{i=1}^{n} x_i$	summation of the variable x_i	4
n	number of measurements	4
δx	a part of the variable x	5
δy	a part of the variable y	5
$\dfrac{dy}{dx}$	the first differential coefficient	5
$f'(x)$	the first differential coefficient	5
$\dfrac{d^2 y}{dx^2}$	the second differential coefficient	5
$f''(x)$	the second differential coefficient	5
V or v	velocity variable	5
s	distance variable	5
$f^{(n)}(x)$	nth differential coefficient	5
$\int f(x)\,dx$	integrate the function with respect to x	7
ρ	density	9
m	mass	9
w	thickness	9
M_y	first moment of force about y axis	9
M_x	first moment of force about x axis	9
A_y	first moment of area about y axis	9
A_x	first moment of area about x axis	9
$(\bar{x}, \bar{y})$	centroid position	9
KE	kinetic energy	10
I_y	second moment of area about y axis	10
I_x	second moment of area about x axis	10
$P(\text{event})$	probability of an event occurring	12
$\{1, 4, 6\}$	an event with outcomes 1, 2, and 6	12
$P(X = x)$	the probability of obtaining the discrete random variable X with a value x	13
X	the random variable	13
p	the probability of a success in one trial	13
q	the probability of failure in one trial	13

Table A-2 (*continued*)

Symbol	Explanation	Chapter
λ	the Poisson mean	13
M	measurement values	14
$P(a \leqslant X < b)$	probability of obtaining the continuous random variable X between a and b	14
Z	the standardized random variable	14
j	complex number $= \sqrt{-1}$	15

Table A-3   Areas under the normal curve

$$Z = \frac{X - \mu}{\sigma}$$

$$f(u) = \frac{1}{\sqrt{2\pi}} e^{-u^2/2}$$

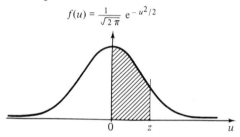

Z	Area	Z	Area	Z	Area	Z	Area
0.00	0.0000	0.25	0.0987	0.50	0.1915	0.75	0.2734
0.01	0.0040	0.26	0.1026	0.51	0.1950	0.76	0.2764
0.02	0.0080	0.27	0.1064	0.52	0.1985	0.77	0.2794
0.03	0.0120	0.28	0.1103	0.53	0.2019	0.78	0.2823
0.04	0.0160	0.29	0.1141	0.54	0.2054	0.79	0.2852
0.05	0.0199	0.30	0.1179	0.55	0.2088	0.80	0.2881
0.06	0.0239	0.31	0.1217	0.56	0.2123	0.81	0.2910
0.07	0.0279	0.32	0.1255	0.57	0.2157	0.82	0.2939
0.08	0.0319	0.33	0.1293	0.58	0.2190	0.83	0.2967
0.09	0.0359	0.34	0.1331	0.59	0.2224	0.84	0.2995
0.10	0.0398	0.35	0.1368	0.60	0.2257	0.85	0.3023
0.11	0.0438	0.36	0.1406	0.61	0.2291	0.86	0.3051
0.12	0.0478	0.37	0.1443	0.62	0.2324	0.87	0.3078
0.13	0.0517	0.38	0.1480	0.63	0.2357	0.88	0.3106
0.14	0.0557	0.39	0.1517	0.64	0.2389	0.89	0.3133
0.15	0.0596	0.40	0.1554	0.65	0.2422	0.90	0.3159
0.16	0.0636	0.41	0.1591	0.66	0.2454	0.91	0.3186
0.17	0.0675	0.42	0.1628	0.67	0.2486	0.92	0.3212
0.18	0.0714	0.43	0.1664	0.68	0.2517	0.93	0.3238
0.19	0.0753	0.44	0.1700	0.69	0.2549	0.94	0.3264
0.20	0.0793	0.45	0.1736	0.70	0.2580	0.95	0.3289
0.21	0.0832	0.46	0.1772	0.71	0.2611	0.96	0.3315
0.22	0.0871	0.47	0.1808	0.72	0.2642	0.97	0.3340
0.23	0.0910	0.48	0.1844	0.73	0.2673	0.98	0.3365
0.24	0.0948	0.49	0.1879	0.74	0.2704	0.99	0.3389

Table A-3 (*continued*)

Z	Area	Z	Area	Z	Area	Z	Area
1.00	0.3413	1.49	0.4319	1.98	0.4761	2.47	0.4932
1.01	0.3438	1.50	0.4332	1.99	0.4767	2.48	0.4934
1.02	0.3461	1.51	0.4345	2.00	0.4772	2.49	0.4936
1.03	0.3485	1.52	0.4357	2.01	0.4778	2.50	0.4938
1.04	0.3508	1.53	0.4370	2.02	0.4783	2.51	0.4940
1.05	0.3531	1.54	0.4382	2.03	0.4788	2.52	0.4941
1.06	0.3554	1.55	0.4394	2.04	0.4793	2.53	0.4943
1.07	0.3577	1.56	0.4406	2.05	0.4798	2.54	0.4945
1.08	0.3599	1.57	0.4418	2.06	0.4803	2.55	0.4946
1.09	0.3621	1.58	0.4429	2.07	0.4808	2.56	0.4948
1.10	0.3643	1.59	0.4441	2.08	0.4812	2.57	0.4949
1.11	0.3665	1.60	0.4452	2.09	0.4817	2.58	0.4951
1.12	0.3686	1.61	0.4463	2.10	0.4821	2.59	0.4952
1.13	0.3708	1.62	0.4474	2.11	0.4826	2.60	0.4953
1.14	0.3729	1.63	0.4484	2.12	0.4830	2.61	0.4955
1.15	0.3749	1.64	0.4495	2.13	0.4834	2.62	0.4956
1.16	0.3770	1.65	0.4505	2.14	0.4838	2.63	0.4957
1.17	0.3790	1.66	0.4515	2.15	0.4842	2.64	0.4959
1.18	0.3810	1.67	0.4525	2.16	0.4846	2.65	0.4960
1.19	0.3830	1.68	0.4535	2.17	0.4850	2.66	0.4961
1.20	0.3849	1.69	0.4545	2.18	0.4854	2.67	0.4962
1.21	0.3869	1.70	0.4554	2.19	0.4857	2.68	0.4963
1.22	0.3888	1.71	0.4564	2.20	0.4861	2.69	0.4964
1.23	0.3907	1.72	0.4573	2.21	0.4864	2.70	0.4965
1.24	0.3925	1.73	0.4582	2.22	0.4868	2.71	0.4966
1.25	0.3944	1.74	0.4591	2.23	0.4871	2.72	0.4967
1.26	0.3962	1.75	0.4599	2.24	0.4875	2.73	0.4968
1.27	0.3980	1.76	0.4608	2.25	0.4878	2.74	0.4969
1.28	0.3997	1.77	0.4616	2.26	0.4881	2.75	0.4970
1.29	0.4015	1.78	0.4625	2.27	0.4884	2.76	0.4971
1.30	0.4032	1.79	0.4633	2.28	0.4887	2.77	0.4972
1.31	0.4049	1.80	0.4641	2.29	0.4890	2.78	0.4973
1.32	0.4066	1.81	0.4649	2.30	0.4893	2.79	0.4974
1.33	0.4082	1.82	0.4656	2.31	0.4896	2.80	0.4974
1.34	0.4099	1.83	0.4664	2.32	0.4898	2.81	0.4975
1.35	0.4115	1.84	0.4671	2.33	0.4901	2.82	0.4976
1.36	0.4131	1.85	0.4678	2.34	0.4904	2.83	0.4977
1.37	0.4147	1.86	0.4686	2.35	0.4906	2.84	0.4977
1.38	0.4162	1.87	0.4693	2.36	0.4909	2.85	0.4978
1.39	0.4177	1.88	0.4699	2.37	0.4911	2.86	0.4979
1.40	0.4192	1.89	0.4706	2.38	0.4913	2.87	0.4979
1.41	0.4207	1.90	0.4713	2.39	0.4916	2.88	0.4980
1.42	0.4222	1.91	0.4719	2.40	0.4918	2.89	0.4981
1.43	0.4236	1.92	0.4726	2.41	0.4920	2.90	0.4981
1.44	0.4251	1.93	0.4732	2.42	0.4922	2.91	0.4982
1.45	0.4265	1.94	0.4738	2.43	0.4924	2.92	0.4982
1.46	0.4279	1.95	0.4744	2.44	0.4927	2.93	0.4983
1.47	0.4292	1.96	0.4750	2.45	0.4929	2.94	0.4984
1.48	0.4306	1.97	0.4756	2.46	0.4931	2.95	0.4984

Table A-3 (*continued*)

Z	Area	Z	Area	Z	Area	Z	Area
2.96	0.4985	2.99	0.4986	3.2	0.4993	3.5	0.4998
2.97	0.4985	3.0	0.4987	3.3	0.4995	3.6	0.4998
2.98	0.4986	3.1	0.4990	3.4	0.4997	3.7	0.4999

Table A-4   Formulae for differentiation

$y = f(x)$	$\dfrac{dy}{dx} = f'(x)$
ax^n	nax^{n-1}
$\sin(x)$	$\cos(x)$
$\cos(x)$	$-\sin(x)$
$\tan(x)$	$\sec^2(x)$
$\exp(x) = e^x$	$\exp(x)$
$\ln(x)$	$\dfrac{1}{x}$
$u \cdot v$	$u \cdot \dfrac{dv}{dx} + v \cdot \dfrac{du}{dx}$
$\dfrac{u}{v}$	$\dfrac{v \cdot (du/dx) - u \cdot (dv/dx)}{v^2}$

Function of a function or chain rule

1. $\dfrac{dy}{dx} = \dfrac{dy}{du} \cdot \dfrac{du}{dx}$

2. $\dfrac{d^2 y}{dx^2} = \dfrac{d(dy/dx)}{du} \cdot \dfrac{du}{dx}$

Table A-5   Formulae for integration

$f'(x)$	$\int f'(x)\,dx$
x^n	$\dfrac{x^{n+1}}{n+1} + C$
$\cos(x)$	$\sin(x) + C$
$-\sin(x)$	$\cos(x) + C$
$\sec^2(x)$	$\tan(x) + C$
$\dfrac{1}{x}$	$\ln(x) + C$
$\exp(x)$	$\exp(x) + C$
$\ln(x)$	$x[\ln(x) - 1] + C$

Table A-6   Second moments of area

Plane figure	Axis	Second moment of area
Rectangle, $a \times b$	about edge a	$\dfrac{ab^3}{3}$
	about an axis through the centroid parallel to edge a	$\dfrac{ab^3}{12}$
Triangle	about an edge b with a perpendicular height H	$\dfrac{bH^3}{12}$
Circle, radius r	about a diameter	$\dfrac{\pi r^4}{4}$
	about polar axis	$\dfrac{\pi r^4}{2}$
Semicircle, radius r	about a diameter	$\dfrac{\pi r^4}{8}$

INDEX